ATLANTIC HURRICANES

ATLANTIC HURRICANES

GORDON E. DUNN

Chief Meteorologist, U. S. Weather Bureau, Miami
Director, National Hurricane Center, Miami

BANNER I. MILLER

Research Meteorologist, National Hurricane Center

Louisiana
State University Press

PREFACE

PROGRESS IN THE FIELD OF TROPICAL METEOROLOGY, WHICH includes the study of hurricanes, for many years lagged far behind the development of the science of meteorology in the Temperate Zone. The reasons were largely economic; since most comparatively well-to-do countries, which could afford major weather services, were located in middle latitudes, consequently almost all meteorological research was confined to the weather problems of that area. The increasing weather needs of international aviation and the military requirements of World War II, however, have greatly stimulated research in tropical meteorology during the past three decades, and remarkable progress has been made since the war. Largely under the impetus of the National Hurricane Research Project, it is probable that no other single problem in meteorology is receiving more intensive study at the present time than that of hurricanes.

Why the interest in tropical cyclones, when, after all, hurricanes are relatively rare occurrences? Some 17,000 Americans have lost their lives in hurricanes since 1900. It is likely from now on that the annual hurricane damage in the United States will average more than $100,-000,000 and that once every ten or fifteen years a single tropical cyclone will cause property damage of $1,000,000,000 or more. Residents in Cameron, Louisiana, and along the beaches of the Carolinas and New England have seen and felt the death and destruction of this most destructive of all weather phenomena. The hurricane is a most fascinating subject to both layman and meteorologist alike.

In this book, the authors have attempted the difficult task of explaining the complicated facets of the hurricane for the layman while giving a reasonably technical and scientific, although nonmathematical, description of their physical processes for the student. The book begins with climatology, since it is necessary to know when and where hurricanes occur, how they normally travel, etc., before beginning a serious study of the subject. Then the physical processes involved in formation, intensification, and dissipation of hurricanes are discussed. The techniques used in tracking hurricanes (aircraft reconnaissance, radar, etc.) and how they are used are described. Forecast procedures are discussed and evaluated.

There are many unsolved problems in tropical meteorology today — perhaps none have been solved completely. The authors have presented the currently accepted hypotheses, many based on developments during the past several years, and have mentioned a few which are still untested. In any field which is being researched as intensively as that of hurricanes, the accepted theories of today can become obsolete rather quickly. It is hoped that the National Hurricane Research Project within the next few years will provide data and techniques which will lead to significant progress in the solution of the problems of hurricane energetics, eye mechanics, formation, and intensification, thereby clarifying several of the more clouded areas in this book.

While it is desirable that the reader have some meteorological background, the authors have tried to write in terms the layman will understand. Writing about a technical subject without using some of the language peculiar to that particular profession was found to be impossible. For this reason a brief glossary of meteorological terms used in the book is included in the Appendix, and it is hoped this glossary will help the nonprofessional reader through Chapters 6, 7, 10, and 11. The general reader should have no difficulty with the remainder of the book.

The writers are indebted to many of their colleagues for much of the material. Some of the illustrations have been adapted from other authors, and whenever it was possible to do so, the original source has been indicated. Figures 4 and 7-13 have been prepared from data contained in the *Marine Climatic Atlas of the World* [107], and Figures 5 and 6 from the *Atlas of Climatic Charts of the Oceans* [108]. The authors are grateful to the American Meteorological Society for permission to reproduce several illustrations, some from the *Compendium of Meteorology*. The United States Weather Bureau, the National Hurricane Research Project, the United States Navy, the United States Air Force (Air Weather Service), and several individuals have contributed photographs.

Particular thanks are due Mr. Robert H. Simpson and Dr. Joanne S. Malkus, who read the manuscript and offered many valuable suggestions. Others who were particularly helpful include Messrs. R. C. Gentry, Charles True, and Walter Dorsey of the National Hurricane Research Project, and Allen Marshall, Don Gerhard, and Robert L. Carrodus of the Weather Bureau Office, Miami, Florida.

Gordon E. Dunn
Banner I. Miller

TABLE OF CONTENTS

LIST OF FIGURES

LIST OF TABLES

ATLANTIC HURRICANES

1
A HURRICANE STRIKES

AT 9:30 A.M. EST, SEPTEMBER 26, 1955, ONE OF THE teletype-writers in the United States Weather Bureau's hurricane-forecast center at Miami, Florida, chattered out a weather report. It came from the Navy reconnaissance plane investigating hurricane Janet and read as follows:

5U93 NAVY FIVE 96669 13300 20154 78244 00700 05045 81810 20000 2////30003 40545 ONE FIVE TWO FIVE X SEVEN EIGHT ONE ZERO X ZERO FIVE ZERO X FOUR FIVE X BEGINNING PENETRATION

Decoded this means:

Navy reconnaissance flight 5U93, observation number five, using English units and heights in feet, at 1330 GMT (8:30 a.m. EST), Monday, located in latitude 15.4° N, longitude 78.2° W, oblique and horizontal visibility 3-10 miles, altitude 700 feet, flight wind 050° (NE), 45 knots (52 mph), present weather light intermittent showers, past weather same, overcast above the plane and some scud below plane, surface pressure 1,003 (millibars) (29.62 inches), surface wind 050° (NE), 45 knots (52 mph), beginning penetration into the vortex of the hurricane.

Nothing more has ever been heard from Lieutenant Commander Grover B. Windham, his crew of nine, and the two newspapermen aboard the plane.

On the next day, September 27, during the late forenoon another Navy reconnaissance plane transmitted a weather report which read:

NAVY SEVEN EYE CENTERED ONE SIX FIVE FIVE NORTH EIGHT TWO FOUR THREE WEST AT ONE FIVE FOUR ZERO ZEBRA RADAR LANDFALL ACCURATE WITHIN FIVE MILES X MAXIMUM WIND IN EXCESS OF 100 KNOTS BY LARGE AND UNREADABLE AMOUNT X 65 KNOT WIND EXTENDS 80 MILES WEST QUAD X EYE FREE OF UPPER CLOUDS X

RADAR COVERAGE FEASIBLE AND VERY DESIRABLE X
MINIMUM PRESSURE NINE THREE EIGHT MILLIBARS.

This may be translated as follows:

The eye of hurricane Janet is centered at latitude 16.9° N and longitude 82.7° W at 10:40 a.m. EST. Position can be determined quite accurately within five miles because some land is visible on radar screen. The highest wind is greatly in excess of 100 knots (115 mph) by a large and uncalculable amount. Winds of 65 knots (75 mph) or higher extend outward 80 miles west of the storm's center. The eye is free of upper clouds. Determination of the position of the hurricane's center is feasible by radar and indeed it is very desirable for the plane to stay on the periphery of the storm because of the extreme severity of this hurricane. The pressure in the center of the hurricane is 938 mb (27.70 inches).

Eye-witness Account of Hurricane Janet

About midday on September 27, 1955, one of the most intense hurricanes of the twentieth century passed over Swan Island in the Caribbean, attended by winds of about 200 mph. The only record of the meteorological and other events is that described from memory by John Laban and supplemented by Francis Lewandowski, weather and seismograph observers on the island [51]. The original time sequence as given by Laban has been modified slightly to conform with the known time the eye passed over the island, but this is his account:

September 26, 1955. Weather all day high thin cirrostratus overcast, wind variable in morning ranging from ESE to N, sea condition moderate to rough. During the afternoon, sea increased slightly. Late evening, around 8 p.m., full moon was becoming obscured by thickening cirrostratus with heavy cumulus from E, wind increasing to around 20-25 mph. I was at Gliddenville [a native village] and told four Grand Caymanian women to prepare on the morrow to go with blankets, food-stuff, babies, children, and newspapers, to Navy Seismograph building where U. S. Navy Seismo operator, Francis Lewandowski, had prepared the building for them. Late evening, distant lightning and thunder.

September 27, 1955. Time 1:55 a.m. Just got to bed when there was a wind shift from E to N accompanied by a squall with heavy rain — duration about 10 minutes. Awoke a little late in the morning, prepared quonset building for storm, cut off butane gas, went to Mess Hall, then weather station. Weather condition scattered scud, broken stratocumulus and altostratus overcast. Wind from NE about 20-25 mph. Sea very rough, waves to height of 10-15 feet from ESE or E. In station found all weather personnel up, heard of requests for 6-hourly R/s [radio-sonde] and hourly surface reports. Time around 8:00 a.m. Started our R/s instrument. Took sensitivity for R/s observation — balloon filled — time around 8:30 a.m. Wind increasing, waves higher, a few coco-nut trees starting to uproot.

Breazeale and Brown thought we should take the radiosonde obser-vation earlier, before the wind was too strong. Released R/s at 0909 a.m., overcast, showers, wind NNE, 31 mph, station pressure 29.55 inches.

Run very stable. Breazeale atop inflation building operating SCR-658 [rawin apparatus]. During run, wind increasing fast. Over intercom, Breazeale said winds to gale force — terrific racket at SCR-658. Hurri-cane recon plane made 3 or 4 passes overhead. At this time Breazeale terminated run. Winds dangerously high at SCR-658. Run to about 45,000 feet, evaluated by Brown and me. Winds by Breazeale and Brown, then transmitted all to Miami. Plane makes last pass to within 100 feet of surface. Pilot says, "You boys have your hole ready?" We answer, "Yes." He comes back with "Better get into it — this one (hurricane) is a bad one." Says there is a squall line 50 miles E of station. During this time sea and wind increased, many coconut trees beginning to uproot, coconuts flying, waves to 70 feet on south side from ESE. Wind average over 50 mph. Charles A. Dowd, Jr., (Elect. Tech. — FAA) sends message to his wife and mine that we are OK, etc. Time is around 11:00 a.m. Then Dowd sends message saying antennas going down — abandoning station. Squall almost upon us. Dowd and I cover radio transmitters and receivers with empty U. S. mail bags. We went back into weather room — north corner of building ripping.

Weather rain squalls. Wind over 75 mph from N. Sea ESE, waves to 70 feet. Dowd goes out to west corner of station to see if any flying debris. I go back into building to get three flashlights, put forms in drawers, read wind — over 100 mph average from N. Pressure 29.065. Time a little after 11:00 a.m. We both dash for Mess Hall where cook, Henry Alsted Glidden, had lunch ready. We all pitched in to re-inforce shutters on north side; then had lunch, except Lewandowski, who stayed in Seismo building. Hurried with lunch — shutters ready to fly in. Cleared off most of dining table. We went into kitchen, looked out of kitchen door (south side), saw debris flying — asbestos shingles from station — SCR-658 turns over atop inflation building. Shutters in dining room fly in; we see that kitchen shutters ready to go also. Wind increased to over 120 mph (estimated) about 11:30 a.m. We all move into pantry and wait for about five minutes, when kitchen shutters blow in. I kept pantry door open to equalize pressure. Things are crashing in dining room and kitchen; we go to bathroom, then into Sims' office in last room of building on south side. Racket of crashing things in other parts. Someone suggests we go to Seismo building but it seemed too dangerous. Moved office desk in front of office door to kitchen, time estimated to be about noon. There are seven of us here — Sims, Breazeale, Guarcello, Brown, Dowd, Al Glidden (cook) and I. There is a silence among all, Glidden with fear reflected in his eyes — others with thoughts and prayers to themselves. As for myself, I had dreamed two days previously that the storm would hit us and I had read the message sent to Miami that I was dead — the only fatality. I was asking myself when was I going to get it. I prayed for all of us and those people — men, women and children, down at Gliddenville. I presumed all were dead or injured, they being closer to the sea by about 300 feet. I asked Brown again what the time was — 12:15 p.m. The wind was estimated at over 150 mph now, and the rain was going by between the buildings in a horizontal watery stream. I could barely discern the living quarters about 25 to 30 feet away. About two inches of water was on the floor. Time estimated at about 12:30 p.m. A loud CRASH and we all made a dive for the space under the office desk, 30" x 24". How all our heads got into that space is a wonder. Seconds later we looked up and saw we were without a roof. Some walls were standing and we went over the side of the building platform (made of concrete pillars) and put our heads along the edge of the platform. We were all given a baptism of 500 gallons of diesel fuel when tank burst. We were completely soaked, our eyes smarting, our mouths, ears and heads covered with diesel fuel. Someone suggested we get under the building to avoid flying debris. Then another suggestion — to make 125 foot dash to U. S. Navy Seismo concrete building where Lewandowski was. Sims and Guarcello went first and are knocked off their feet. Then the rest of us made the dash. Lewandowski (*Ski*) is most surprised to see us, especially in our condition of fright and wild stare (diesel fuel in our eyes).

We immediately tried to wipe the diesel fuel from our eyes but there were no dry cloths around. A few moments were spent in talking, cussing the fuel oil in our eyes, scratches and abrasions on our feet, etc. Someone said that the people from Gliddenville are coming up and there was a sort of let-up in the wind and rain. The eye of the hurricane was approaching. We dashed out to the desperate people — men carrying children and

Fig. 1. Weather Station on Swan Island following the passage of Hurricane Janet.
(Photograph Courtesy Civil Aeronautics Administration)

babies in thin blankets and bags — men and women with fright in their
eyes. Some of the men had cuts and scratches but no one was seriously
hurt. Thank God, all are accounted for. All we could see was havoc and
damage [Figure 1]. All that was left of the Mess Hall that we had been
in was the proverbial toilet — atop the concrete platform.

We are all in the Navy Seismo building. We are pretty crowded —
have to set up chairs, etc., for some to sit on — there is water on the floor.
Elapsed time spent at this time is about 30 minutes during which the eye
of the hurricane passes. During "Eye" I was unable to see sky due to
blindness from diesel fuel. Wind resumes its howl after we are hit by SE
and S winds — pressure inside Seismo building is painful to ears — rain
resumes — the building vibrates — length of time (EST) from 2:30
p.m. to after 6 p.m. winds subsiding but still hurricane force.

After 6 p.m. the Caymanian boys go down to see what is left of Gliddenville to see what food can be salvaged, etc. A 2-burner oil stove is
found and food that is usable — a meal is made and food is handed out
to all who are hungry. After the meal, preparation for spending the night
in the Seismo building. Agricultural buildings reported in good shape —
the "Ranch" has water, gas and a home butane stove. Al Glidden and I
clean out the ranch for the future cooking and feeding of all on the island.

The sky is partly cloudy but the wind is still gale force. The island seems desolate — out of 10,000 coconut trees, only a few are still standing. Most have been snapped at an average height of 15 feet from the ground. The Caymanian and Honduranian men bed down in the Agricultural barns, others in the Seismo building.

September 28. Preparations of assembling order and sanitation, surveying damage, finding edible food, water and clothing. People are preparing for a comfortable stay. Breazeale and I chlorinate 55,000 gallons of water. Roland Jackson, one of Capt. Donald Glidden's men, some 60 years of age, makes a venture around the island to locate cattle and survey conditions in the former woods and coconut groves. Report of isolated cattle, some beaches on SE side washed clean of all sand — other beaches piled with more sand — the woods and coconut groves almost impenetrable because of fallen trees and shrubs. On the west side of island, estimate that one acre of bluff and soil washed away by pounding high waves. All my 14 chickens survived but are almost entirely denuded. Weather today is windy, high clouds and sunny. Preparations are going on to throw off debris from power shed to get at least one generator going. All able men are put to work — others help in setting up a systematic food preparation and sanitation. A day is spent in throwing off debris from generators. Late that afternoon, Air Force C-54 flys low — later a seaplane and other rescue craft are overhead. Water and rations are dropped. 34th Rescue Squad from Coco-Solo, Canal Zone, drops Walki-Talki, communications set up with aircraft overhead (MATS).[1] In days that follow more air-drops of food. Charles Dowd of FAA has one of the station receivers working — with MATS relaying, we listen on receiver — we have a listening schedule to Miami and MATS.

September 29. Banana boats arrive from Costa Rica to check on us. Brown departs for Tampa. Hamilton Bros. of Tampa sends us free food and any assistance we may need from their ships.

September 30. U.S. Navy arrives to evacuate and survey.

October 1. Guarcello and I depart for Grand Cayman and Miami.

Blinded by the fuel oil, Mr. Laban could not describe very completely conditions in the eye of the storm. Aerology Mate Third Class, Francis D. Lewandowski, United States Navy seismograph tender, remarks:

Eye lasted from 1310 to 1335 approximately. Station near north edge of eye. Always some wind 15 to 35 knots. Stratus type clouds, but sun occasionally visible. Vertical wall cloud occasionally visible through breaks.

---

[1]Military Air Transport Service.

Distant roar audible at all times. About 10 minutes required for wind to subside from about 200 mph to 20-40 mph. Increase of wind after eye passed more rapid than diminution before. Few birds in eye. Sky had hazy milky appearance. No sense of oppression during eye. Wind NNE before eye, S after eye. No particularly lurid sunset evening before storm. Ice box in mess hall exploded during hurricane. No tidal wave. Many fish washed up on land and 4 out of 5 had eyes popped out, due to decrease in pressure.

This was Janet of 1955, one of the fiercest hurricanes in history. On the average, eight of these storms develop in the tropical Atlantic during the summer and fall of each year, some recurving harmlessly northward over the open sea, but about two spread death and destruction along the eastern and southern coastal regions of the United States, and the remainder take a course farther south, devastating some of the islands and countries in the Caribbean and Central America. No other weather phenomena receive such widespread and intense attention from the public, and in both 1954 and 1955 hurricane news was rated among the 10 biggest news stories of the year. Much is still to be learned about these storms which, in recent years, have caused such losses of life and property and have resulted in one natural disaster after another. Their development frequently takes place in the relatively untraversed reaches of the Atlantic Ocean, and both this fact and their infrequency make them difficult to study.

Origin of the Word "Hurricane"

The term "hurricane" comes from the Spanish *huracan,* which in turn is thought to have originated from words in use among some of the Caribbean Indian tribes. In the Mayan dialect "Hunraken" is the storm god. In Taino, an extinct tribe of the Greater Antilles and the Bahamas and especially Haiti, the word for hurricane was also *huracan,* meaning evil spirit. The Galibi Indians of Dutch and French Guiana used the word *hyoracan,* or devil, and the Quiche of southern Guatemala spoke of "Hurakan" the thunder and lightning god. Other Carib Indian words for hurricane were *aracan, urican,* and *huiranvucan* which have been translated as "Big Wind," and similar terms. In any event the hurricane is aptly named. It has also been described more recently as the "meteorological monster of the sea." The Atlantic hurricane is identical to the Pacific typhoon, the tropical cyclone of the Bay of

Bengal and the Arabian Sea, and the willy-willy of Australia. All have essentially the same origin, structure, and behavior.

Why Hurricanes Are Given Girls' Names

In the North Atlantic and North Pacific oceans all hurricanes and typhoons are now given girls' names. For several hundred years hurricanes in the Spanish islands of the Caribbean were named after the particular saint's day on which the hurricane occurred. An example is the "Santa Ana" hurricane which struck Puerto Rico with exceptional violence on July 26, 1825, and "San Felipe" (the first) and "San Felipe" (the second) which passed over Puerto Rico on September 13, the first in 1876 and the second in 1928.

Early in this century a forecaster in Australia named hurricanes in his area after political figures whom he disliked. By properly naming a hurricane, the weatherman could publicly describe a politician (who perhaps was not too generous with weather-bureau appropriations) as "causing great distress" or "wandering aimlessly about the Pacific." Another method of identifying hurricanes was the phonetic alphabet used by the military services during the late World War (Able—Baker—Charlie—etc.). The oldest method is the more cumbersome latitude-longitude description.

The first written mention of lady hurricanes or storms may have been in the novel *Storm,* by George R. Stewart, Random House, 1941. During World War II the practice of giving the storms girls' names became more widespread. In weather-map discussions, forecasters, especially Air Force and Navy meteorologists who plotted the movement of storms over the Pacific Ocean, used this method of identification. It soon became evident that this method in written as well as in spoken communications was shorter, quicker, and less confusing than any other.

These advantages are especially important in exchanging detailed storm information between hundreds of widely scattered stations, airports, coastal bases, and ships at sea. In the past, confusion and false rumors have arisen when two or more storms have been in progress at the same time — an advisory for one of the storms would be mistaken for a warning about another storm located hundreds of miles distant.

Hurricane identifiers should be short, easily pronounced, quickly recognizable, and easily remembered. These requirements can be appreciated when one realizes that a single hurricane can prompt millions of

telephone calls (the weather number in New York City was called by 406,899 persons and in Washington, D.C., by 395,486 persons on September 19, 1955, when hurricane Ione threatened), thousands of additional news bulletins over radio and television stations, and countless telegrams, written messages, advices, warnings, and oral instructions among the millions of people who may be affected.

Names used in alphabetical succession for identifying tropical storms are selected in advance by the Weather Bureau and by the weather services of the Air Force and the Navy. In the Atlantic the first hurricane of the season is identified by a girl's name beginning with the letter *A*; the second hurricane is designated by a girl's name beginning with the letter *B*, and so on for all the remaining hurricanes that come along during that year. Since the record number for tropical cyclones in the Atlantic in one year is twenty-one, it is not likely that the alphabet will be exhausted in any one calendar year. It is expected that a different set will be used each year for ten years and then it may be necessary to repeat names. However, names for the most famous hurricanes, such as Carol of 1954, will be retired for a longer period.

Girls' names are also used for typhoons in the Pacific, but the procedure differs slightly and different names are used.

What Is A Hurricane?

A hurricane is essentially a rotating cyclone of the tropical oceans. When well developed it is a vast whirlwind of extraordinary violence. It is neither the largest nor the most intense of all storms. Temperate Zone storms are usually larger than the hurricane and it cannot match the concentrated fury of the tornado, but because of its considerable size and great intensity it is the most dangerous and destructive of all storms. In 1954 the total hurricane damage exceeded one billion dollars and in 1955 approached or exceeded two billion dollars. In total damage, hurricanes have exceeded any other natural catastrophe.

The term "hurricane" is defined technically as a storm of tropical origin with a cyclonic wind circulation (counter-clockwise in the Northern Hemisphere) of seventy-four mph or higher. The phrase "hurricane winds" is often used the world over to denote any wind of seventy-four mph or higher and is not confined to winds of a real hurricane.

TABLE 1
Beaufort Scale of Wind Force

Beaufort Number	Miles per Hour	Knots	Wind Effects Observed on Land	Terms Used in U.S. Weather Bureau Forecasts
0	Less than 1	Less than 1	Calm, smoke rises vertically	Light
1	1-3	1-3	Direction of wind shown by smoke drift; but not by wind vanes	Light
2	4-7	4-6	Wind felt on face; leaves rustle; ordinary vane moved by wind	Light
3	8-12	7-10	Leaves and small twigs in constant motion; wind extends light flag	Gentle
4	13-18	11-16	Raises dust, loose paper; small branches are moved	Moderate
5	19-24	17-21	Small trees in leaf begin to sway; crested wavelets form on inland waters	Fresh
6	25-31	22-27	Large branches in motion; whistling heard in telegraph wires; umbrellas used with difficulty	Strong
7	32-38	28-33	Whole trees in motion; inconvenience felt in walking against wind	Strong
8	39-46	34-40	Breaks twigs off trees; generally impedes progress	Gale
9	47-54	41-47	Slight structural damage occurs; (chimney pots, slates removed)	Gale
10	55-63	48-55	Seldom experienced inland; trees uprooted; considerable structural damage occurs	Whole Gale
11	64-73	56-63	Very rarely experienced; accompanied by widespread damage	Whole Gale
12 or more	74 or more	64 or more	Very rarely experienced; accompanied by widespread damage	Hurricane

Over the ocean the wind is usually measured according to a scale designed by Admiral Sir Francis Beaufort in 1806; this scale, which is still used today, is shown in Table 1.

Cyclones and Anticyclones; Tornadoes and Waterspouts

Considerable confusion exists among the general public in regard to the terms "cyclones," "anticyclones," "tornadoes," and "waterspouts." It is unfortunate that the popular name for a tornado in the Middle West is "cyclone," which technically means any rotating storm. Less frequently one hears the words "tornado" and "hurricane" used interchangeably. These atmospheric phenomena are described in the following paragraphs.

Cyclone is the name of any atmospheric system in which the barometric pressure diminishes progressively to a minimum value at the center and toward which the winds blow spirally inward from all sides, resulting in a lifting of the air and eventually in clouds and precipitation. Circulation is counterclockwise in the Northern Hemisphere and clockwise in the Southern Hemisphere. The system overspreads an approximately circular or elliptical area of at least 50 miles, generally several hundred, and often over 1,000 miles in diameter. Thus, a cyclone is any system of rotating winds, except a tornado, which is rarely greater than one mile wide, or a whirlwind, which is seldom more than a few yards across. The name does not signify any degree of intensity and is applied to storms of little as well as of great intensity. Cyclones are divided into tropical and extratropical groups, depending upon characteristics of the surrounding air masses. The hurricane is, of course, a tropical cyclone, and is the most ideal vortex in the atmosphere, one which can be used as a yardstick for comparative study of other severe storm types.

Anticyclone is an area of high pressure from the center of which air spirals out in all directions. This implies sinking air and consequently good weather. However, at all levels above the friction layer, anticyclones may comprise either indraft or outdraft circulations, although the latter is much more common. There are two kinds of anticyclones or HIGHS, cold and warm. Cold anticyclones are those which move rapidly south or southeastward out of the polar regions and are com-

Fig. 2a. Tornado observed at Dallas, Texas, April 2, 1957. (Photograph by Commercial Photographers, Inc.)

paratively shallow or short-lived. Warm anticyclones, such as the Azores-Bermuda HIGH, are deep systems extending high into the upper atmosphere and are often stationary or quasi-stationary over the oceans. They are very persistent and exercise a profound influence over the weather in adjacent areas. For example, changes in the position and intensity of the Azores-Bermuda HIGH are attended by characteristic and often pronounced departures from normal temperature and precipitation in the eastern United States and by changes in the hurricane tracks.

Tornado is the most violent storm produced by nature. Its most noticeable characteristic is the pendant, usually funnel-shaped cloud (Figures 2a and 2b) which is nearly always, if not invariably, present. Destruction, always instantaneous and frequently complete, occurs when this cloud dips to the ground. The funnel cloud on the ground is attended by a terrific roar, as if from a hundred freight trains. Buildings may be reduced to rubble and the air is filled with dangerous debris. Heavy objects are often picked up and carried long distances. The speed of the whirling wind which moves counterclockwise around the central axis of the funnel has been estimated at 450–500 mph. Tornadoes usually move along their path at 30-40 mph but forward speeds may vary from zero to 60 mph.

Although tornadoes occur over land areas in many parts of the world, they are far more frequent in the United States than in any other country. They have occurred in every state in the Union but are most fre-

Fig. 2b. Another view of the Dallas tornado. (Photograph by Charles B. Raymond)

Fig. 3. Waterspouts near Miami, Fla., July 25, 1958. (Photograph by Jacques Wolfe)

quent and destructive between the Rockies and the Appalachians. The area of maximum frequency is from northern Texas northeastward to Iowa, and the incidence decreases toward the coast line of the Gulf of Mexico and toward the Great Lakes and the Canadian border.

Tornadoes develop in connection with three general weather types: (1) along the squall line ahead of colder weather moving from the west or northwest; (2) in connection with thunderstorm squall lines during hot, humid weather; and (3) in the forward portion on the outer periphery of advancing hurricanes. A scattering of tornadoes occurs under other conditions, such as in cold air of an occluded cyclone and even in noncyclonic circulations. The average tornado path in the United States is about 400 yds. wide and 16 mi. long, and tornadoes are most frequent in the spring.

Waterspouts develop over water and are somewhat similar to tornadoes, although less violent. A pendant or funnel-shaped cloud extends from the base of a cumulonimbus cloud to the surface of the water. Rotation of the winds around the axis of the funnel is usually counterclockwise. Waterspouts have passed over ships of some size without significant damage. They often cross the coast line and penetrate inland a few blocks with usually minor destruction. Over the ocean or seas, salt water rises in the bottom of the spout only a few feet. Above that the water is fresh, indicating it has resulted from condensation rather than from suction from the sea. A typical waterspout funnel is shown in Figure 3.

THE NORMAL WEATHER IN THE TROPICS

The General Circulation

THE AZORES-BERMUDA AREA OF HIGH PRESSURE, OR SIMPLY HIGH, is the weather control, or "center of action," for the Atlantic and often for the eastern United States during the summer and early fall. The central pressure of this HIGH averages about 30.30 inches (1,026 mb) at this season. Figure 4 shows the mean position of the HIGH during August. The center is located southwest of the Azores, but the system extends from the Iberian Peninsula through the middle Atlantic Ocean to the southeastern United States. During the hurricane

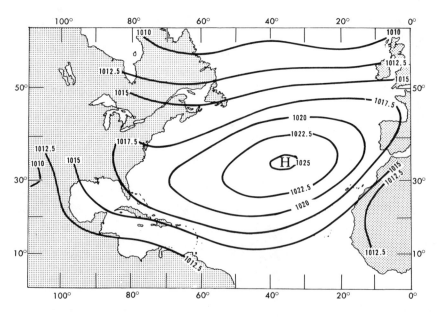

Fig. 4. Mean Sea-Level Pressure (millibars) over the North Atlantic during August.

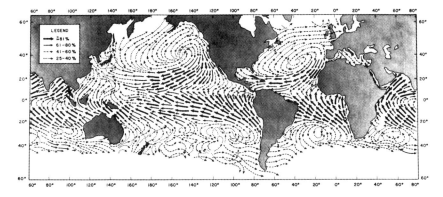

Fig. 5. Prevailing Winds over the oceans during August. Scale at upper left
indicates relative constancy of the wind.

season this center oscillates north and south with varying degrees of
intensity. Persistent departures from normal in either position or
strength have a profound influence on hurricane frequency and paths.

North of the anticyclone are the prevailing westerlies and to the
south are the northeast and east trade winds. Over the Atlantic Ocean
south of the equator are found the southeasterly trades, flowing out of
a similar anticyclonic cell in the South Atlantic Ocean. The prevailing
winds during August are shown in Figure 5, and those for February, in
Figure 6. During summer the zone between the two trade-wind systems
moves northward some 6°–10° but, lagging behind the sun, reaches its

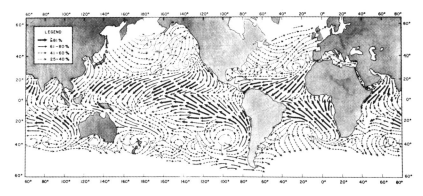

Fig. 6. Prevailing Winds over the oceans during February. Scale at upper left
indicates relative constancy of the wind.

northernmost position in the Cape Verde region in August and early September. To the south of this area the southeasterly trade wind is deflected to the northeast, i.e., it becomes a southwest wind and is known as the southwest monsoon. The southwest moonsoon occurs in other regions of the world, notably in the region of India. In both area and depth the Atlantic monsoon is small and weak compared to the Indian monsoon. The Atlantic monsoon advances northward in July, reaches a latitude of about 12° N in August, and then begins to recede in September.

Figure 7 shows the normal sea-level pressure over the Atlantic during February. It will be noted that the mean position of the Azores-Bermuda HIGH is farther south during winter and that the central pressure is somewhat less. These factors effectively reduce both the lateral and vertical extent of the easterly current to the south of the HIGH center. This is one reason why hurricanes are seldom observed during the winter season in the Atlantic.

The previous discussion has been concerned with surface wind conditions only. At higher elevations within the atmosphere the flow patterns may be, and frequently are, quite different. In order to study conditions at these upper levels, forecast offices prepare detailed analyses

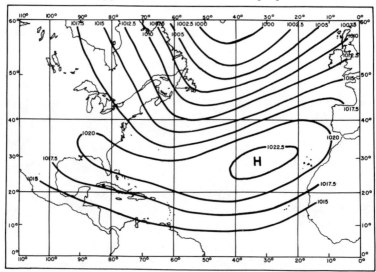

Fig. 7. Mean Sea-Level Pressure (millibars) over the North Atlantic during February.

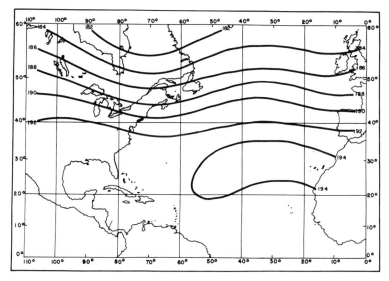

Fig. 8. Mean 500-mb Heights (hundreds of feet) over the North Atlantic during summer.

of the weather elements at various elevations ranging from about 5,000 to more than 50,000 feet above the surface. The information needed to prepare these charts is obtained by means of radiosondes carried aloft by balloons. The wind field may be analyzed by drawing streamlines and isotachs. Another analytical technique (used by all forecast centers in the Temperate Zone) consists of drawing height (contour) lines on a constant-pressure surface. These contours are analogous to the isobars on the surface map. In the Temperate Zone the 500 mb chart is the most universally used and is generally accepted as the most useful upper air chart. The 500-mb chart has been carried over to the tropics, although the value of contour analysis is much less at the lower latitudes. In addition the 500-mb level in the tropics often lies within a transitional zone between the lower easterlies and the westerlies or eddy circulations which lie above. For these reasons many tropical meteorologists prefer the use of one level below and one above the 500-mb chart to obtain a better picture of the two circulation regimes usually found within the tropics, particularly during summer.

Figures 8 and 9 show the average heights of the 500-mb surface during the summer and winter seasons. During summer (Figure 8) the prevailing westerlies over the ocean are restricted on the average to

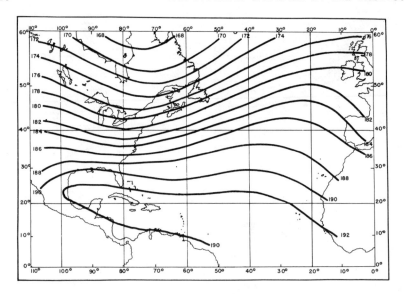

Fig. 9. Mean 500-mb Heights (hundreds of feet) over the North Atlantic during winter.

latitudes north of 35°–40°N. The presence of the Azores-Bermuda HIGH is still evident at this level, although it is much smaller than it was at sea level. A comparison of Figures 4 and 8 reveals that the center of the HIGH at 500 mb is about 5° south of its position at the surface. This small slope indicates relatively weak horizontal temperature gradients, which is characteristic of the tropical and subtropical regions during summer and which seems to be a prerequisite for hurricane formation. Under the center of the high (south of about 30° N) the prevailing winds over the eastern portions of the Atlantic are from the east or northeast. Over the western Atlantic the direction varies, being easterly as the western portion of the Azores-Bermuda HIGH strengthens and oscillates northward, and westerly as it weakens or moves southward. This variability, however, is usually restricted to the belt between 25° and 35° N, as south of 25° N the prevailing direction is usually easterly.

In the winter (Figure 9) the strong westerlies aloft are found as far south as southern Florida. The easterly belt is restricted to a narrow zone south of about 15°–20° N and even this region is frequently invaded by air from the middle latitudes; occasionally an intense outbreak of polar air penetrates the tropics, although greatly modified as it pushes southward over the warm oceans. The influence of the Azores-Bermuda HIGH is reflected by the bulge northward of the height lines over the eastern Atlantic, i.e., the high-pressure area has become a ridge of high pressure. In February the remaining center, located over the Greater Antilles, is far south of the surface position of the HIGH (Figure 7). This great slope indicates a strong horizontal thermal gradient, which is generally unfavorable for hurricane development.

At the still higher elevation of 200 mb, which is about 40,000 feet above sea level, the wintertime circulation is very similar to that prevailing at lower levels, as shown by Figure 10. The prevailing westerlies now overlie almost the entire tropics, and the wind speeds are much greater than they are at 500 mb.

During the summer, however (Figure 11), the circulation at great heights over the tropical regions becomes quite complicated. South of the prevailing westerlies, which at this elevation are also to be found generally north of 35°–40° N, the circulation pattern breaks up into small eddylike HIGHS and LOWS. There are occasionally prolonged periods during the summer when deep easterlies, extending to elevations of 40,000 to 50,000 feet, cover vast areas within the tropics, but

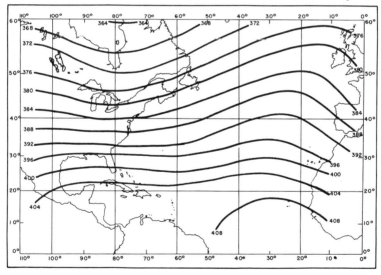

Fig. 10. Mean 200-mb Heights (hundreds of feet) over the North Atlantic during winter.

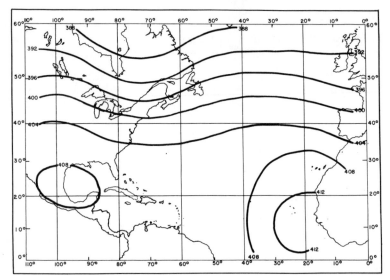

Fig. 11. Mean 200-mb Heights (hundreds of feet) over the North Atlantic during
          summer.

recent studies made at the National Hurricane Research Project in
Miami, Florida, seem to indicate that this simple pattern is frequently
broken up by small vortices which move westward across the Atlantic,
over the Caribbean, and into the Gulf of Mexico. The frequency of
the high-level LOWS, which are relatively small in comparison to the
LOWS of the Temperate Zone, varies greatly from three or four to as
many as twelve in a month. They are accompanied by below-normal
high-level temperatures. Their frequency is about the same as that of
the easterly wave, which is to be defined later, and there appears to be
some connection between the two, although this relationship is not as
yet clearly understood.

Air and Water Temperatures

The air and water temperatures over the ocean in August and
February are shown in Figures 12 and 13. In August there is a gradual
increase in the water temperatures across the subtropical portion of the
ocean, ranging from 77° F. off the coast of Africa to 85° F. in the
Gulf of Mexico. Air temperatures are quite similar; in fact the mean

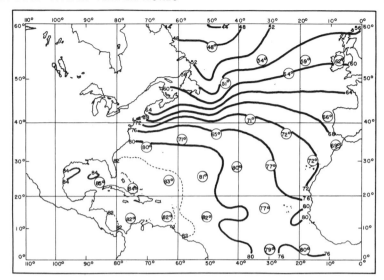

Fig. 12. Mean Air Temperatures (solid or dashed lines) and Water Temperatures
(circled numerals) over the North Atlantic during August.

air temperature is within ± 1° F. of the mean water temperature over
the entire tropical and subtropical area.

In February the water temperatures off the coast of Africa have
dropped to 71°–74° F. and those in the Gulf of Mexico to about 74° F.
The warmest portion of the area is now the Caribbean, where temperatures of 77°–79° F. are found south of the Greater Antilles and
just to the north of the Isthmus of Panama. The air temperatures
are more variable than during August. Over the Caribbean the mean
air temperature is still within one degree of the mean water temperature, but along the Gulf Coast the air averages about 14° colder than
the water. Off the South Atlantic coast of the United States the difference is even greater.

Air and water temperatures are of utmost importance in the hurricane
problem, and this subject will be discussed in detail in Chapters 6
and 7.

Returning again briefly to Figure 4, during the summer the Azores-
Bermuda HIGH, despite occasional accretions of modified polar air
from North America and Europe, is essentially a source of warm and
stable air. By stable, as applied to an air mass, meteorologists mean
that ascending air motion is suppressed. Aloft in the great Azores-

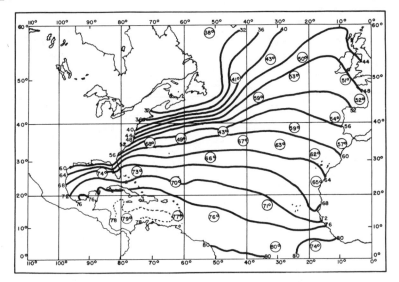

Fig. 13. Mean Air Temperatures (solid or dashed lines) and Water Temperatures (circled numerals) over the North Atlantic during February.

Bermuda HIGH air is gradually sinking, and since this sinking carries the air to a lower level where the atmospheric pressure is higher, the air is warmed by compression. This warming also causes the relative humidity to drop, since no additional moisture is added to the air. At the surface on the south side of the HIGH the air mass moves in the form of trade winds for hundreds of miles over water. The surface air attains a temperature approximately equal to that of the ocean over which it passes, and because of evaporation from the surface of the ocean, it becomes very moist to a depth of several thousand feet. The depth of the moist layer increases steadily as one moves southward toward the equator. The lower moist layer is separated from the warm, dry overlying subsiding layer by an inversion. (Normally as one ascends to higher levels within the atmosphere, the temperature drops, as everyone who has left a hot and humid city during the summer to spend a vacation at a mountain resort is well aware. However, it is frequently observed that this temperature trend is reversed and the temperature is found to rise as one ascends to a higher elevation. The region through which this rise occurs is known as an inversion.) Inversions are characteristically found at an elevation of 5,000 to 8,000 feet over the tropical oceans.

Within the trade-wind area there are no surface-temperature discontinuities which cannot be explained by the presence of cloudiness, precipitation, land and sea breezes, and daytime heating of the land areas. In the middle and upper atmosphere twenty-four-hour temperature changes of 2°–4° C. are occasionally noted. These are mostly dynamic in origin, i.e., they are the result of rising or sinking air, cooling by evaporation, or entrainment. Some of them, however, particularly those associated with the high-level vortices mentioned previously, may be advective in nature, i.e., they can be followed from place to place and day to day. There are no marked changes in the surface dew points from day to day, although these will normally be observed to be a few degrees lower on days when the trade-wind inversion is found at unusually low levels, falling from the customary 75° F. to 70° F. They are also occasionally slightly lower on the lee sides of islands.

Tropical Rainfall

Until recently almost all meteorological textbooks emphasized "the monotonous sameness" of day-to-day weather in the tropics, and the Hawaiian language contains no word for weather. The legend has grown that "one can set one's watch by the shower which always begins at 3:00 p.m.," and that social and business engagements are made by the shower rather than by clock, i.e., "I'll meet you after the shower," not, say, at 5:00 p.m. This is largely a myth, as actually there is considerable variation from day to day as periods of frequent and perhaps heavy shower activity alternate with periods of comparatively fine weather. There will be several days with fair-weather cumuli and perhaps a few isolated small showers followed by a period with considerable middle cloud, frequent showers, and thundershowers.

Olascoaga [74] analyzed rainfall data for Argentina, and by combining data for the entire country for all seasons concluded that 10 to 15 per cent of the rainy days accounted for about 50 per cent of the total rainfall, and that 50 per cent of the days with the smallest rainfall totals accounted for only one-tenth the annual total. Argentina is not primarily a tropical region (it extends from the subtropics to the subarctic regions), but Riehl [82] believes that Olascoaga's results apply to most regions, and he cites results based on rainfall studies of Hawaii, Puerto Rico, Hongkong, and the Philippines to support this opinion.

This points to the conclusion that organized weather disturbances account for most of the rainfall in the tropics as well as in the Temperate Zone. This obviously does not apply, however, to areas which receive large amounts of rainfall caused by orographic lifting. Some areas, notably the mountainous regions of Hawaii, receive large amounts of rainfall distributed throughout the year, and traveling disturbances may produce less rainfall than would normally be expected from orographic effects alone.

The normal vertical structure of the air in the trade-wind belt consists of a moist lower layer, capped by an inversion above which the air is relatively dry. This places an effective upper limit on the development of convective activity, and "normal" cloud tops in the tropics fall within the 6,000-10,000-foot range. One must hasten to add, however, that even clouds with this limited vertical extent are capable of producing significant, even heavy, rainfall in tropical regions. These showers are usually of short duration, however, and the amounts they produce do not account for a very large percentage of the yearly accumulation. On the windward slopes of mountains, where orographic lifting assists convection in breaking through the trade-wind inversion, showers may occur almost daily, and the percentage of the annual rainfall produced in this manner may greatly exceed that produced by any other means.

The disturbances that produce the bulk of the rainfall in the Temperate Zones are the huge migratory extratropical cyclones and their

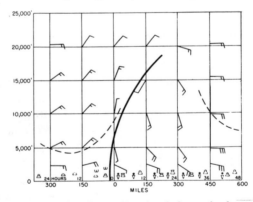

Fig. 14. Model of an Easterly Wave. Depth of the moist layer is indicated by the broken line. The horizontal distances entered are measured from the position of the wave crest, and the time scale gives the average amount of time needed for a wave to pass a particular station. (After Riehl)

associated frontal structures. In the tropics the hurricane is the most prolific single rain producer, but its relatively infrequent appearance at any given locality makes it unlikely that the hurricane greatly affects the long-range rainfall averages. The disturbances that produce the routine rainstorms of the tropics are of interest, not primarily because of their rain-producing ability, but because hurricanes may develop from them. The rainfall is of interest because the occurrence of "abnormal rainfall" is one of the best indications that a disturbance is forming, and the distribution of the rainfall and cloud structure about the disturbance yields very important clues for the forecaster and often points to development or lack of development of the disturbance into a hurricane. For these reasons some of the most common of these disturbances will be discussed.

Easterly Waves

The importance of the easterly wave in tropical-cyclone forecasting was first recognized by Dunn [16], who observed a series of centers of falling and rising pressure moving from east to west across the islands in the Caribbean. These centers of pressure change are known as isallobaric centers. When upper-air observations became available, the centers were found to be associated with the westward progression of the easterly wave. The isallobaric field, however, still remains one of the most effective means of keeping track of these disturbances.

The easterly wave is essentially a trough of low pressure, which is embedded in the deep easterly current located to the south of the Azores-Bermuda high-pressure area. Figure 14, which was developed by Riehl [80], shows an idealized model of this type of disturbance. Subsidence and divergence precede the wave. (Simply expressed, divergence means that more air is going out of a specified area than is entering it. It is associated with sinking air, or subsidence, and fine weather. The opposite of divergence is convergence, and it is associated with ascending air, cloudiness, and precipitation.) Ahead of the wave the normal east or northeast trade wind backs to northeast or north, the pressure falls, the trade-wind inversion lowers, and little or no cloudiness is observed. As the wave trough approaches, the depth of the moist layer increases, and towering cumuli begin to form. Behind the wave convergence and ascent occur, the pressure begins to rise, heavy cumulus and cumulonimbus clouds become numerous, and middle and high cloud decks develop as the moist air extends to higher and higher levels. Shower and thundershower activity and convergence reach a maximum 200-300 miles behind the surface trough. The ascending motion reaches a maximum at an elevation of about 30,000 feet. The above portrays the stable type of wave, which means that the trough may travel 2,000 or 3,000 miles with little or no change in the shape of the wave, and no vortex develops.

A wave in the easterlies is present over some part of the Caribbean almost every day from June through September, with a somewhat lesser frequency in May, October, and November, and a weather station in the eastern Caribbean may expect a wave passage on the average about twice a week. There are many individual variations between waves, and not all fit the simple description given above. Most of these waves are stable, but it is the variation from the normal wave pattern that causes the forecaster to suspect that the wave is becoming unstable and is developing into a hurricane vortex.

The Intertropical Convergence Zone (ITC)

The existence of a zone of convergence between the hemispheres has been suggested by the prevailing-wind charts of Figures 5 and 6. Over the North Atlantic the prevailing winds throughout the tropics and subtropics are from the northeast and east, while in the South Atlantic they are from the southeast or southwest. These two air currents tend to flow together or converge, and the region within which this is taking place is known as the "intertropical convergence zone," frequently abbreviated as ITC. It is also known as the "equatorial trough" or the "equatorial convergence zone" or the "equatorial shear line." This convergence zone follows the sun. Its mean position in the Eastern Atlantic reaches its northernmost location at about 12° N latitude in August, and in February it is usually found within 1° to 3° of the equator. Day-to-day variations in its position may differ substantially from the mean position during both winter and summer.

Ascending motion, clouds, and precipitation are typically associated with the ITC. Its intensity varies greatly. At times it is a veritable mass of clouds extending to elevations of 30,000 to 40,000 feet, and aircraft flying through it encounter weather and turbulence comparable to that found within some of the more vicious Temperate Zone squall lines. Its width may reach 50 to 100 miles. At other times it becomes so weak that it can hardly be located, and virtually no weather or cloudiness can be found along it. In fact the ITC as a continuous narrow line circling the globe exists in a statistical sense only. The intense activity tends to be associated with convergence produced by perturbations or eddies moving along or out of the equatorial trough. Alternately divergence and minimal activity follow the westward-moving eddies. Transition from maximum to minimum may occur within a few hours.

Aloft however, the ITC is occasionally found as an equatorial trough as far north as Puerto Rico and Cuba. Riehl [82] has described an example. The trough reached its maximum intensity at about 30,000 feet, and it was unusually persistent. Cold air was found in the trough, but warmer air was present both to the north and to the south, indicating that the cooling was due to vertical motion. There were westerly winds to the south of the trough. These were not the usual prevailing westerlies found in the Temperate Zones, but were of Southern Hemispheric origin.

When the ITC is located within a few degrees of the equator only small vortices form along its course, but when it migrates northward (or southward in the Southern Hemisphere), the influence of the rotating globe becomes great enough to transfer sufficient spin to converging currents to permit tropical cyclones to develop. In the Atlantic area this occurs principally in the Cape Verde region and in the western Caribbean just north of the Isthmus of Panama.

The area where the trade-wind systems of the two hemispheres meet has often been called the "doldrums" or region of "equatorial calms." The doldrums are roughly synonymous with the ITC, although the definition of the latter does not imply that the winds are light and variable. In fact it is when the opposing trades are at their greatest strength that the ITC is most active. Many authorities at one time believed that most tropical cyclones originate within the doldrums. It is true that a few hurricanes develop out of disturbances which can be traced back to the general area of the doldrums, but most of the growth from minor disturbance to full hurricane intensity takes place after the initial disturbance moves away from the doldrums. It is very rare indeed for a storm to reach hurricane intensity in the doldrums, and it is obvious today that the importance of the doldrums as a hurricane breeding ground has been greatly overemphasized.

The Polar Trough

This disturbance originates outside the tropical or subtropical areas. It is a trough of low pressure embedded within the prevailing westerlies to the north of the Azores-Bermuda HIGH, and it moves from west to east. Whenever the subtropical high cell is weak and the depth of the easterly current to the south is relatively low, e.g., 10,000-15,000 feet, or whenever the polar trough is unusually strong, the southern portion of the trough may penetrate into the tropics. This only occurs aloft, however, and the eastward-moving trough overrides the lower easterly current, to which it is opposed. This trough often produces considerable bad weather. It occurs quite frequently during the winter and with lesser frequency during the early summer and late fall, when the Azores-Bermuda HIGH is weak or south of its normal position, which results in a rather shallow easterly current. It occurs rarely during the height of the hurricane season; thus the importance of the polar trough in the development of tropical cyclones is greatest early and late in the season.

Occasionally the extension of the polar trough into the tropics will break off, or "fracture," from its parent trough in the westerlies; afterwards the fractured portion may begin to move westward. Riehl [82] has suggested that these fractured troughs later become easterly waves and that the origin of many, but not necessarily all, easterly waves may be explained by this process.

These three disturbances, easterly waves, the intertropical convergence zone, and the polar trough, account for much of the weather observed in the tropics. There are other mechanisms for producing the convergence necessary to explain the observed weather, but these three are by far the most important. Their roles in the process of hurricane formation will be discussed in more detail in Chapter 7.

3

HURRICANE CLIMATOLOGY

Classification of Tropical Cyclones

TROPICAL CYCLONES ARE KNOWN BY VARIOUS NAMES, SUCH as: hurricanes, cyclones, storms, lows, disturbances, depressions, and in the tropical North Pacific, typhoons. The intensity of these may vary greatly, from the vicious hurricane such as Janet (Chapter 1), packing winds of over 200 mph, down to the weak, but possibly developing, disturbances discussed in Chapter 2. A classification of tropical cyclones according to intensity has, therefore, been generally accepted by most meteorological organizations in and near the tropics. This has been done to eliminate confusion and make the terms in common usage as meaningful as possible. It is imperative that a classification, once agreed upon, remain relatively unchanged; otherwise the statistics of past years become less useful and extremely difficult to interpret. Changing the classification system could even lead to erroneous conclusions concerning trends or cycles in cyclone frequency.

The following classification is the one most commonly employed in the Atlantic area, but unfortunately its usage is not universal. It will be used in the discussions to follow:

1. *Tropical disturbance.* Rotary circulation slight or absent on the surface but possibly better-developed aloft. There are no closed surface isobars and no strong winds. This type of disturbance is common throughout the tropics.

2. *Tropical depression.* One or more closed surface isobars. Wind force equal to or less than Beaufort force 7 (32-38 mph).

3. *Tropical storm.* Closed isobars, wind force more than Beaufort force 7, or 39 mph or more. When used in official weather Bureau advisories the wind velocity is less than Beaufort 12. Frequently however, this term includes cyclones of hurricane intensity as well. The terms "tropical storms"

and "tropical cyclones" have been used interchangeably in much of the literature on tropical meteorology, but the term "tropical cyclone" is not used in United States Weather Bureau advisories. For sake of clarity it is strongly urged that the term "tropical cyclone" include tropical disturbances of all intensities and "tropical storm" include only those with winds between 39 and 73 mph.

4. *Hurricane.* Wind force Beaufort 12, or 74 mph or more. It is equivalent to the typhoon of the Pacific area. It, of course, must originate in tropical or subtropical regions.

Another system of classification makes use of the stage of hurricane development as well as the intensity factors. A storm of tropical origin may appear on the weather charts for a period of three weeks or more. During this whole time the storm is never static and its characteristics are constantly changing from day to day and even from hour to hour. The physical processes of the storm itself and its environment are continually affecting its development, structure, shape, and intensity. McDonald [58] first described the four stages in the normal cycle of development and decay, and he called these: (1) Preliminary, or incipient stage, (2) deepening stage, (3) expanding stage, and (4) decline or decaying phase. Dunn [18] used different terms in dividing the life history of hurricanes into four similar stages: (1) The formative stage, which begins when an organized circulation develops in an easterly wave or in the vicinity of the ITC and ends when the disturbance reaches hurricane intensity; (2) the stage of immaturity, during which the hurricane continues to deepen and reaches its maximum intensity, is most symmetrical, and covers a relatively small area; (3) the stage of maturity, when the isobars are expanding, there is no further deepening, and the actual intensity is often decreasing although the area covered by gales and hurricane winds is the largest of any period of the storm; and (4) the stage of decay, when the hurricane either moves inland and dissipates or recurves northward and assumes extratropical characteristics. The passage from one phase to the next is a gradual one.

Tropical cyclones observed in the Cape Verde region and in the nearby oceanic areas are usually in stage 1; stages 1, 2, and 3 are observed in Puerto Rico and the Bahamas, 3 and 4 at New Orleans and Cape Hatteras, and 4 in New England. Investigators should exercise caution in deductions regarding the behavior and characteristics of storms observed in any one location, since these features vary from one stage to another as well as from storm to storm.

When and Where Hurricanes Occur

Tropical cyclones form in much the same way and in the same seasons of the year all over the world. Atlantic hurricanes form in a homogeneous air mass, and there are no significant discontinuities in temperature or moisture in the area of development. Almost invariably, however, one of the three disturbances described in Chapter 2, e.g., easterly waves, the intertropical convergence zone, or old polar troughs, serve as one of the essential requirements for hurricane formation.

It may be that none of the tropical oceans in either hemisphere is entirely free from tropical cyclones, but there is no record of a true tropical cyclone of hurricane intensity having occurred in the South Atlantic Ocean or in the South Pacific east of about 140° W longitude. The absence of hurricanes in the South Atlantic is apparently due to the fact that the intertropical convergence zone moves only one or two degrees south of the equator during the Southern Hemisphere summer. In addition the sea-surface temperatures are much lower than they are in the North Atlantic.

The principal areas of hurricane, typhoon, or tropical-cyclone (depending upon local terminology) occurrence are shown in Figure 15. Hurricanes develop over the southern portions of the North Atlantic Ocean, including the Gulf of Mexico and the Caribbean Sea, mostly

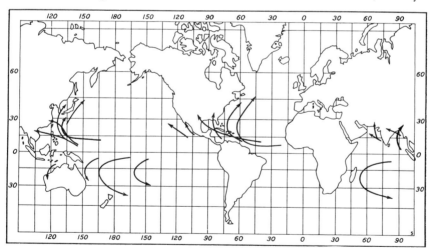

Fig. 15. Areas where Tropical Cyclones form.

from June through October, infrequently in May and November, and very rarely during other months of the year. Hurricane Alice, which occurred in the vicinity of the Lesser Antilles during January, 1955, is the only one definitely known to have developed in that month [10]. Another out-of-season storm passed through the same area on March 8, 1908, and Basseterre, St. Kitts, recorded hurricane winds and a barometric pressure of 29.28 inches. During some winters several tropical cyclones will develop in the southern Atlantic, but almost none of these ever reach hurricane intensity. One such storm passed near Puerto Rico during January, 1951, and another developed in the western Gulf of Mexico and crossed Florida, near Miami, on February 2, 1952.

There are more hurricanes (typhoons) in the southwest portion of the North Pacific Ocean than anywhere else in the world. On the average more than twenty tropical cyclones develop in that area per year (see Table 2). Most of these form to the east of the Philippine Islands, and may move westward across the Philippines into the China Sea or northwestward toward Formosa and the China coast, thence recurving toward Japan or the open Pacific.

About six tropical cyclones per year develop off the west coast of Central America or Mexico, but less than half reach hurricane intensity. These usually move northwestward off the coast, but occasionally one will recurve into Mexico, and some of the cities on the west coast of Mexico are subject to visitations from these storms. Once in a long while one will come close enough to the southern California coast to cause squally weather there. On somewhat more frequent occasions these eastern Pacific hurricanes will move into the Gulf of Lower California and, while the winds will diminish, the moisture will continue to be carried northward, resulting in beneficial rains in Arizona. Several eastern Pacific hurricanes have crossed Central America and regenerated in the Caribbean Sea or in the Gulf of Mexico.

The hurricane season off the west coast of Mexico is about the same as in the Atlantic. Only about one storm out of twenty has struck the coast north of latitude 25° N, and about one out of fifty has reached the coast north of latitude 30° N. (San Diego, California, is about 150 miles north of latitude 30° N.) The last hurricane to strike the California coast was in September, 1939, and it caused a loss of forty-five lives and property damage of about $2,000,000, mostly in the Los Angeles and Santa Barbara areas.

TABLE 2

Average Frequency of Tropical Cyclones (by Months)

	Jan.	Feb.	March	April	May	June	July	Aug.	Sept.	Oct.	Nov.	Dec.	Year
North Atlantic Ocean (1887-1955)													
All tropical Cyclones..	*	0	*	0	.1	.4	.5	1.5	2.6	1.9	.5	*	7.5
Hurricane intensity...	*	0	*	0	*	.2	.2	.9	1.6	.8	.1	*	3.8
North Pacific Ocean— off west coast of Mexico (1910-1940)													
All tropical Cyclones..	*	*	*	*	.1	.8	.7	1.0	1.9	1.0	.1	0	5.7
Definitely Hurricane intensity..........	*	*	*	*	.1	.2	.2	.5	.7	.5	0	0	2.2
North Pacific Ocean— long. 170° E westward (1901-1940)													
All tropical Cyclones† .	.4	.2	.3	.4	.7	1.0	3.2	4.2	4.6	3.2	1.7	1.2	21.1
North Indian Ocean— Bay of Bengal (period unknown)													
All tropical Cyclones‡ .	.1	0	.2	.2	.5	.6	.8	.6	.7	.9	1.0	.4	6.0
North Indian Ocean— Arabian Sea (period unknown)													
All tropical Cyclones‡ .	.1	0	0	.1	.2	.3	.1	0	.1	.2	.3	.1	1.5
South Indian Ocean— Madagascar eastward to 90° E (period unknown, possibly 1839-1922)													
All tropical Cyclones§ .	1.3	1.7	1.2	.6	.2	0	0	0	0	0	0	.1	5.1
South Indian Ocean— Northwest Australia, excluding Queensland (period unknown, possibly 1839-1922)													
All tropical Cyclones§ .	.3	.2	.2	.1	0	0	0	0	0	0	0	.1	.9
South Pacific Ocean...	According to Visher [111], the average number of tropical cyclones is in excess of 27 per year. However, this includes several more or less separate areas of development. A number of island groups such as Fiji, Samoa, Hebrides, Tongo, and New Caledonia average 2 or 3 a year. Data are insufficient for monthly percentages, but the tropical cyclones are apparently well concentrated in the period December through March.												

*Less than 0.1.
†Very few of the storms listed in the winter months reach hurricane intensity. The proportion of storms in other months reaching full hurricane intensity is unknown.
‡Few of the midwinter and midsummer storms reach full hurricane intensity, and the midwinter storms may not be true tropical cyclones.
§The intensities of these storms are not indicated.

According to Jean A. Brown, forecaster at the Weather Bureau Office in San Francisco, the few hurricanes which have reached or neared southern California have been preceded there by several days of extremely hot weather. Existence of these high temperatures indicates the presence of a strong upper-level thermal anticyclone over the southwestern United States, which tends to drive a tropical storm off the coast northwestward and prevent its recurving into Mexico. However, the arrival of a migratory upper-level trough, which replaces the extension of the thermal HIGH, causes storms to recurve northeastward toward the California coast. Fortunately, this is a relatively rare occurrence.

The remaining place of origin of hurricanes in the Northern Hemisphere is the Bay of Bengal and the Arabian Sea off the east and west coasts of India. The tropical cyclones, as they are known in this area, develop from perturbations which originate along the intertropical convergence zone. They occur mostly in the late spring and in the fall, not during the summer, since the ITC is usually over land during the summer and close to the foothills of the Himalayas. Occasionally the ITC will move southward during the summer to the vicinity of Calcutta at the head of the Bay of Bengal, and tropical cyclones will develop over the wet monsoon-flooded plains of Bengal. However, land friction is sufficient to prevent intensification to hurricane force, although winds

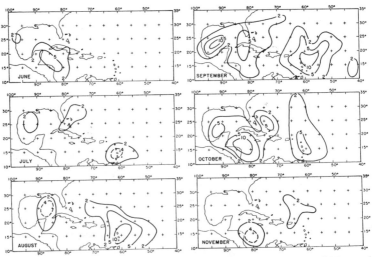

Fig. 16. Total frequency of Tropical-Cyclone Tracks starting within each 5° square during the period 1887–1950. (After Colón)

of 60 mph will occasionally occur in the province of Bengal as these storms begin moving northwestward across northern India. In the fall, tropical cyclones are accompanied by torrential rains which, falling on ground already soaked by the summer monsoon rains, often result in disastrous flooding.

In the Southern Hemisphere hurricanes occur in three principal areas: (1) in the South Indian Ocean in the vicinity of and to the east of Madagascar, (2) off the northwest coast of Australia, and (3) in the South Pacific ocean off the east coast of Australia and north of New Zealand. In the Southern Hemisphere the wind blows clockwise around the center of low pressure. Hurricanes are confined to November through April, corresponding to the summer and fall months of the Northern Hemisphere.

Origin of Hurricanes in the Atlantic Area

Easterly waves in which hurricanes frequently develop may move more than two thousand miles before any indication of intensification can be detected. Even after the transition from stable to unstable wave has begun, a period of three to six days, sometimes longer, is often required for the initial small vortex circulation to grow to full hurricane intensity. During this period the wave may have traveled an additional 1,500 to 2,000 miles. When should it be said the hurricane formed? When the initial disturbance began to intensify, when the tropical storm reached hurricane intensity, or perhaps at some other point in its life history?

Two procedures have been devised to determine approximately the regions of maximum hurricane formation. Colón [9] has used the beginning of published tracks as an indication, although he is quick to say that the beginning of the track is not usually the point of formation, since the initial disturbance usually existed for some time prior to intensification. Colón based his study on the period 1887-1950, and during the earlier years disturbances of storm or even hurricane intensity could exist east of the Lesser Antilles for days before they arrived within the reporting network and were detected, although this is not often the case today, with more data and better detection methods available. The results of Colón's tabulations are shown in Figure 16.

Dunn [17] devised a different procedure and plotted the points at which the disturbances reached hurricane intensity. He used storms of

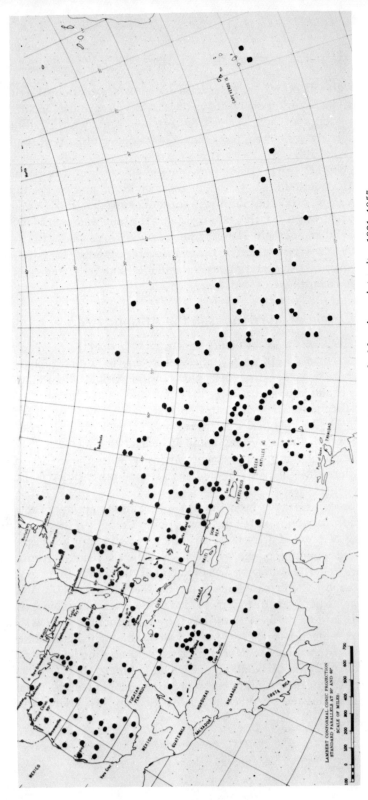

Fig. 17. Locations where Tropical Cyclones reached hurricane intensity, 1901–1957.

the 1901-1957 period and plotted only those for which he was reasonably confident that this point could be established accurately. These points are shown in Figure 17. During the past decade it has been possible to locate these positions very accurately on the basis of airplane-reconnaissance reports. Many tropical cyclones are first encountered by ships on the New York–Capetown route, and frequently several ships may send in reports on the day of discovery. Excellent inferences may be made in regard to the previous history of the storm from the lowest pressure and the size of the storm's circulation. It is believed that 85 per cent of the positions west of longitude 60° W are correct within $2\frac{1}{2}$°. The area of greatest uncertainty is southeast of Bermuda. East of longitude 60° W the positions become more and more questionable as the supporting data become scantier. In this area, the errors will have a bias, and in almost all cases the position, if in error, should be farther to the east than plotted.

Three hurricane developments have been placed in the Cape Verde area, although a definite report of hurricane winds can be found in only one storm. In the majority of instances, evidence available at this late date indicates only that an unstable wave passed through the islands and that hurricane intensity was actually reached some 10° to 15° or more to the westward. Hurricane positions from 1901 through 1915 are the least reliable.

On Figure 17, one concentration will be noted just to the east of Swan Island and another just to the east of the Leeward and Windward Islands. The only two 5° squares where none reached hurricane intensity are between Hispaniola and Venezuela. Mitchell [64] stated, "In every instance the *first evidence* of storm development, although rather obscure in some cases, was found either over the western third of the Caribbean Sea (west of Long. 78° W) or to the east of the eastern limits of the Caribbean Sea." This statement has been misquoted to the effect that hurricanes do not develop in the eastern and central portions of the Caribbean. Certainly, comparatively few storms reach hurricane intensity in this area, particularly between longitude 67° and 75°, perhaps due to the significant divergence in the lower tropospheric easterly flow as the easterly trade is diverted into the semipermanent low over the Amazon Valley. On the other hand two recent severe hurricanes — Hazel of 1954 and Janet of 1955 — attained great intensity in this area, although both were immature hurricanes when they entered the Caribbean.

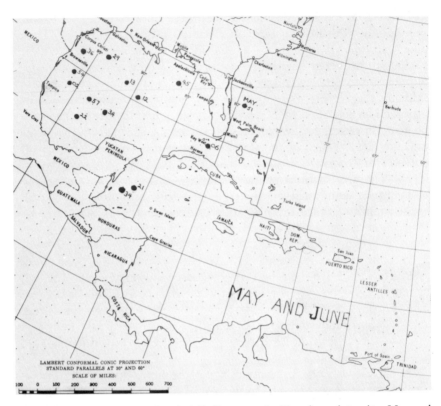

Fig. 18. Locations where Tropical Cyclones reached hurricane intensity, May and June, 1901–1957. The two digits at each location indicate the year.

Of the 251 hurricanes plotted on Figure 17, approximately 41 developed in perturbations moving away from the intertropical convergence zone (ITC) in the Panama region, although almost all of the major development occurred a considerable distance away from the ITC. Most of the remaining hurricanes (210) developed in easterly waves. Even the developements in the Cape Verde Islands may be associated with easterly waves rather than the ITC, although evidence is not conclusive. Whether here and in other low-latitude developments east of the Leeward Islands, some of the initial impulses come from the ITC is difficult to say, since the area can hardly be said to be within the field of observation. It is evident that the great majority of Atlantic hurricanes do not undergo their principal development in the doldrums or in the ITC, but rather in the trade-wind current. Indeed a comparison of the areas of hurricane formation in the Atlantic with the *Atlas of Climatic Charts of the Oceans* [108] indicates that many of the tropical storms reach hurricane intensity in the region where the constancy and strength of the trades is the greatest and frequency of calms the least.

Hurricane formation in May (1) and June (13), Figure 18, is confined to the extreme western Caribbean and the Gulf of Mexico, with one exception — the one May Hurricane forming off the east coast of Florida in 1951.

July hurricane positions are plotted on Figure 19. Nine of the sixteen reached hurricane intensity along a narrow band from the Lesser Antilles northwestward to a point off the east coast of Florida. One in

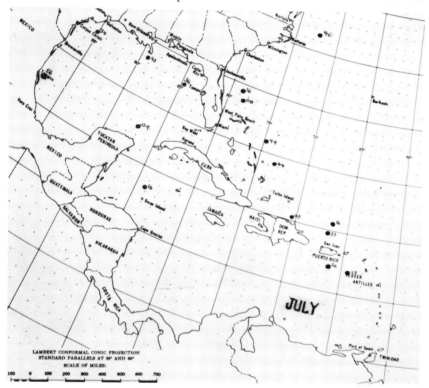

Fig. 19. Locations where Tropical Cyclones reached hurricane intensity, July, 1901–1957. The two digits at each location indicate the year.

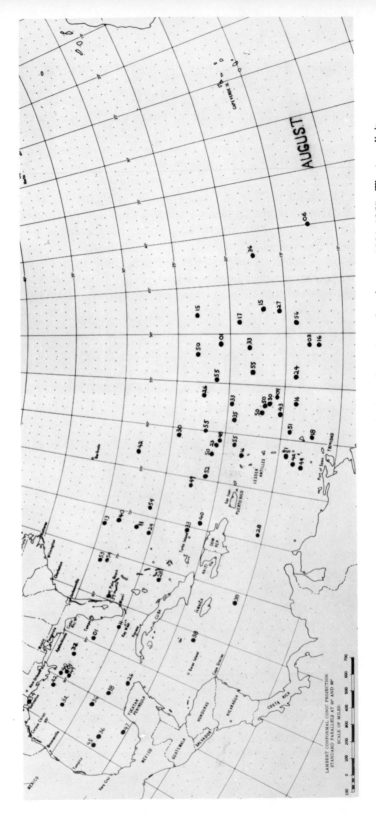

Fig. 20. Locations where Tropical Cyclones reached hurricane intensity, August, 1901–1957. The two digits at each location indicate the year.

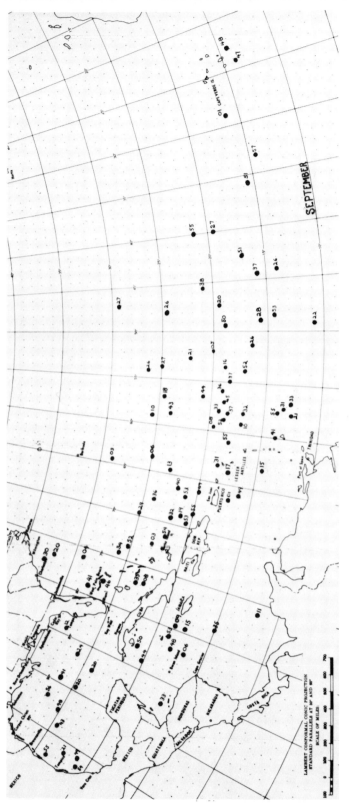

Fig. 21. Locations where Tropical Cyclones reached hurricane intensity, September, 1901–1957. The two digits at each location indicate the year.

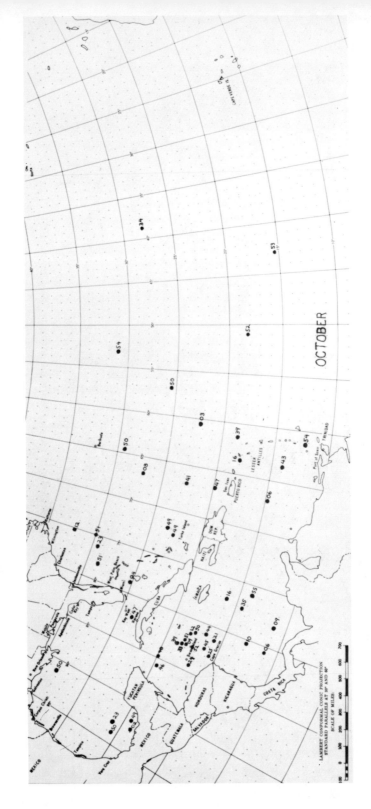

Fig. 22. Locations where Tropical Cyclones reached hurricane intensity, October, 1901–1957. The two digits at each location indicate the year.

1946 reached hurricane intensity in about latitude 36.5° N and longitude 72.5° W, the northernmost point of development noted during the period 1901-1957. Five hurricanes formed in the Gulf of Mexico, one in the northwestern Caribbean and none east of longitude 58° W.

The sixty-eight hurricanes in August are well scattered between latitude 11° N and 30° N in the Atlantic and Gulf of Mexico, with the greatest concentration in and east of the Leeward and Windward Islands, Figure 20. Only three August hurricanes formed in the Caribbean Sea west of longitude 62.5° W, and two of these were in 1938. There is no authenticated case of a storm reaching hurricane intensity near the ITC in the vicinity of the Cape Verdes. The heavy concentration in and east of the eastern Antilles lies astride the trade wind of greatest strength and constancy.

September's ninety-five hurricanes, Figure 21, are spaced rather similarly to August's except for a significant number forming in the northwestern Caribbean and close to the Mexican coast in the Gulf of Mexico.

The principal concentration in October, Figure 22, is in the northwestern Caribbean, with marked diminution in all other sections. Formation in the Gulf of Mexico is largely confined to the Bay of Campeche.

Frequency of Atlantic Hurricanes

The frequency of tropical storms and those reaching hurricane intensity for the period 1901-1958 by months and for all areas in the Atlantic is given in Table 3. The "storm" classification includes all tropical cyclones whether or not they reached hurricane intensity.

During recent years there has been frequent speculation on the possibility that the annual number of hurricanes is on the increase. Over the past seventy years an average of eight tropical cyclones per year has occurred. This average has increased to nine per year over the past forty years and to ten per year during the past twenty years. This increase is believed to be due in part to better detection, but there also appears to have been a significant increase in the number of hurricanes beginning around 1930. A gradual warming of the atmosphere apparently began about that time, and the greater number of tropical cyclones is probably due to that warming trend. During the past several years the warming trend has apparently been reversed, and in 1956 and 1957 the number of cyclones fell off to eight.

TABLE 3
Frequency of Tropical Storms and Those of Hurricane Intensity (by Months), 1901–1958

		Mar.	May	June	July	Aug.	Sept.	Oct.	Nov.	Dec.	Total
1901	Storms		0	1	2	1	3	2	1	0	10
	Hurricanes		0	0	1	1	1	0	0	0	3
1902	Storms		0	2	0	0	1	1	1	0	5
	Hurricanes		0	1	0	0	1	1	0	0	3
1903	Storms		0	0	1	1	4	2	1	0	9
	Hurricanes		0	0	1	1	3	2	1	0	8
1904	Storms		0	1	0	0	1	3	1	0	6
	Hurricanes		0	0	0	0	1	1	0	0	2
1905	Storms		0	0	0	0	3	2	0	0	5
	Hurricanes		0	0	0	0	0	1	0	0	1
1906	Storms		0	2	0	1	3	4	1	0	11
	Hurricanes		0	1	0	1	2	2	0	0	6
1907	Storms		0	1	0	0	2	1	0	0	4
	Hurricanes		0	0	0	0	0	0	0	0	0
1908	Storms	1	0	0	1	1	3	2	0	0	8
	Hurricanes	1	0	0	1	0	2	0	0	0	4
1909	Storms		0	2	2	2	2	1	2	0	11
	Hurricanes		0	0	1	1	1	1	0	0	4
1910	Storms		0	0	0	1	2	1	0	0	4
	Hurricanes		0	0	0	0	2	1	0	0	3
1911	Storms		0	0	0	2	1	1	0	0	4
	Hurricanes		0	0	0	2	1	0	0	0	3
1912	Storms		0	1	1	0	2	3	1	0	8
	Hurricanes		0	1	0	0	1	2	1	0	5
1913	Storms		0	1	0	1	1	1	0	0	4
	Hurricanes		0	1	0	1	1	0	0	0	3
1914	Storms		0	0	0	0	1	0	0	0	1
	Hurricanes		0	0	0	0	0	0	0	0	0
1915	Storms		0	0	0	2	3	0	0	0	5
	Hurricanes		0	0	0	1	3	0	0	0	4
1916	Storms		0	0	3	3	4	3	1	0	14
	Hurricanes		0	0	3	3	2	2	1	0	11
1917	Storms		0	0	0	1	2	0	0	0	3
	Hurricanes		0	0	0	0	2	0	0	0	2
1918	Storms		0	0	0	3	2	0	0	0	5
	Hurricanes		0	0	0	2	1	0	0	0	3
1919	Storms		0	0	1	0	2	0	0	0	3
	Hurricanes		0	0	0	0	1	0	0	0	1
1920	Storms		0	0	0	0	4	0	0	0	4
	Hurricanes		0	0	0	0	4	0	0	0	4

TABLE 3 (Continued)

		Mar.	May	June	July	Aug.	Sept.	Oct.	Nov.	Dec.	Total
1921	Storms	0	1	0	0	3	1	0	0		5
	Hurricanes	0	1	0	0	2	1	0	0		4
1922	Storms	0	1	0	0	1	2	0	0		4
	Hurricanes	0	1	0	0	1	1	0	0		3
1923	Storms	0	0	0	0	2	3	0	0		5
	Hurricanes	0	0	0	0	2	2	0	0		4
1924	Storms	0	1	0	2	2	2	1	0		8
	Hurricanes	0	0	0	2	1	1	1	0		5
1925	Storms	0	0	0	0	1	0	0		1	2
	Hurricanes	0	0	0	0	0	0	0		1	1
1926	Storms	0	0	1	2	5	1	1	0		10
	Hurricanes	0	0	1	2	4	1	0	0		8
1927	Storms	0	0	0	1	3	2	1	0		7
	Hurricanes	0	0	0	1	3	0	0	0		4
1928	Storms	0	0	0	2	3	1	0	0		6
	Hurricanes	0	0	0	2	1	1	0	0		4
1929	Storms	0	1	0	0	1	1	0	0		3
	Hurricanes	0	1	0	0	1	1	0	0		3
1930	Storms	0	0	0	1	1	0	0	0		2
	Hurricanes	0	0	0	1	1	0	0	0		2
1931	Storms	0	1	1	2	4	1	1	0		10
	Hurricanes	0	0	0	0	2	0	0	0		2
1932	Storms	1	0	0	2	4	2	2	0		11
	Hurricanes	0	0	0	2	2	0	2	0		6
1933	Storms	1	1	3	6	6	3	1	0		21
	Hurricanes	0	1	1	2	4	1	0	0		9
1934	Storms	1	1	1	2	2	3	1	0		11
	Hurricanes	0	1	1	1	1	1	1	0		6
1935	Storms	0	0	0	1	3	1	1	0		6
	Hurricanes	0	0	0	1	2	1	1	0		5
1936	Storms	0	3	2	6	5	1	0	0		17
	Hurricanes	0	2	1	3	2	0	0	0		8
1937	Storms	0	0	1	2	5	1	0	0		9
	Hurricanes	0	0	0	0	2	0	0	0		2
1938	Storms	0	0	0	2	1	3	1	0		7
	Hurricanes	0	0	0	2	1	0	0	0		3
1939	Storms	0	1	0	1	1	1	1	0		5
	Hurricanes	0	0	0	0	0	1	1	0		2
1940	Storms	1	0	0	3	2	2	0	0		8
	Hurricanes	0	0	0	3	1	0	0	0		4

TABLE 3 (Continued)

		Jan.	Feb.	Mar.	Apr.	May	June	July	Aug.	Sept.	Oct.	Nov.	Dec.	Total
1941	Storms	0	0	0	0	0	0	0	0	4	2	0	0	6
	Hurricanes	0	0	0	0	0	0	0	0	3	1	0	0	4
1942	Storms	0	0	0	0	0	0	0	3	3	3	1	0	10
	Hurricanes	0	0	0	0	0	0	0	3	0	0	1	0	4
1943	Storms	0	0	0	0	0	0	1	2	4	3	0	0	10
	Hurricanes	0	0	0	0	0	0	1	1	2	1	0	0	5
1944	Storms	0	0	0	0	0	0	2	3	3	2	0	0	10
	Hurricanes	0	0	0	0	0	0	1	2	2	1	0	0	6
1945	Storms	0	0	0	0	0	1	1	4	3	1	0	0	10
	Hurricanes	0	0	0	0	0	1	0	1	1	1	0	0	4
1946	Storms	0	0	0	0	0	1	1	1	1	1	1	0	6
	Hurricanes	0	0	0	0	0	0	1	0	1	1	0	0	3
1947	Storms	0	0	0	0	0	0	1	2	3	3	0	0	9
	Hurricanes	0	0	0	0	0	0	0	2	1	2	0	0	5
1948	Storms	0	0	0	0	2	0	1	3	2	1	1	0	10
	Hurricanes	0	0	0	0	0	0	0	2	2	1	1	0	6
1949	Storms	0	0	0	0	0	0	0	3	8	2	1	0	14
	Hurricanes	0	0	0	0	0	0	0	2	3	2	0	0	7
1950	Storms	0	0	0	0	0	0	0	3	4	6	0	0	13
	Hurricanes	0	0	0	0	0	0	0	3	4	4	0	0	11
1951	Storms	0	0	0	0	1	0	0	3	4	2	0	0	10
	Hurricanes	0	0	0	0	1	0	0	2	3	2	0	0	8
1952	Storms	0	1	0	0	0	0	0	1	3	2	0	0	7
	Hurricanes	0	0	0	0	0	0	0	1	3	2	0	0	6
1953	Storms	0	0	0	0	1	0	0	3	4	4	1	1	14
	Hurricanes	0	0	0	0	0	0	0	2	3	1	0	0	6
1954	Storms	0	0	0	0	0	1	1	1	4	2	1	0	10
	Hurricanes	0	0	0	0	0	1	0	1	3	2	0	0	7
1955	Storms	1	0	0	0	0	0	0	5	5	2	0	0	13
	Hurricanes	1	0	0	0	0	0	0	3	5	1	0	0	10
1956	Storms	0	0	0	0	0	1	1	1	4	0	1	0	8
	Hurricanes	0	0	0	0	0	0	1	1	1	0	1	0	4
1957	Storms	0	0	0	0	0	2	0	1	4	1	0	0	8
	Hurricanes	0	0	0	0	0	1	0	0	2	0	0	0	3
1958	Storms	0	0	0	0	0	1	0	4	4	1	0	0	10
	Hurricanes	0	0	0	0	0	0	0	3	3	1	0	0	7

	Jan.	Feb.	Mar.	Apr.	May	June	July	Aug.	Sept.	Oct.	Nov.	Dec.	Total
Total Storms	1	1	1	0	8	29	29	97	168	96	27	2	459
Total Hurricanes	1	0	1	0	1	14	15	64	104	48	12	1	261

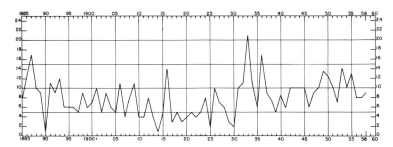

Fig. 23. Annual Variation in the Number of Tropical Cyclones, 1885–1958.

Figure 23 shows the yearly variation in the number of storms from 1885 to 1958. The annual variation is greater than any possible longer-period variation, and in order to smooth out the former, five-year running averages have been computed (see Figure 24). The value for 1920, for example, is the average for the years 1918-1922 inclusive. One slight maximum is evident at the beginning of the period and another beginning in the early 1930's. It is considered significant that following the abrupt increase in the five-year averages which occurred in the early 1930's, the frequency has remained at a higher level and has not dropped back to the average which prevailed from about 1895 to 1930. The periods around 1900 and following 1910 are characterized by low tropical-cyclone frequencies. The highest five-year average was thirteen and the lowest four.

The yearly variability is of course greater than that of the five-year averages. During the past seventy years the largest number of tropical cyclones in any one year was twenty-one in 1933; only one was noted in 1890 and 1914 and two in both 1925 and 1930. At one time in 1893 and more recently on several occasions (see Figure 25) three hurricanes were in progress at the same time in the Gulf, the Caribbean, or the Atlantic.

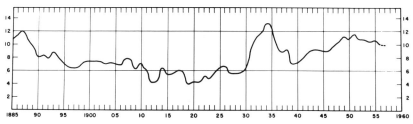

Fig. 24. Five-Year Running Average of Tropical-Cyclone Frequencies.

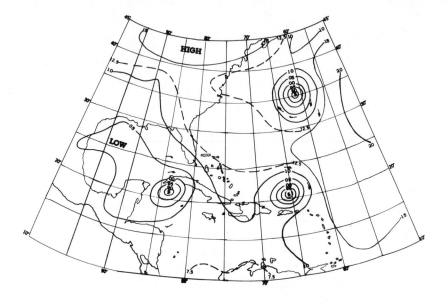

Fig. 25. Weather Map of 7:30 A.M., September 2, 1950, showing three hurricanes in progress at one time.

The variation by months of hurricanes and other tropical cyclones in the North Atlantic area for the period 1887-1958 is shown in Table 4:

TABLE 4
Monthly Variation of Hurricanes in the North Atlantic Areas, 1887–1958

	Full Hurricane Intensity	Not of Hurricane Intensity	All Tropical Cyclones	Per Cent of Cyclones Reaching Hurricane Intensity
January	1	0*	1	100
February	0	1*	1	0
March	1	0*	1	100
April	0	0	0	0
May	2	8	10	20
June	15	20	35	43
July	20	17	37	54
August	97	34	131	74
September	120	73	193	62
October	63	68	131	47
November	11	18	29	38
December	1	2	3	33
Total	331	241	572	58

*Probably other tropical cyclones during these months.

Storms are placed in the month in which they began. The advance and decline of the hurricane season can easily be seen from Table 4. One out-of-season hurricane was reported in the Windward Islands in March, 1906, and another in January, 1955. May is an unimportant hurricane month, since only two hurricanes have been reported.

June storms are usually small in area but may be rather intense, and hurricane Audrey, 1957, falls within this category. A storm appears on the average about every other year, but one of hurricane intensity is noted only about every six years.

Tropical cyclones are only slightly more common in July than in June. They are usually larger in size and are somewhat more likely to reach hurricane intensity. However, none of the major hurricanes of the last seventy-two years have occurred in July.

A marked increase in the frequency and in the percentage of tropical cyclones which reach hurricane force occurs in August. Some of the most severe hurricanes of record have occurred in this month.

The height of the hurricane season is reached in early September. One third of all tropical cyclones in the Atlantic occur in this month, although many do not reach hurricane intensity.

Following a temporary lull during the last half of September, there is a decided increase again early in October. After the middle of October the hurricane season declines rapidly, and only a few of the tropical cyclones reach hurricane intensity after the second decade of this month.

The season continues to decline rapidly in November, and some of the storms included in this list developed in westerly troughs. December is an unimportant month for tropical cyclones. A hurricane was in progress on December 1, 1925, but developed in November and is included in the November list.

TABLE 5

Probabilities of Tropical Cyclone Occurrences per Month
(After Colón)

	May	June	July	Aug.	Sept.	Oct.	Nov.
At least 1 storm	0.09	0.34	0.39	0.75	0.92	0.83	0.36
2 or more storms	0.02	0.06	0.11	0.52	0.72	0.59	0.03
3 or more storms	0.00	0.02	0.03	0.19	0.42	0.34	0.03

Thus, in any September there is a 92 per cent chance that there will be at least one tropical cyclone somewhere in the Atlantic and a 42 per cent chance there will be three or more storms. This Table is based on tropical cyclones of all intensities observed during the period 1887-1950.

Gentry, Moore, and Marshall [29] have calculated the frequency of hurricanes for the 52-year period, 1900 through 1951, for different sections of the United States coast line, which calculation has been extended through 1957 in Table 6. The areas are listed in descending order of frequency per unit length of smoothed coast line. The total number of hurricanes shown for each area is significant only· when compared with those for other sections of similar size.

TABLE 6

Frequency of Hurricanes for Various Sections of the United States Coast Line, 1900–1957

Area	No. of Tropical Cyclones Giving Hurricane Force Winds	Relative Ratio
Extreme southern Florida (Miami—Cape Sable southward through Florida Keys)	18	12.0
Alabama and northwest Florida	20	7.6
Texas	24	7.2
North Carolina	17	6.2
Eastern Florida (north of Greater Miami)	16	5.2
Louisiana and Mississippi	18	4.0
Virginia	8	4.0
Florida West Coast (south of Apalachee Bay and north of Cape Sable)	14	3.7
South Carolina	5	3.1
Maryland, Delaware, and New Jersey	6	1.8
New York and New England	8	1.5
Georgia	3	1.1

The variation in frequency (by months) of hurricane occurrences from 1879 to 1958 in various segments of the United States coast line is shown in Table 7.

Approximately 60 per cent of all tropical cyclones reach hurricane intensity. Only about 25 per cent approach close enough to the coast line of the United States to cause hurricane winds over any land area. No state except Florida averages one full hurricane per year. Extreme southern Florida and the northwest Florida coast between Apalachicola and Pensacola are the most frequently visited of any section of the United States. However, there will be periods when hurricanes will be relatively frequent and then there may be a period of five to twenty years or more with few, if any, at any particular point.

TABLE 7

Number of Hurricanes (by Months) Affecting Various Coastal Areas, 1879–1958

	Texas	La. Miss. Ala.	Fla. Gulf	Fla. Atlantic	S. C. Ga.	N. C.	North Atlantic States	New England
June	6	2	3	0	0	0	0	0
July	4	1	4	2	0	0	0	0
August	13	7	3	8	7	10	2	3
September	8	15	15	10	4	10	5	4
October	4	4	12	13	4	2	2	1
November	0	0	1	2	0	0	0	0
December	0	0	0	1	0	0	0	0

Monthly Variation in Hurricane Tracks

Tropical-cyclone development is a seasonal phenomenon wherever it occurs, embracing principally the summer and fall months in each hemisphere. If one looks at a chart showing the hurricane paths over any considerable period, the tracks appear to have little rhyme or reason. No two hurricanes follow the same or parallel paths from the time of origin to the time of dissipation. Tracks cross and recross and recurve in all areas without seeming to obey any physical law. Some recurve, some do not, some loop, some slow almost to a standstill, and some will accelerate 1,500 per cent in twenty-four hours. If, however, the tracks are plotted by months or by ten-day periods a little order appears. In almost all the hurricane-susceptible areas the mean storm track, and to a lesser extent the place of most frequent origin, changes in a logical manner from month to month during the storm season. However, from year to year the individual storm tracks vary considerably, and it is rather difficult to decide on a mean track.

June storms develop in the northwestern Caribbean or in the Gulf of Mexico, and the Texas coast line is the most vulnerable of any section of the United States. A few recurve toward Florida but these are usually quite weak. Several early- and late-season hurricanes have formed from remnants of Pacific storms that have crossed Central America, of which the June 11-17, 1936, hurricane is an example.

Tropical cyclones in July are slightly larger in size than those in June. They tend to have a rather strong westerly component and are about as likely to reach the coast line of one state in the hurricane belt as another.

The main hurricane season begins in August with a marked increase in number and intensity. Since many of the hurricanes during this month develop to the east of the surface-plotting chart normally used prior to the early 1940's, the earlier forecasters gave them the name "Cape Verde Hurricanes." During August and early September, some storms do reach hurricane intensity within 10° to 15° longitude of the Cape Verdes and if they remain on a fairly straight westerly course and move steadily along at around 15 mph, they will approach the United States coast line as very large and severe hurricanes. The Miami and West Palm Beach hurricanes of 1926 and 1928 were good examples of the Cape Verde type. However, the great majority of August and early September hurricanes develop west of longitudes 45° and 50° and should not be included in the Cape Verde classification. The trades are normally strongest in August, and August hurricanes usually have strong westerly components and have the highest average hourly movement (in the tropics) of any month. If they recurve up the Atlantic, they usually travel on a comparatively smooth parabolic curve.

The climax of the hurricane season is reached during the first half of September. Forecasters often say there is a greater likelihood of a hurricane on the map during the Labor Day week end than at any other time. During the first half of the month most of the storms come from the Antilles or to the eastward, but during the last half of the month many will also develop in the western Caribbean, and storms gradually begin to develop greater northerly components as the polar westerlies move southward. There is a rather marked decrease in frequency during the latter half of the month.

There is a minor increase in frequency again in early October as hurricanes develop in the northwestern Caribbean, often within 150 miles of Swan Island. All have strong northerly components and recurve fairly quickly. Rarely do hurricanes move as far west as Texas after September 15. The frequency and average intensity declines rapidly after mid-October. Florida, Cuba, and Jamaica are frequent targets for October storms.

Cycles and Climate

Is our climate changing and do we have hurricane cycles? The best-known and most definite climatic cycles are those from ice age to interglacial period to ice age again. There is strong evidence there have been at least four ice ages. The ice ages last for about 50,000,000 years and the interglacial periods about 250,000,000 years. Superimposed upon these major climatic cycles are numerous other cycles of various lengths and degrees. That is, a minor short-term warming trend may be superimposed upon a longer-term cooling cycle, which, in turn, is superimposed upon a still longer warming cycle. The meteorological history of the earth which is known to man comprises only a very insignificant period of time.

There is evidence of a very significant, probably a very short-term cycle, climatic change during the past several decades. Codfish, once plentiful over the Grand Banks off the Canadian Maritime Provinces, are now found closer to Greenland. Glaciers are retreating. Armadillos from Mexico are invading the Gulf coastal areas. The permanent snow line in certain mountainous areas has moved several hundred feet up the mountainside. Flora and fauna in many sections have advanced noticeably northward. Indeed, the meteorological records indicate a warming during the past three decades of some 2° F. This may seem of little significance, but if the earth continued to warm at this rate for another five hundred years or less, some of our most productive areas would become virtually uninhabitable deserts and the most profound changes would occur economically and politically. On the other hand a fall of 10° F. would bring on another ice age. The warming trend which was most pronounced in the thirties seems to have slowed, and there are now some indications of a reversal. The winters of 1955-1956 and 1956-1957 were cold and snowy in many areas of the Northern Hemisphere.

The higher temperatures have led to warmer ocean temperatures. In August, 1955, ocean temperatures were 7° F. warmer than normal off the coast of Maine. Figure 24 shows there has been a slight but significant increase in the annual average of hurricanes since 1930 which coincides with the beginning of the warming of the earth's atmosphere. Also beginning about the same time, the New England and Middle Atlantic States began to be affected more frequently by hurricanes. The August 22-23, 1933, hurricane which moved on a northwesterly course near Cape Hatteras and south of Norfolk up Chesapeake Bay was the first of the series. Severe hurricanes struck New England in 1938 and again in 1944 and perhaps culminated with Carol and Edna in 1954 and the record-breaking floods of Diane in 1955.

The general warming of the earth's atmosphere, at least in the Northern Hemisphere, has tended to push the principal boundary between the tropical and polar air masses — the polar front — farther north than normal. Since the strong westerlies are associated with the polar front, this wind stream or jet also was north of its normal position. And, according to Willett [114], a leading student of long-range weather trends, the final stage of a warm cycle such as this is the development of a blocking circulation pattern, which, in the Atlantic, forces hurricanes that normally would recurve harmlessly northeastward over the open Atlantic, into the northeastern United States instead. Associated with this blocking, the Azores-Bermuda anticyclone, which is the weather control for the Atlantic, is found situated farther north and abnormally strong. The anticyclonic circulation around this HIGH, under these circumstances, results in a stronger and more persistent southerly component in the winds in the eastern United States carrying hurricanes imbedded in this air stream inland over the area from the Carolinas to New England and Canada.

Namias [69, 70] has pointed out the persistent anomaly (departure from long-period normal) of the circulation pattern of recent years. This flow pattern has been associated with a greater than normal south-to-north transport of warm, moist tropical air, or in other words, a more northward steering of hurricanes north of latitude 35°. As Namias points out, this encourages storms to retain devastating tropical characteristics for a longer period. Namias is uncertain concerning the causes of the abnormal circulation patterns and does not dismiss completely the possibility that they are completely internal mechanisms of the earth-atmosphere system.

According to Dr. Willett, the wind circulation determines the weather and the circulation depends upon atmospheric conditions that are determined by, or coincide with, changing conditions in the gaseous atmosphere of the sun; consequently there is a relationship between sunspot activity and temperature and precipitation on the earth. The relationship is complex, but sunspot activity can be forecast with some accuracy, and if the relationships found in the comparatively recent past hold, Dr. Willet forecasts an end to the present warm dry cycle within the immediate future and that within ten years (by 1965), hurricanes will return to their traditional track in the Caribbean, the Gulf of Mexico, and the Atlantic. However, even if this occurs, many points in these areas will still have long periods without hurricanes. And along with this change in cycle would be associated a small but significant decrease in frequency.

4

CHARACTERISTICS OF THE HURRICANE
A Hurricane Comes and Goes

ANY STUDENT OF HURRICANES BECOMES MORE AND MORE impressed with their individuality; no two identical tropical cyclones have ever been observed. Although they always differ in detail and often in certain major characteristics, nevertheless there is also a very real similarity among tropical cyclones, particularly when in the same latitude. Let us see what the normal sequence of weather events might be as a hurricane in late August passes over one of the small islands in the Antilles.

The day is Tuesday and it is a little warmer than usual with plenty of hot tropical sunshine. There is no high or middle cloud, only a few fair-weather cumuli and no sign of a cooling shower anywhere, not even where they are almost always observed over the mountains in the west. The wind is easterly as usual, but instead of the customary 20 mph at midday, it is only about half that much and occasionally the palm fronds barely move. Early in the afternoon on the east side of the island the ocean begins to present a somewhat abnormal appearance, and an hour or two later a very discernible long, low swell is noted rolling in from the east-southeast. The swell is somewhat stronger than the normal trade-wind swell and it is coming in from a slightly different direction. Some of the fishermen are heard to say that there is a hurricane somewhere off to the east, but since this happens four or five times each year and hurricanes apparently rarely affect this particular island, no one is disturbed. The barometer is normal.

It is Wednesday morning; the sky is clear and the barometer is several hundredths of an inch higher than yesterday. The long, high swells are now definitely rolling in and, breaking, crash on the shore with a sound that can be heard nearly half a mile inland. Counting them, it appears that six swells pass a given point every minute in contrast to the usual ten or eleven. This would indicate a hurricane of

58

moderate intensity. As the hours pass, the weather feels unusually oppressive and sultry, the winds are variable and fitful with occasional dead calms — there is no trade wind. By midafternoon fine wisps of cirrus appear in the southeast; by sunset they have passed the zenith, moving a little faster than usual, and the cirrostratus is solid and milky in the east and southeast. The sunset is red and orange, and very beautiful, but not much different from those observed on many other days during the year. This is the second consecutive day with no showers. The fishermen now glance frequently and anxiously out at the heavy swells and surf. The weather signs are more ominous and they decide to stay up tonight. Others check their supply of kerosene and food and get an additional supply of ice for their old-fashioned refrigerators. They take a look at their shutters and get ready their hammer and nails.

It is after midnight when occasional gentle but rather gusty breezes begin to rustle through the tropical foliage, and the sound is somewhat different from usual. The moon still shines dimly through the high cloud. The morning dawns later and darker than yesterday and smooth altostratus clouds obscure the sun. The barometer has fallen more than a tenth of an inch during the night and the wind is now steady northeast and gusty, 10 to 20 mph. As one native meets another or groups gather together, you pick out the words: "Hurricane coming." The pounding of hammers is heard everywhere as shutters are nailed across the windows. The women are gathering mops, rags, and cloths for later use. Fishermen and others with boats are taking them up the river to hoped-for places of safety.

Between 7:00 and 8:00 a.m. the roar of drumming raindrops is heard from far off. It comes rapidly closer, passing over with a hard burst of rain lasting only a few minutes, then retreats, growing fainter off to the west. It is now 9:00 a.m., the wind is now north-northeast, gusting 30 to 35 mph, the sea is tremendous — hard to estimate the height of the waves — the surf wild and noisy, the clouds are matted, dark in the east, and scud clouds are moving rapidly overhead. The barometer has fallen another tenth of an inch. Shortly the pounding of another shower is heard in the northeast and in a minute or two a rainstorm arrives, with gusts of wind longer and stronger than before. Even when the squall passes, the rain does not completely cease.

By 10:00 a.m. the wind is north, 45 to 50 mph, and increasing with every passing squall, and the barometer is down more than another tenth. The tree limbs are thrashing; the coconut palms bent from the constant northeasterly trades lean even more in the gale. One last look at the ocean before the door is closed and bolted — it is white with blowing spray and blends with the sky a short distance offshore. Within minutes the wind reaches hurricane force and continues to rise higher and higher, driving water in around the windows; water gurgles under the door, water everywhere.

During the next two hours the howling and screaming of the wind becomes indescribable, the house quivers and shakes and seems to want to rise off the foundation, torrents of rain gush all around. The wind is in excess of 100 mph and is now dealing destruction over the island. One hears splitting of limbs, the crashing of trees, the occasional thud of a coconut against the house, the noise of unseen objects flying through the air and hitting other objects. One is almost numbed by fear but work has to be done. The dank air seems chilly and clammy and it is almost as wet inside as outside. The mop and rags are in constant use but the water rises deeper and deeper on the floor. It seems impossible, but the wind continues to increase, its pitch higher and higher. Verily it seems like a monstrous living thing trying to tear the house apart. One easily imagines he can see the marker on the aneroid barometer move toward lower pressure.

Suddenly one realizes the tone of the wind has changed. The sound and fury have lessened, and in no more than 10 minutes the wind subsides to a fitful breeze, the rain ends, the sky lightens, and a few brief rays of sunshine filter down on a stricken island. We are in the eye of the hurricane. The barometer reads 28.5 — this is a hurricane of about average intensity for the tropics.

The twenty minutes of grace are used in making repairs and preparing for the second onslaught of this monster of the sea. There seems something unnatural about the air; it is oppressive, hard to breathe, and too silent after the tumult of a few minutes ago. Out over the ocean the waves are high, confused, and turbulent. No piers can be seen. Are they destroyed or only covered by the hurricane tide? The ocean seems about two hundred feet nearer than usual. A new noise like a distant express train is heard, the wind is rising, it is getting dark again, and there is an abrupt renewal of the screaming wind and gushing rain as if the unseen giant were now trying to break in on the opposite side of the house. Two more hours — will it ever stop? Yes, it is getting less. Another hour or two and the rain has stopped, the winds are subsiding. The sun comes out for a few minutes before dark, the events of the day are already becoming a memory — only the stricken island and our water-soaked and battered homes remind us.

The Wind

The world's record winds have never been measured, because no wind instruments have been devised to withstand their fury. These occur within the tornado, in which winds have been estimated as high as 400 to 500 mph. The fastest wind ever measured did not occur in a hurricane but at Mt. Washington Observatory, New Hampshire, where 188 mph, with gusts to 229, was recorded April 12, 1934. This same observatory, however, clocked 186 mph in connection with the passage of the famous New England hurricane of September 21, 1938. In both cases the wind speeds were greatly affected by the orographic effect of the mountain upon which the observatory is located.

Some extreme wind velocities are shown in Table 8. At Havana, Cuba, in October, 1944, a velocity of 163 mph was measured. In the Florida hurricane of September, 1947, a reliable one-minute wind velocity of 155 mph was measured at Hillsboro Light near Pompano Beach. Earlier this same storm had passed over Hope Town in the Bahamas, and the maximum wind was estimated at 160 mph. Probably neither of these extremes represent the actual maximum winds in the storm. Wind estimates varied from 130 to 150 mph from several points between Cape Fear, North Carolina, and Myrtle Beach, South Carolina, when the destructive Hazel passed over these locations in October, 1954. In San Juan, Puerto Rico, on September 13, 1928, the wind averaged 135 mph for a five-minute period, and the one-minute maximum was estimated at 144 mph. During the hurricane of August, 1949, the wind instrument at West Palm Beach, Florida, was blown away when the velocity reached 110 mph with gusts to 125. The highest wind was estimated at 120 mph with gusts to 130. A privately owned anemometer, the accuracy of which is unknown, recorded gusts to 155 mph. The anemometer at the airport terminal building at Chetumal, Mexico, registered 175 mph before it collapsed with the approach of hurricane Janet, September 28, 1955. The wind continued to increase and was estimated at more than 200 mph.

Even these speeds were undoubtedly exceeded in the Labor Day storm that struck the Florida Keys in 1935. Engineers have calculated that winds of 200 to 250 mph would have been required for some of the damage done during this severe hurricane. Winds of 150 mph probably occur not infrequently, but these are not often measured because few anemometers withstand winds of such force, and, too, the centers of hurricanes frequently pass inland at isolated points and the maximum winds seldom occur at locations where wind-measuring equipment is installed. There are some indications that winds within the 150–160-mph class struck Cameron, Louisiana, during hurricane Audrey in June, 1957.

TABLE 8
Maximum Winds Recorded in Hurricanes

	Date	Place	
1.	*Jan. 11, 1878	Mt. Washington, N.H.	†186 mph Robinson 140 mph true velocity
2.	Sept. 18, 1926	Miami Beach, Fla.	128 mph for 5 min., 123 mph true 138 mph for 2 min., 132 mph true
3.	Sept. 13, 1928	San Juan, P.R.	150 for 5 min., 135 true; estimated 160, 1 min., 144† true
4.	*April 12, 1934	Mt. Washington, N.H.	188 mph ,gusts 229, extreme 231, true 225 mph
5.	Sept. 21, 1938	Milton, Mass.	‡121 for 5 min., 186 for shorter period
6.	Sept. 21, 1938	Mt. Washington, N.H.	186 mph
7.	Oct. 18, 1944	Havana, Cuba	163 mph
8.	Sept. 17, 1947	Hillsboro Lighthouse, Fla.	155 mph extreme, 121 maximum
9.	Aug. 26, 1949	Jupiter Lighthouse, Fla.	132 mph, extreme 153
10.	Sept. 27-28, 1955	Chetumal, Mexico	175 mph

*The Mt. Washington velocities were not observed during hurricanes.
†Extreme.
‡Probably some orographic effect.

These measurements represent the wind velocities at land stations. At sea the surface friction is less than it is over land. Extreme wind measurements at sea are virtually unobtainable except by aircraft reconnaissance, because surface ships usually flee the paths of severe hurricanes, unless they are caught unawares, which, with present-day warn-

Fig. 26. Anemometers and Wind Vanes at Miami Weather Bureau Office. Cumulus clouds and altostratus in the background.

ing systems and high-speed communications, is almost a thing of the past. However, there is reason to believe that hurricane winds over the open seas exceed those observed at land stations.

Since the beginning of routine hurricane-reconnaissance flights in 1944, hardly a season has passed that failed to see aircraft wind reports of at least 140 to 150 mph or more. While it is true that these winds are estimated, the estimates are usually considered reliable. In 1951, for example, a flight was made into a hurricane off Puerto Rico, and the following postflight summary was filed:

Flight departed Ramey AFB, P.R., at dawn, and in a little more than an hour we were in hurricane winds and commenced circumnavigation, keeping an average distance of 70 miles from the center. On reaching the northwest quadrant, commenced gradual penetration until due west of center, then put the wind on the port wing and probed until winds reached 125 knots (144 mph) and plane became almost uncontrollable. At this

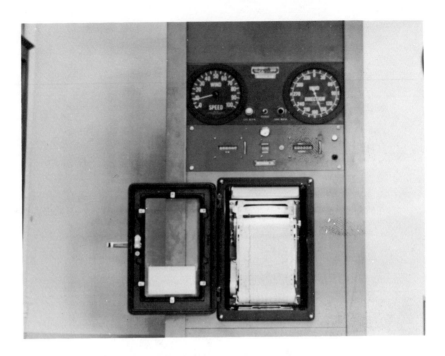

Fig. 27. Gust Recorder.

point radar showed edge of core to be 8 miles east. Unable to continue further, were forced to slide southward, eventually leaving the storm. Lowest observed pressure 979 mb (28.91 inches).

Winds in the south side of this severe hurricane were later estimated by aircraft at 140 knots (161 mph), and the center was still impenetrable. This indicated that the maximum winds on the stronger northern side of the storm were probably between 160 and 200 mph. Again in 1953 aircraft estimated the maximum winds in hurricane Carol in excess of 130 knots (150 mph), and the lowest pressure 930 mb (27.45 inches), on September 3 and 4.

More recently in hurricane Carrie (1957), winds of 150 mph were reported by aircraft when the storm was still midway between the African coast and the Lesser Antilles. At that time winds of hurricane force covered a diameter of 145 miles and gales extended over an area 230 miles wide.

The data in Table 8 represent the average wind for a period of either five minutes, one minute, or for one mile of wind travel. These winds are usually measured by means of the conventional three-cup anemometer shown in Figure 26. The accuracy of anemometers decreases rapidly with increasing wind velocity, so that large corrections have to be applied to the indicated reading in order to obtain the true wind velocity. The anemometer also has the disadvantage of being slow to

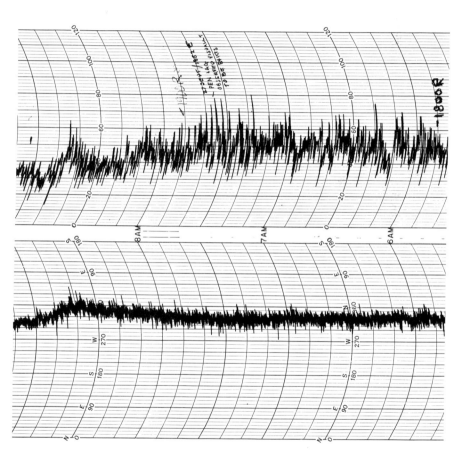

Fig. 28. Gust-Recorder Trace made at Marine Corps Air Station, Cherry Point, N.C., during the passage of Hurricane Helene, September 27, 1958. Note the variation in wind direction as well as in speed.

respond to rapid fluctuations in wind speed, and as a result the peak gusts in hurricanes have seldom been recorded.

Recently a number of "gust recorders" have been installed at key Weather Bureau stations in order to determine the peak gusts. The recording portion of this type of wind system is shown in Figure 27, and an example of the variability of the wind in a hurricane is revealed by Figure 28 (Helene, 1958). Gust recordings made in other hurricanes have indicated that extreme gusts exceed the highest sustained winds by 30 to 50 per cent. If these are correct, gusts of over 200 mph can be expected in connection with hurricane winds of 150 mph. It is these powerful gusts in hurricanes that makes their winds so destructive.

Most hurricanes will have maximum winds of at least 100 mph at some time during their life histories. Hughes [40] has worked out the average wind speeds around Pacific storms by using about 500 individual wind reports made by reconnaissance flights at a height of about 1,000 feet above the ocean. These data (Figure 29) show a maximum of about 90 knots (103 mph) to the right of the direction of motion, looking downstream. Individual storms will quite naturally be expected to differ considerably from this mean picture. That the stronger winds occur to the right is, however, typical of a moving hurricane. It is due

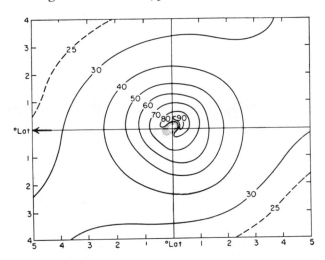

Fig. 29. Mean Wind Speed (knots) around a Tropical Cyclone. Based on aircraft reconnaissance, winds measured near 1,000 feet. Arrow at left indicates the direction in which the storm is moving. (After Hughes)

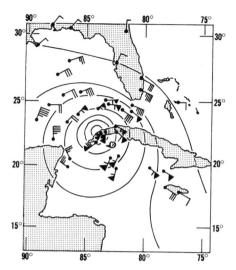

Fig. 30. Wind Circulation around a typical hurricane in the Northern Hemisphere. Outer isobar is 30.00 inches, with isobars at 0.20-inch intervals.
Single barbs indicate 10 knots and pennants 50 knots.

in part to the fact that on the right side the forward motion of the
storm is added to the observed wind velocity and on the left it is
subtracted. A stationary storm would be more symmetrical.

In the Northern Hemisphere winds around the tropical cyclone (or
any other cyclone for that matter) blow counterclockwise, while in the
Southern Hemisphere they blow clockwise. This is illustrated in Figures
30 and 31. At the same time the winds incline inward toward the
center until they reach the edge of the eye of the storm. The angle of
inflow is not the same in every quadrant, but it averages about 20° to
30° across the isobars, except at the inner edge of the wall cloud, where
there is no longer any inflow. The angle of inflow seems to vary considerably with individual storms, their maturity, size, latitude, and other
meteorological situations in which the hurricanes are located. The intense, immature storms seem to have the most symmetrical wind fields,
and the strongest winds are located in the wall cloud around the eye. In
mature or decaying storms the maximum winds may be found far from
the center. In poorly developed storms hurricane winds may be observed
in only one quadrant, usually the northeast if the storm is moving
westward.

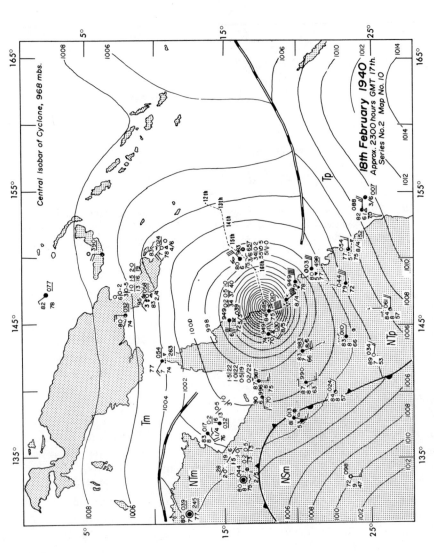

Fig. 31. Wind Circulation around a tropical cyclone in the Southern Hemisphere. Outer isobar is 30.00 inches, with isobars at 0.20 inch intervals. Single barbs indicate 10 knots and pennants 50 knots.

Barometric Pressures

The flow of the atmosphere, or wind, is due to differences in pressure between two points. The pressure effect, if wind were comparable to the simple flow of water through a pipe, would be such that air would move from high to low pressure by the most direct available route. The most direct route is the one along which the pressure is changing most rapidly, and is called the pressure gradient, line *AB* in Figure 32. The pressure gradient is perpendicular to the isobars and is measured in the direction of diminishing pressure. In the atmosphere, pressure gradients are largely the result of temperature differences.

If the pressure-gradient forces were the only ones acting on the air, the wind would blow along *AB* (Figure 32) and accelerate as air moved from *A* to *B* because the pressure gradient is increasing in that

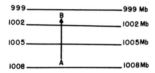

Fig. 32. Pressure Gradient directed along Line *AB*.

direction. Such a flow would soon cease unless the pressure gradient were continuously maintained by a heat source or a pressure head, as in a channel. The sea breeze, which flows across the coast from the relatively cold water toward the heated land during the day, is an example of wind flow along the pressure gradient, the latter being maintained by differential heating of the land and water. Several other factors influence the wind, however, and large-scale atmospheric flow is a balance between two or more forces, of which the following are the most important:

1. *Coriolis Force.* This is an apparent force which is caused by the rotation of the earth. It is proportional to the wind speed, and its magnitude depends upon the sine of the latitude. It is zero at the equator and reaches a maximum at the poles. It is always at right angles to the direction of motion, acting to the right in the Northern Hemisphere and to the left in the Southern Hemisphere. (For a mathematical derivation of the Coriolis force the reader is referred to a textbook on general meteorology.[1]) If the pressure gradient and Coriolis forces were the only two factors

[1]H. R. Byers, *General Meteorology,* McGraw-Hill Book Co.

acting, the wind would blow in a straight path parallel to the isobars (assuming that the latter are not curved). Such a flow is called the *geostrophic wind*.

2. *Centrifugal Forces*. While the geostrophic approximation of the true wind is often a good one in regions where the isobars are straight, near the centers of high- and low-pressure areas, the air trajectories assume a pronounced curvature. According to Newton's first law of motion, flow in a curved path results in centrifugal forces acting on the air particles, and this force is directed outward from the center of curvature. In regions of low pressure (counterclockwise flow) centrifugal force opposes the pressure gradient, while in high-pressure areas (clockwise flow) the two are in the same direction. Air flowing in such a manner that the pressure gradient, Coriolis, and centrifugal forces are in balance is known as the *gradient wind*. Near the center of a hurricane the pressure gradient and centrifugal forces become so large that they greatly exceed the Coriolis force, and the latter is frequently neglected in calculating the actual wind. Such a flow (balance between the pressure gradient and centrifugal forces) is called the *cyclostrophic wind*.

3. *Friction*. Frictional forces act oppositely to the motion of the air, thus retarding the flow. This reduces the magnitude of the Coriolis force and the pressure-gradient force becomes dominant. This imbalance of forces results in flow across the isobars from high to low pressure. Angle between the wind and the isobars varies from as low as 10° to as much as 45° depending upon roughness of terrain. Magnitude of frictional forces increases with approximately the square of the wind speed.

4. *Isallobaric Wind*. Whenever the pressure distribution is changing rapidly with time, an additional force becomes important. This results in an isallobaric component of the wind, and it is directed perpendicular to the isallobaric gradient.

It is clear that strong winds, such as those that exist near the center of a hurricane, can exist only in regions with strong pressure gradients. The pressure at the center of a hurricane must be very low in order to concentrate a rapid decrease in pressure in a short distance, thereby creating the devastating winds characteristic of the hurricane. The barometric pressure in the center of a hurricane is, therefore, a measure of its intensity, although not an absolute measure. All cyclonically rotating storms are areas of low pressure, and as a rule the more intense the storm the lower the pressure in the center. For this reason the barometric pressure is one of the things meteorologists are most interested in measuring as accurately as possible.

Fig. 33. Aneroid Barometer. (Courtesy Bendix Aviation Corp., Friez Instrument Div.)

Mercurial barometers are used for the most accurate measurements of weight of the atmosphere. Since these are somewhat large, complicated, and expensive, most barometers found in homes, on ships, and in other places where weather is of some interest are of the aneroid type (Figure 33). In instruments of this type, an aneroid diaphragm expands or contracts as the pressure of the air changes. By means of a series of levers and a chain, these changes are converted to rotary motion which causes the pointer to move on the dial. A red or black aligning pointer, which permits back reference to a previous setting, is attached to the face of the dial. For reference purposes this pointer may be set at a given reading to determine the rise or fall of the barometer. Most of the aneroid barometers in the United States are scaled in inches. The lowest point on the scale is 26.5 inches, which would normally suffice for the most severe storm. In the northern portion of the United States the needle would rarely go below 29.0, and in the tropics the needle will remain near 30.0 inches day after day unless a hurricane is in the vicinity. In order to compare one barometer reading with another, or with those appearing on a weather chart, it is necessary that the aneroid barometer be adjusted to indicate sea-level

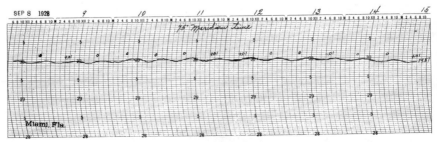

Fig. 34. Barograph Trace showing the daily fluctuations of atmospheric pressure.

readings. Everywhere there is a double daily fluctuation in the barometer (Figure 34), which is known as the diurnal atmospheric-pressure variation, but it has no meaning as far as our daily weather is concerned. This fluctuation is quite noticeable in the tropics but is often masked in the Temperate Zone, especially during the winter season, by passing areas of high and low pressure.

Barograph traces for small hurricanes are shown in Figures 35 and 36; for the mature Cape Verde type, in Figure 37; for the severe hurricane Janet (1955) at Chetumal, Mexico, in Figure 38; and for a hurricane at a northern latitude, in Figure 39.

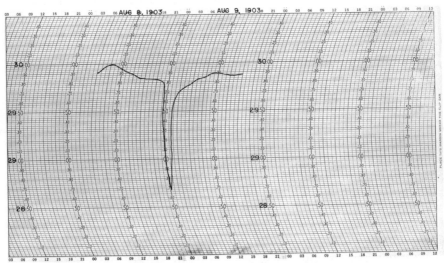

Fig. 35. Barograph Trace showing the passage of an immature hurricane at low latitude (Martinque, F.W.I., August 8-9, 1903).

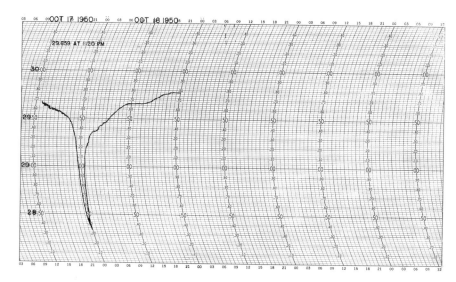

Fig. 36. Barograph Trace accompanying the passage of a small, intense hurricane (Miami, Fla., October 17–18, 1950).

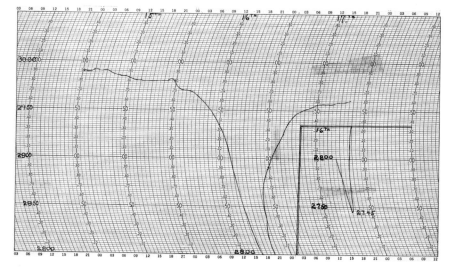

Fig. 37. Barograph Trace indicating the passage of a mature Cape Verde-type hurricane (West Palm Beach, Fla.. September 15–17, 1928).

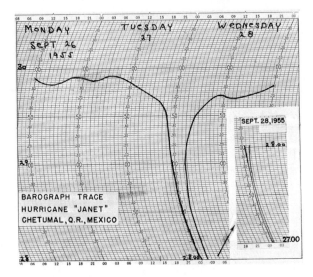

Fig. 38. Barograph Trace indicating the passage of Hurricane Janet (Chetumal. Q.R., Mexico, September. 1955).

The lowest sea-level barometer readings for the entire world have all been recorded in hurricanes, and the lowest credible values are listed in Table 9.

There were other very low barometer readings reported in the nineteenth century, especially around the Philippines and India. In view of the primitiveness and the general unreliability of observations at that time and the obvious tendency to report readings to the nearest tenth, quarter, or even half inch, it is believed they cannot be given full credence.

The lowest accepted sea-level barometer reading in the United States, 26.35 inches, occurred at Lower Matecumbe Key, Florida, on Septem-

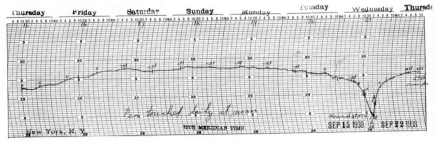

Fig. 39. Barograph Trace showing the passage of a hurricane at a northern latitude (New York, N.Y., September 20–22, 1938).

TABLE 9
Record Low Barometer Readings

Number	Place	Location	Date		Pressure
1	SS *Sapoeroea*	460 mi. east of Luzon	Aug. 18,	1927	26.18 in.
2	Matecumbe Key	Florida	Sept. 2,	1935	26.35 in.
3	Basilan	Frank Helm Bay, P.I.	Sept. 25,	1905	26.85 in.
4	Cossack	Australia	Jan. 7,	1881	27.00 in
5	Chetumal	Mexico	Sept. 27-28,	1955	27.00 in.
6	SS *Phemius*	In western Caribbean	Nov. 5,	1932	27.01 in.
7	SS *Laisang*	26.7° N 123.0° E	Aug. 2,	1901	27.03 in.
8	Havana	Cuba	Oct. 10-11,	1846	27.06 in.
9	False Pt.	India	Sept. 22,	1885	27.14 in.

Other low readings in the United States.

	Place	Location	Date		Pressure
	Miami	Florida	Sept. 18,	1926	27.61 in.
	West Palm Beach	Florida	Sept. 16,	1928	27.43 in.
	Long Island	New York	Sept. 21,	1938	27.90 in.

ber 2, 1935. No doubt lower pressures, and probably much lower, have occurred in tornadoes. Frankenfield [24] mentions a reading of 27.30 inches in a tornado at St. Louis, Missouri, on May 27, 1896, but it is not clear whether this pressure was recorded in the tornado vortex.

The most extreme pressure gradients in the world, except in tornadoes, are found in hurricanes in lower latitudes and during the immature and early mature stages. Depperman [13] cites several examples in the Philippines: The SS *Pathfinder* anchored at Aras, Samar, recorded a fall in barometer of 1.07 inches in 27 minutes. In the Tacloban typhoon there was a drop of 1.14 inches in 30 minutes with a measured fall by mercurial barometer of 0.49 inches in 5 minutes. The SS *Virginia* in the central Caribbean on September 20, 1943, experienced a barometer reading of 28.74 inches at 8:00 p.m. and 27.40 inches at 8:20 p.m., a fall of 1.34 inches in 20 minutes. It then rose to 28.60 by 9:00 p.m. Altogether the barometer in this immature hurricane fell more than 2 inches in less than 90 minutes. The diameter of the circle enclosed by the 29.5 isobar was estimated at 50 miles and the calm center and relatively flat pressure area was 12-15 miles wide, therefore the pressure gradient is calculated at 2.10 inches in 19 miles or 0.11 inch per mile. In the intense Labor Day storm of 1935 on the Florida Keys one estimate was made of a pressure gradient of one inch in 6 miles. Cline [8] found in the storms which he studied an average pressure gradient of 0.02 inch per mile, indicating a considerable spread of the isobars in the later hurricane stages normally found on the Gulf coast, with the occasional exception of the June storms. Usually the observing network is not sufficiently dense to determine accurately the actual pressure gradient, although if the rate of movement is known exactly the gradient can be computed.

Size

In addition to the strength of the maximum winds in a hurricane, the size is usually expressed in two ways. These are by the diameters of the hurricane winds (74 mph or more) and the gale winds (about 40 mph or more). A third way is to express the size by the diameter of the outer closed (roughly circular or elliptical) isobar, but this is not usually contained in hurricane advisories.

A look at Figure 29 shows that the average diameter of the hurricane-force winds is a little over 100 miles and that gales cover an area 350 to 400 miles across. These figures come pretty close to expressing the dimensions of the average-sized hurricane. In this respect also hurricanes are subject to great individual variations.

As a rule, in the early stages of development and even for the first few days after the storm reaches hurricane intensity, the diameter may be quite small, almost a pin point on the usual weather chart. As it becomes older it also becomes larger, although the maximum winds may not show any increase in velocity. The most intense hurricane of record, the Labor Day storm on the Florida Keys in 1935, had a path of destruction no more than thirty-five to forty miles wide. The severe hurricane of October, 1950, was attended by destructive winds only about 14 miles wide as it moved north-northwestward over Miami. The degree of damage increased from light to heavy within a space of one-quarter to one-half mile.

Hurricane Hazel on October 14, 1954, packed hurricane winds over a diameter in excess of 120 miles and gales covered a width of 300 miles. Carol, 1953 (not the famous New England hurricane, which occurred in 1954), while it was still southeast of Bermuda, had hurricane-force winds over a width of 150 miles and gales 400 miles in diameter. Among the all-time great storms was the "Great Atlantic Hurricane" of September, 1944, which on September 12, possessed hurricane winds over an estimated width of 200 miles and gales 600 miles in diameter. Some Pacific typhoons are even larger, however, and a few of these have been observed with diameters of 1,000 miles.

Life Span

The average life of a hurricane is about nine days. August storms normally live the longest, with an average span of twelve days. July and November storms last about eight days.

The factors which determine the lifetime of a hurricane are the time and place of origin and the general circulation features existing in the atmosphere at the time of occurrence. Very few storms dissipate as long as they remain over tropical or subtropical waters unless some abnormal features of the wind-flow patterns surrounding the storms act to bring cold or dry air into the hurricane circulation. The presence of such abnormal circulation features also inhibits the formation of tropical cyclones, and once a storm has developed it is a very rare circumstance for the situation to change with sufficient rapidity to cause the hurricane to dissipate over warm water.

Obviously cyclones developing in the Cape Verde region in August and September, when the Azores-Bermuda HIGH is at its greatest strength, will have the longest life span, since these storms normally travel westward for a few days before recurving northward around the western edge of the subtropical ridge. In contrast, those that form in the Caribbean and the Gulf of Mexico will have shorter lives, simply because the region of formation is so near to land areas that they do not have far to travel before landfall takes place.

A number of Atlantic hurricanes have been tracked for three or four weeks. There is evidence in one or two cases that the circulations from which the storms developed may have been noted in tropical Africa. This was true of the New England hurricane of 1938. The famous San Ciriaco hurricane of 1899 passed over the entire length of Puerto Rico on August 8, being one of the most destructive in the history of the island. It passed over the Bahamas, where it was quite severe, and from the sixteenth to the eighteenth it was off Cape Hatteras, where it was described as the most severe in the memory of the oldest inhabitants. This storm has since been traced back to the Cape Verde region on August 3, and it was still observed on the weather map in the vicinity of the Azores Islands on September 7, giving it a lifetime of about five weeks. More recently, hurricane Carrie (1957), was first detected on September 6, and at that time it had already reached great intensity. Its origin could be tracked back to very near the African coast on the second. This storm was still of hurricane intensity on September 22, when it was located near the Azores. It finally became extratropical and moved into the British Isles.

After leaving the tropics some hurricanes encounter in the westerlies moist, active troughs of low pressure. These supply new energy that may keep the hurricanes active for long periods of time. One such storm was the Galveston hurricane of 1900. This storm was tracked from the middle of the tropical Atlantic Ocean into the Gulf of Mexico and to the Texas coast. From there it recurved and became an active storm in the Great Lakes region. It then crossed the Atlantic Ocean and moved across northern Europe into Siberia. Many hurricanes cross the Atlantic in the trade-wind belt, moving from east to west, and then recross the Atlantic from west to east in the prevailing westerlies north of the Azores-Bermuda HIGH. Once these storms leave the tropics, however, they lose their earlier characteristics rapidly and can no longer be considered true tropical cyclones.

The Eye

The wind circulation around a hurricane can be conveniently divided into three parts: (1) The outer portion in which the wind increases steadily as one approaches the center. This region extends from the periphery of the storm where the wind may be no more than 20-30 mph to within 20-30 miles of the center, where velocities of 120-150 mph may be reached. (2) The region of maximum winds surrounding the eye. Winds are relatively constant within this area, which normally has a radius of 15-25 miles. (3) The eye, or innermost portion, of the storm.

The eye of the hurricane is unique. It is not observed in any other meteorological phenomena. In many ways it is the most spectacular part of the storm. As the center of the eye is approached the wind diminishes with amazing rapidity from extreme violence to 15 mph or less, but probably never to an absolute calm. For example as the eye of the violent hurricane of September, 1926, passed over downtown

Fig. 40a. Wall Cloud around the eye of Typhoon Marge, August, 1951. Composite photograph. (Courtesy R. H. Simpson)

Miami the wind decreased to about 10 mph, but at the same time Allison Hospital (now St. Francis) on Miami Beach 6¼ miles away was reporting the wind at 80 mph. Numerous observers several miles within the relatively calm eye have remarked on hearing the roar of the hurricane winds around the edge. As one passes into the calm area the rain ceases, the middle deck of cloud vanishes, the low cloud often remains but with clear patches here and there through which the sun may shine, or the stars may be visible if at night. Cirrus and cirrostratus clouds are almost always present. Some aerial photographs made in and near the eye are shown in Figures 40a and 40b. Simpson [96] describes the eye of typhoon Marge as he approached it on August 15, 1951, on airplane reconnaissance as follows:

> Soon the edge of the rainless eye became visible on the (radar) screen. The plane flew through bursts of torrential rain and several turbulent bumps. Then, suddenly, we were in dazzling sunlight and bright blue sky.
> Around us was an awesome display. Marge's eye was a clear space 40 miles in diameter surrounded by a coliseum of clouds whose walls on one side rose vertically and on the other were banked like galleries in a great opera house. The upper rim, about 35,000 feet high, was rounded off smoothly against a background of blue sky. Below us was a floor of low clouds rising to a dome 8000 feet above sea level in the center. There were breaks in it which gave us glimpses of the surface of the

Fig. 40b. Photograph of Hurricane Cleo from an elevation of 15,500 feet. Note
circular structure of clouds in lower center. (Courtesy National Hurricane Research Project)

ocean. In the vortex around the eye the sea was a scene of unimaginably
violent, churning water.

Observers have described conditions in the relatively calm center as
"oppressive," "sultry," and "suffocating" and full of strange odors,
e.g., "like escaping gas." This reaction is apparently largely psycho-
logical and due to the rapid transition from hurricane winds and the
comparative coolness of torrential rains to relatively calm conditions. A
few minutes of sunshine would raise the temperature and the discomfort factor somewhat. Some writers have cited several examples of
extraordinary rises in temperature in the eye. However, it is believed
that all could be explained on the basis of insolation or foehn effect.
Although the eye is quite warm at intermediate levels, an inversion pre-

vails at or somewhat above the stratocumulus level (approximately two thousand feet) in the eye with more or less normal conditions below.

The average diameter of the wind eye is about fourteen miles. The smallest eye which has ever come to the author's attention was one with a diameter of four miles in a storm in the formative stage, but diameters of twenty to twenty-five miles in large mature storms are not unusual. The frictional effect as the storm passes overland tends to increase the size of the eye, and it often assumes an elongated shape in the direction of the storm's movement. In several instances the eye has been reported as seventy to ninety miles long. While many exceptions are reported, the size of the eye tends to vary in proportion to the maturity and size of the hurricane. In the Atlantic, tropical cyclones with central pressures as low as 29.40 inches almost invariably have an eye, while storms with minimum pressures above 29.55 inches rarely do. A storm of this slight intensity may have an area of relatively light winds but no wall cloud. Storms with central pressure above 29.55 will, of course, be poorly organized with altostratus and more or less random convective cells, but somewhere between 29.55 and 29.40 inches most Atlantic storms become sufficiently organized to possess a recognizable eye, although the wall cloud may not completely surround it. In fact the wall cloud is often not completely closed in cyclones with much lower central pressures. A few representative wind eyes follow in Table 10.

TABLE 10

Diameters of Some Hurricane Eyes

Place	Date	Diameter	Duration	Barometer
West Palm Beach	Sept. 1928	25 mi.	1½ hr.	27.43 in.
Miami	Sept. 1926	13 mi.	45 min.	27.61 in.
Keys	Sept. 1935	9-10 mi.	55 min.	26.35 in.
Nassau	Sept. 1929	16-20 mi.	4 hr.	27.64 in.
S. Fla. coast	July 27, 1936	4 mi.	20 min.	29.38 in.

The length of time required for the eye to pass over any one point is, of course, dependent upon the size of the eye, the length of the chord of the circle which passes over the point, and the rate of movement of the storm.

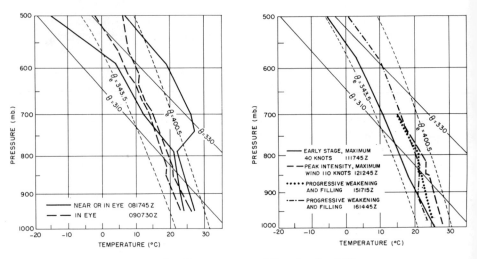

Fig. 41. *A*, Eye Temperatures of Connie; *B*, of Diane.

It is well known that birds tend to "ride with the wind," and often many thousands of birds are blown into the center of the storm. Exhausted birds will sometimes completely cover the deck of a ship which has found its way into the center of the hurricane. Hurricanes kill many birds, but apparently some can travel long distances in these storms, since tropical or semitropical birds have been found in New England following the passage of a hurricane.

Temperatures within the eye of the hurricane are much warmer than they are throughout the rest of the storm, although this difference is less at the surface than it is at the higher levels. Warm air is lighter than cold air, and it is this warm air within the eye of the storm that accounts for the low-pressures observed at the surface.

During recent years numerous aircraft and dropsonde[2] observations have been made inside the eye, although these have of necessity been made at levels of 500 mb (about 19,000 feet) or less. As a result of these observations the temperature structure of the hurricane eye in the

---

[2] A dropsonde is a small radio transmitter which is attached to a small parachute and dropped by an aircraft in flight. As it falls it transmits temperature, relative humidity, and pressure data back to a receiver in the plane. The dropsonde is similar to the radiosonde used by land stations, the latter being sent aloft by the use of helium-filled balloons.

lower troposphere is pretty well known. Figure 41 shows some of the eye temperatures that occurred within Connie and Diane (1955).

Jordan [45] has summarized the available data. He found that the eye temperatures and relative humidities varied with the intensity of the storm in accordance with Table 11:

TABLE 11

Mean Values of Temperatures (°C.) and Relative Humidities (Per Cent) at Different Levels Within the Eye of Intense, Moderate, and Weak Hurricanes*

	Mean Temperature (°C)			Mean Relative Humidity			Mean Tropical Atmosphere		
	Intense	Mod-erate	Weak	Intense	Mod-erate	Weak	T.	R.H.	Height
Surface	25.7	25.7	24.9	90	90	84	24.7	81	
900-mb	23.6	22.9	20.8	89	91	89	18.3	79	3,470 ft.
800-mb	19.3	19.0	17.4	86	89	86	13.1	62	6,750 ft.
700-mb	16.6	14.4	12.1	80	83	79	7.9	47	10,400 ft.
600-mb	11.8	8.7	6.4	64	72	62	1.0		14,530 ft.
500-mb	5.1	−0.4	−2.4	45	70	75	−7.6		19,260 ft.

*Corresponding values for the tropical standard atmosphere [43] are shown for comparison. (After C. Jordan.) These data indicate that the eye temperatures are warmer in intense than in weak storms, and indeed such is the case. They also suggest that for the intermediate levels (600 mb and 500 mb) the air is drier in the more intense storms.

Simpson [95] has given a graphical description of the temperature measurements in the eye of typhoon Marge as follows: "For 4½ hours we cruised in the eye of the typhoon, taking observations and making photographs of the clouds. Among the most significant measurements were those of temperature. We found the air in the eye considerably warmer than in the surrounding vortex. At 8000 feet its temperature was some 14° F higher; at 18,000 feet the eye temperature was more than 32° F higher than that of the outer fringes of the vortex. This astounding temperature gradient indicated that the storm had as great a concentration of potential energy as has ever been detected in the atmosphere." The temperature at the 500-mb level was 16° C., the highest ever recorded at that level.

Such a warm temperature could be produced only by sinking from above and warming by compression as the air moved to a higher pressure. It can be shown that the temperature observed in the eye of typhoon Marge would have required dry adiabatic descent from near the 200-mb level (about 40,000 feet). The dry adiabatic rate is 10° C. per kilometer, or about 5.5° F. per 1,000 feet. If a slightly lower rate of warming is assumed, descent might have begun near 100 mb, which is above 53,000 feet. Descent begins at a higher level in the more intense hurricanes than in moderate or weak storms, and the resulting temperatures in the middle levels of the atmosphere are also higher. It is this descending motion within the eye which dries out the air, and this makes the eye relatively cloud free except for stratocumulus near the surface.

Not all the air within the eye, however, descends from extremely high levels. Continued descent would result in temperatures far in excess of those ever observed, and the relative humidities would approach zero instead of the quite sizable figures shown in Table 11. It is inconceivable that the same air remains within the lower portions of the eye throughout the life history of the storm, and it must be concluded that some air flows into the eye from the outside. This, of course, brings up the problem of what happens to the momentum possessed by the air prior to entering the eye. An attempt to answer that question is beyond the scope of this book, although Malkus [56] has recently proposed a very interesting mechanism by which this may be accomplished.

Present knowledge, direct and deductive, about how the hurricane eye is formed may be summarized as follows:

1. In severe hurricanes, warming by subsidence within the eye must take place, because no other atmospheric process can account for temperatures high enough to explain the low pressures in the eye and the strong pressure gradients around the center.

2. Within deep and mature hurricanes, descent must begin at high elevations (near 40,000 or 50,000 feet) in order to explain the high temperatures that have actually been observed at mid-tropospheric levels.

3. Throughout the lower layers of the storm some air probably flows into the eye from the outside, because the relative humidities are too high and the temperatures too low for descent to have taken place from the upper atmosphere. This mixture of moist air and the drier eye air results in evaporation of the liquid water introduced from the outside, thus cooling the eye temperatures somewhat. The eye is apparently filled with a

mixture of air, part of which has descended from varying elevations and part of which has flowed into the eye from the outside.

4. Recent calculations made by Malkus [55] indicate that strong subsidence within the eye may not be necessary to explain the warming required to account for the pressure fall within hurricanes of moderate intensity, i.e., the addition of heat and/or moisture to the subcloud air before ascent begins can raise the equivalent potential temperatures of the air enough to result in the required warming aloft. This will be discussed in more detail in Chapter 6.

5. Moisture may also be injected into the eye at very high levels [46], as cumulonimbus towers extend to 40,000 feet or higher, at which level they spread out as the ascending air runs out of buoyancy upon striking a stable upper layer, or "lid," on the convection process. As the clouds spread out they may eventually extend over the eye, thus permitting ice particles to fall out and descend within the eye. Kessler [46] has presented some radar photographs of hurricane Edna which demonstrate this occurrence. This is a means of getting moisture into the eye without the necessity of introducing troublesome angular momentum.

Vertical Structure

So far, with the exception of the thermal structure of the eye, discussions of the hurricane have been limited to surface or near-surface characteristics. It is not solely a low-level phenomenon, however, but extends to great heights within the atmosphere. Theoretical calculations made by Haurwitz [32] in 1935, indicated that the cyclonically rotating wind system of a hurricane must extend to 30,000 feet or more. During and since World War II enough winds-aloft observations have been made around tropical cyclones to permit a rather detailed study of their upper-level characteristics. E. Jordan [42] and later Miller [60] have performed such analyses, and some of their most important findings will be discussed briefly.

Both the size and the intensity of the hurricane decreased with elevation, but the decrease in the wind velocity was more rapid in the outer portions of the storm than near the center. The cyclonic circulation at 7,000 feet covered a diameter of almost 600 miles. A cyclonic circulation could still be detected at 45,000 feet, but it was small, and this was surrounded by anticyclonic eddies which began at a distance of about 200-250 miles from the center. The wind patterns for these two levels are shown in Figures 42a and 42b.

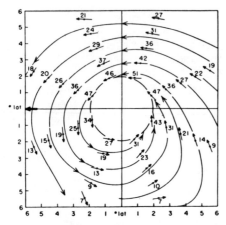

Fig. 42a. Total Wind Speed (knots) around a hurricane at 7,000 feet. Arrow at left indicates the direction of the cyclone motion. (After E. Jordan)

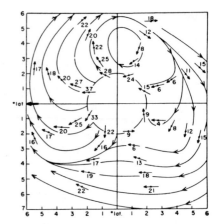

Fig. 42b. Total Wind Speed (knots) around a hurricane at 45,000 feet. Arrow at left indicates the direction of the cyclone motion. (After E. Jordan)

The radial components, i.e., the flow of air into or out of the storm, for the two levels are shown in Figures 43 and 44. Net inflow occurs at 7,000 feet, although the average is only about 30 per cent of the net inflow Hughes [40] found at 1,000 feet. At 45,000 feet there is strong outflow, amounting to as much as 30 knots on the forward

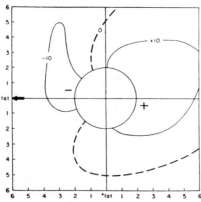

Fig. 43. Radial Velocity (knots) at 7,000 feet. Positive values indicate inflow. Arrow at left indicates the direction of the cyclone motion. (After E. Jordan)

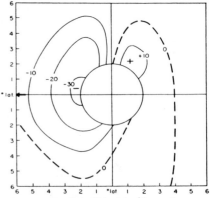

Fig. 44. Radial Velocity (knots) at 45,000 feet. Positive values indicate inflow. Arrow at left indicates the direction of the cyclone motion. (After E. Jordan)

side of the storm. In a steady state mass inflow into the storm must balance the mass outflow. If the inflow is greater, the storm must fill, and if the outflow is greater the pressure in the center of the storm would fall and intensification would result. E. Jordan suggests that the major inflow occurs within the lowest 10,000 feet and that compensating outflow takes place above 30,000 feet.

The decrease in the tangential wind speed between the 7,000- and 45,000-foot levels is more pronounced than Figures 42a and 42b would seem to indicate. The tangential wind speed, i.e., a wind tangent to a circle drawn through a given point, is indicative of the cyclonic or rotary motion of the storm. The wind values of Figures 42a and 42b include the radial component as well as the motion of the storm. Computation of the tangential components near the center of the storm shows that they had a value at 45,000 feet equal to only about 25 per cent of the speed at 7,000 feet.

E. Jordan's work was carried out in 1952, and since that time a large

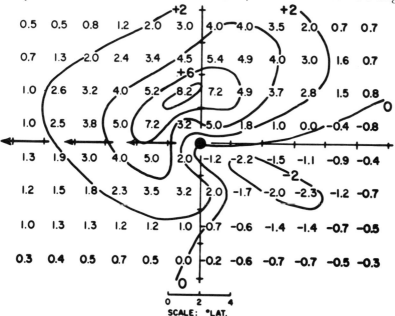

Fig. 45. Radial Velocity (relative to the center of the hurricane) for the 0–1 kilometer layer. Speeds in meters per second (mps). Positive values indicate inflow. Arrow at left indicates direction in which the center is moving.

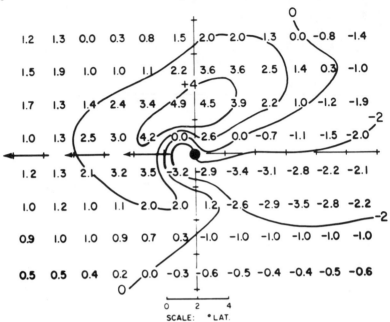

Fig. 46. Radial Velocity (relative to the center of the hurricane) for the 1–3
kilometer layer. Speeds in meters per second (mps). Positive values
indicate inflow. Arrow at left indicates direction in which the center is
moving.

number of winds-aloft observations have been made in the vicinity of
hurricanes, particularly in the Atlantic area. Miller [60] used these to
extend the work begun by Jordan. The over-all results are quite similar,
although there appear to be some significant differences. Miller
processed his data by layers extending from the surface up to 16 kilometers, instead of using selected levels as Jordan had done.

   Miller computed the radial components relative to the center of the
storm. He found that the greatest inflow occurred within the 0-1
kilometer layer, but that the inflow pattern had changed only slightly
through the 1-3 kilometer layer. For both layers the major inflow
was into the right front quadrant of the storm as shown in Figures 45
and 46. Both figures reveal an *outflow*, however, in the left rear quadrant. This strongly suggests that air is flowing *through* the storm.
Above 10 kilometers there is net outflow, which agrees with Jordan's
findings. Throughout the 12.5-16.0 kilometer layer outflow becomes

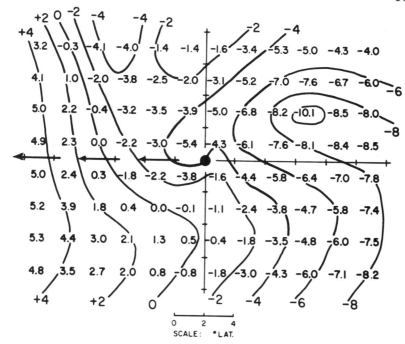

Fig. 47. Radial Velocity (relative to the center of the hurricane) for the 12.5–16.0 kilometer layer. Speeds in meters per second (mps). Positive values indicate inflow. Arrow at left indicates direction in which the center is moving.

predominant (Figure 47). Miller's data showed that the *mass* inflow through the 0-1 kilometer layer was almost exactly balanced by the mass outflow above 10 kilometers. This strongly suggests that the net inflow from 1 to 10 kilometers is very nearly zero, with air probably flowing into the storm in one quadrant and out from another.

Figure 48 shows the mean wind pattern around a hurricane for the 12.5–16.0 kilometer layer. A closed cyclonic circulation can no longer be detected, although a very small center probably exists. The motion appears to be predominately anticyclonic, i.e., the rotation is clockwise instead of counterclockwise, as was the case at the surface. The entire region of the storm is covered by a huge anticyclone, whose center is just to the rear of the surface position of the hurricane. The strongest winds are no longer near the center, but are to be found along the outer portions of the two rear quadrants. The strong winds over the right

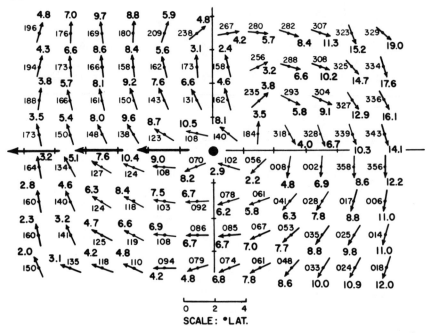

Fig. 48. Mean Wind around a hurricane at the 12.5–16.0 kilometer layer. Speeds in meters per second (mps). Heavy arrows indicate direction in which the center is moving.

rear quadrant are apparently due to the hurricane, and are an indication of the export of kinetic energy to the surroundings as air that has been lifted from the surface during intensification flows out of the region of the cyclone.

The studies of E. Jordan and Miller were based on average conditions in several tropical cyclones. Individual hurricanes may be expected to vary greatly from the mean. During the past three years the National Hurricane Research Project has collected enough data to permit rather detailed analyses of some individual hurricanes [99]. Two such analyses made for Carrie (1957) are shown in Figures 49 and 50.

The most striking feature of the data is the striated character of the wind and temperature profiles. As the plane left the eye, a series of wind maxima and minima were observed within a distance of less than eighty miles. The temperature profile shows similar variations and not a steady decrease outward from the hurricane core. In general there is a pronounced tendency for temperature falls through the rainy areas,

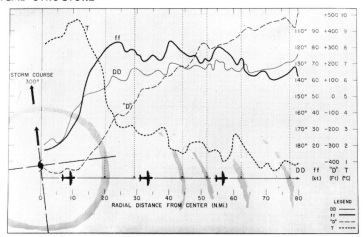

Fig. 49. Profiles of Wind, Temperature, and D-values from the center of Hurricane Carrie north-northeastward, September 15, 1957. "DD" is wind direction in degrees from true north, "FF" is wind speed in knots, and "T" is temperature in °C. "D-value" refers to the difference between the observed height and the standard (atmosphere) height of the pressure surface along which the aircraft flew. (Courtesy National Hurricane Research Project)

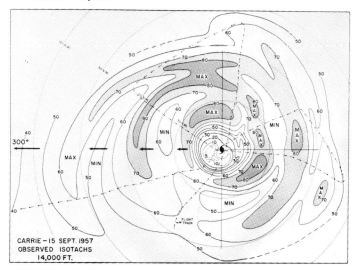

Fig. 50. Wind Speeds (knots) at 14,000 feet for Hurricane Carrie, September 15, 1957, showing the striated structure of the winds. (Courtesy National Hurricane Research Project)

but these do not occupy unique positions relative to the rain bands observed by radar.

The winds at 14,000 feet (Figure 50) show that the striations have continuity from quadrant to quadrant. Flights at other levels revealed that vertical continuity was also maintained. As yet it is too early to determine the exact physical significance of these variations, or if they are nothing more than "noise," or possibly important elements of a rather complex circulation. Collection and detailed analysis of data from individual hurricanes must be continued before any definite conclusions can be formulated.

5

SOME RELATED PHENOMENA

THE MAJOR CHARACTERISTICS OF THE HURRICANE HAVE BEEN described in the previous chapter. There are numerous related features accompanying this monster of the tropical oceans, among which are the hurricane swells and surges, the rains, tornadoes in hurricanes, lightning, and thunderstorms. These will now be discussed briefly.

Swells and Surges

Everyone is familiar with the fact that wind blowing across a stretch of open water creates waves upon the surface of the water. The wave heights (over open oceans) depend upon the wind velocity, the length of time the wind has been blowing, the "fetch," or distance over which the wind has blown in a relatively straight path, and upon the state of the sea at the time the wind started to blow. The relationships between these variables are quite complicated and beyond the scope of this book, and the reader who is interested in additional information is referred to works on oceanography, such as that of Sverdrup [100]. As long as the wind-produced waves remain in deep water and at some considerable distance from the coast line there is little mass transport of water along the wave front. As the waves approach the shore, several factors combine to cause a rise in the level of the sea, which may produce severe inundation and great destruction. This is the deadly "hurricane surge," and it will be discussed in detail in Chapter 12.

Some of the highest ocean waves are generated by the winds of the tropical cyclone. In the Atlantic it has been found that, in an average hurricane, waves of thirty-five to forty feet are developed and that in great hurricanes waves may exceed forty-five feet. The crossing of two waves may send up peaks of fifty to fifty-five feet. These heights may be exceeded in the Pacific, although the differences are not very large.

In 1935 the Japanese fleet accidently sailed into a typhoon, and one of the ships (the *Susaki*) reported wave heights of twenty to thirty meters (about sixty-six to ninety-eight feet), but these heights are unusual. Arakawa and Suda [1] believe that waves in excess of twenty meters (about sixty-six feet) are very rare.

Neglecting the other factors that influence wave heights, a rough estimate can be obtained from the speed of the wind alone; this is shown in Table 12. Cline [8] simplified this relationship even further and estimated the wave heights (in feet) by dividing the average wind speed (in mph) by 2.05. Both Cline's method and the data of Table 12 should be used with caution, since several factors other than wind speed affect the wave heights.

The highest waves are produced just to the right of the hurricane center, with the observer facing the direction toward which the center is moving. There are two reasons for this: First, the strongest winds are known to occur within this region, and second, the winds operate upon the waves for the greatest length of time in the direction in which the storm is advancing. The waves move in a relatively straight line, while the winds turn to the left in accordance with the hurricane circulation.

It can be shown that ocean waves travel with a speed somewhat slower than that of the winds which generated them. The forward motion of a hurricane averages about 12 mph, but since the largest waves are set up by winds which may average more than 100 mph, these waves will often move 30-50 mph or more and eventually pass through the wind system of the cyclone. As the waves tend to move out of the hurricane area into regions of weaker winds or calms, they decrease in height. These decaying waves, which may persist for a long time, are generally termed "swells." Swells are distinguished from waves by two features: (1) They possess a relatively smooth undulating form without the steep and ragged crests characteristic of wind-driven waves, and (2) the movement of the swells is frequently different from that of the wind.

The major swells generated by the right side of the hurricane may move several hundred, even one or two thousand miles ahead of the center [101]. Since the hurricane winds are blowing in a curved path, however, lesser swells move from the storm area in all directions. These are shown in Figure 51. The movement of swells out of the hurricane

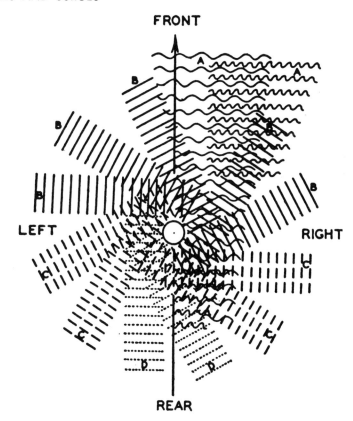

Fig. 51. Generation of Swells by a hurricane. (After Tannehill)

area, as actually observed in the typhoon of September, 1935, is shown in Figure 52.

In the Atlantic trade-wind region the average length of wind-driven waves (the distance from one crest to that of the succeeding wave) is about 210 feet and the wave period is 5.8 seconds. Hurricane-generated swells possess a considerably longer wave length and a corresponding longer wave period.

Arakawa and Suda [1] described the winds, waves, and swells encountered by the main squadron of the Imperial Japanese Fleet as it inadvertently steamed directly through the typhoon of September 26, 1935. These simultaneous observations of weather and sea conditions furnished the meteorologists with some of the best data on record. The

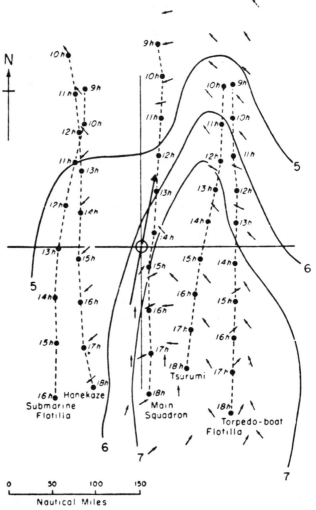

Fig. 52. Composite Chart showing swells in typhoon of September 26, 1935.
Intersection of cross lines indicates the center of the typhoon. Dots indicate positions of naval units at hourly intervals (JMT). Small arrows
denote the direction of the swells. Lines of constant swell character are
shown. (After Arakawa and Suda)

wind velocities throughout the typhoon circulation are shown in Figure
53a. The considerably stronger winds in the right semicircle will be
noted. The typhoon was moving rapidly slightly east of north at about

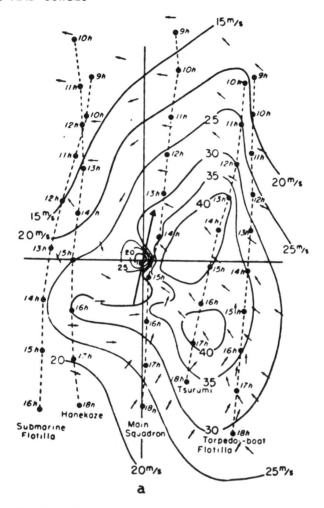

Fig. 53a. Wind Velocities (meters per second) observed in the typhoon of September 26, 1935. (After Arakawa and Suda)

44 mph; thus a high proportion of the speed of translation is added to
the winds on the right and subtracted from those on the left. The
relationship between the wind and the state of the sea is shown in
Figure 53b, and a streamline analysis of the wind field is shown in
Figure 53c. Arakawa and Suda remark that the wind pattern suggests
the formation of fronts as the vortex moved into more northerly lati-

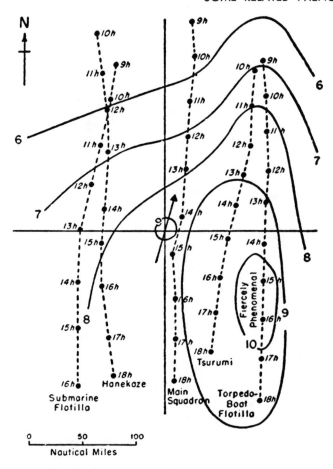

Fig. 53b. State of the Sea in typhoon of September 26, 1935. Lines of constant
wave height are drawn for each unit of the sea scale (Table 12). (After
Arakawa and Suda)

tudes. However, the lines of convergence and divergence are rather
similar to the wind shifts noted in Atlantic hurricanes in connection
with squall lines and the spiral rain bands observed on radarscopes.
The extreme deformity in the convergence line in the right rear quadrant can probably be interpreted as evidence of a strong local convective cell present in that locality. This possibility is supported by the
localized high winds found there. The concentration of clouds and

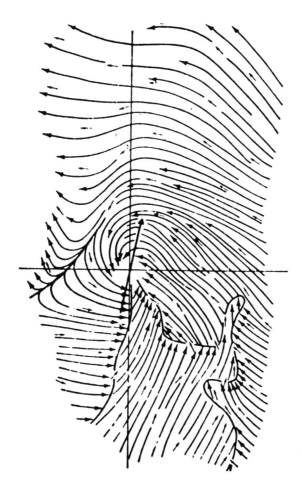

Fig. 53c. Streamline analysis of the Wind Pattern in typhoon of September 26, 1935.

precipitation in the front quadrants can be seen in Figure 53d. This distribution is similar to that found in hurricanes in the more northerly latitudes in the Atlantic.

Hurricane swells pounding on the beach produce a sound well known to coastal residents. Reid, [79] reporting on the September hurricane of 1917 at Pensacola, Florida, stated that the roar of the hurricane surf could be heard in Pensacola, which is about six miles from the open

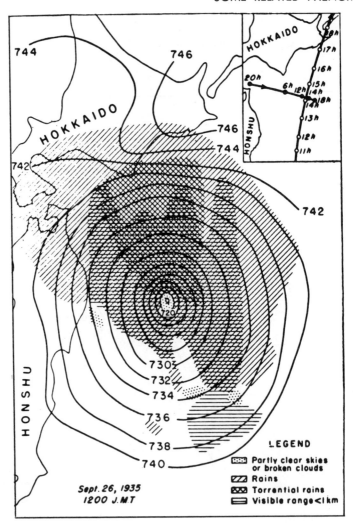

Fig. 53d. Weather and Pressure Distribution to the east of Japan at 1200 JMT, September 26, 1935. Inset (upper right) shows the path of the typhoon. (After Arakawa and Suda)

Gulf, while the center of the storm was still some one hundred miles from the coast.

Another term frequently heard in connection with the rise in the level of the sea along the shore is the "hurricane tide." The rise in

TABLE 12

Code Values, Sea Description, and Wave Heights as Used by the Japanese

Sea Scale Code Figures	General Description	Wind Force Equivalent (In Beaufort number)	Wave Height Equivalent (In feet)
0	Dead calm	0	0
1	Very smooth	1	.1
2	Smooth sea	2-3	1-2
3	Slight sea	4	2-3.3
4	Moderate sea	5	3.3-4.9
5	Rather rough sea	6	4.9-8.2
6	Rough sea	7	8.2-13.1
7	High sea	8-9	13.1-23.0
8	Very high sea	10	23.0-42.7
9	Phenomenal or precipitous sea	11-12	42.7

the water level may begin when the hurricane is as much as five hundred miles from the shore, and it will continue until the storm moves inland or beyond the area. The hurricane tide is often confused with the hurricane surge; but the latter is usually interpreted as a rapid rise in the water level. It reaches the coast about the same time as the center of the hurricane, whereas the hurricane tide is a more gradual rise, which may commence many hours before the center of the storm arrives. Both the hurricane and the surge will be discussed in more detail in Chapter 12.

Tornadoes in Hurricanes

There are many instances of tornado occurrences associated with hurricanes. Most of these have been observed in Florida, Cuba, and the Bahamas, or along the Gulf and South Atlantic coasts of the United States. The tornado is not normally considered a tropical phenomenon. The greatest frequency is in the United States Midwest during the spring and early summer [23], although they have been observed in every state in the union and at other times of the year.

Malkin and Galway [54] have made a study of tornadoes associated with hurricanes, and their conclusions may be summarized as follows:

1. Tornadoes in hurricanes have been observed only in the forward semicircle or along the advancing periphery of the storm.

2. Tornadoes are about as likely to occur at one time of day as another.

3. They are less severe than the usual inland tornado.

4. Limited evidence indicates the absence of a low-level temperature inversion, sharp vertical moisture stratification, and excessive instability. Also the path of the tornado associated with a hurricane is relatively short and narrow in comparison with the average tornado.

Some of the more important tornado cases are shown in Table 13.

TABLE 13
Tornadoes Associated with Hurricanes
(after Malkin and Galway)

Place	Date	Time	Remarks
Charleston, S.C.	1811		
Charleston, S.C.	1814		
Goulds, Fla.	Sept. 10, 1919	1308 EST	Moved E to W, same direction as hurricane (right rear quadrant).
Ft. Lauderdale, Fla.	Sept. 28, 1929	No time available	All these moved from SE to NW in direction of hurricane winds at the time. They possibly developed over the ocean as waterspouts.
Miami, Fla.	Sept. 28, 1929		
Stuart, Fla.	Sept. 28, 1929		
Boca Raton, Fla.	Sept. 28, 1929		
Miami, Fla.	Oct. 4, 1933	Midnight early morning of 5th	At least one moved E to W while hurricane was moving NE. Tornadoes in NW quadrant of hurricane.
Hollywood, Fla.	Oct. 4, 1933		
Ft. Lauderdale, Fla.	Oct. 4, 1933		
Melbourne, Fla.	June 24, 1945	0257 EST	Along forward edge of hurricane.
Houston, Texas	Oct. 11-12, 1947	Night of 11th and morning of 12th.	Within northeastern portion of hurricane.
Apalachicola, Fla.	Sept. 19, 1947	0030 EST	On periphery of hurricane.
Ocala, Fla.	Sept. 23, 1947	0430 EST	On northern edge of hurricane.

TABLE 13 (Continued)

Place	Date	Time	Remarks
Jacksonville, Fla.	Sept. 23, 1947	0900 to 1100 EST	On northern edge of hurricane.
Homestead, Fla.	Sept. 21, 1948	No time given	Occurred in NE sector of hurricane.
Ft. Lauderdale, Fla.	Oct. 5, 1948	Late afternoon & early evening	In forward edge of hurricane.
Apalachicola, Fla.	Aug. 30, 1950	1705 EST	Occurred in NE quadrant of hurricane, moved toward the NW.
Jackson County, Fla.	Aug. 31, 1950	Early morning	Occurred in NE quadrant of hurricane.
Stokes County, N.C.	Aug. 31, 1952	Evening	
Franconia, Va.	Sept. 1, 1952	0330 GMT	Along NE fringe of hurricane; moved toward the NNW. Tornado at Potomac, Md., 0400 GMT may have been continuation of this one.
Georgetown, S.C., northward	Aug. 10, 1955	Early evening	5 tornadoes left front quadrant. Hurricane still offshore.
Penderlea, N.C.	Aug. 10, 1955	Early evening	
Gulf, Suwannee and Taylor Counties, Fla.	Sept. 24, 1956	Early evening	3 tornadoes, right front quadrant.
Southern Alabama and adjoining areas	June 28, 1957	Morning	8 or more tornadoes, right front quadrant.

It is difficult to explain the occurrence of tornadoes in hurricanes since nearly all the so-called essential features [21] are normally absent. Pre-hurricane squall lines have been observed on radar [91]. These lines are undoubtedly regions of strong convergence, and it is reasonable to suppose that tornadoes might develop out of some of the more violent convective cells present along them.

Thunder and Lightning

Greatly varying reports are encountered in regard to thunder and lightning in hurricanes. When all of them are analyzed, a pattern emerges which appears to be fairly consistent, but there are always departures from the general picture. The pattern seems thus:

1. During the formative stages of a hurricane, electrical activity is frequently quite intense. It appears to weaken as the storm reaches maturity, and then increases again during the decaying stages. Tanne-hill [102] has this comment: "Frequent and almost continuous light-ning has been observed within the destructive wind circle of many tropical storms. Thunder is often indistinguishable in the deafening roar of the winds, falling of rain, and noise attending the destruc-tion of buildings; on the seacoast the sea adds to the confusion of noises. Thunderstorms are most frequently noted after the center of the cyclone has passed. For this reason, the occurrence of a thunderstorm is considered a sign that the storm will soon break away." However, he goes on to add that it is more reasonable to assume that whenever thunder can be heard it is evidence that the storm has already abated sufficiently that sounds other than those accompanying the hurricane can be heard.

2. Electrical activity is fairly frequent in isolated cumulonimbus clouds around the periphery of the storm and in the intense convective ring around the eye of the hurricane. Reconnaissance aircraft were struck by lightning three times within three days in 1955 while flying in the edge of the eye. The planes were flying between 10,000 and 20,000 feet at the time. During the passage of a hurricane over Miami, Florida, in October, 1947, an almost continuous display of lightning was observed in and around the eye and was described by meteorologists as among the most vivid they had ever witnessed.

During the often long periods when the fully developed hurricane moves over the ocean with little or no change in intensity, there is usually a minimum of thunder and lightning. Of course it would be difficult to hear the thunder over and above the noise of the storm, as Tannehill has pointed out, but even at night very little lightning is observed. This is rather puzzling, and it may be that the rain is so heavy that the sight of the lightning is also obscured, being visible only to nearby observers, of which there are quite naturally few. However, reconnaissance aircraft frequently report lightning in the wall cloud.

Electrical discharges from thunderstorms can be picked up by radio direction-finding equipment. These discharges are termed "sferics," a contraction of the word "atmospherics," meaning natural electrical phenomena detected by radio methods. They have been used with some success in long-range location of active fronts, nontropical cyclones, and thunderstorms. They seem to be the most useful over the oceans, where the usual weather-reporting facilities are lacking. Some success has been reported in the use of sferics in tracking the progress of easterly waves in the Pacific. Attempts have been made to track hurricanes by the use of sferics, but so far the results have not been successful or at best, have been inconclusive. Almost invariably, however, signals could be detected, which indicates that some electrical activity is almost always present somewhere within the boundaries of the hurricane.

Another interesting feature occasionally observed along the coast as a hurricane moves inland is a myriad of minute electrostatic discharges, which appear like millions of tiny fireflies. These apparently originate as a result of frictionally generated static electricity as literally millions of tiny sand particles are picked up and driven along by the hurricane winds. A very spectacular display of this type occurred in connection with the Florida Keys hurricane in 1935.

Hurricane Rains

Some of the world's heaviest rainfalls [90] have occurred in connection with hurricanes. The rainfall is always heavy, probably three to six inches on the average, frequently much more. It is quite likely that the exact rainfall in these storms is never known, since after the wind reaches 50 mph or more, it is possible that not more than 50 per cent is actually caught by the rain gauge. Consequently it is altogether possible that a measure of five inches in a hurricane may, in reality, be around eight inches, or even more.

The total amount of rainfall is dependent upon a number of features, among the most important being: (1) The rate of ascent of air in the storm's circulation; (2) the temperature and lapse rates; (3) the location of the rain gauge in relation to the storm's center; (4) the rate of forward movement of the storm; (5) if the storm is over land, the topography, which may greatly increase the rate of ascent of the air; and finally, (6) the moisture content of the air, which must be continually renewed in order for heavy precipitation to persist.

Some theoretical calculations of rainfall rates have been made. Hughes [40] prepared an average picture of the low-level wind circulation around a tropical cyclone, using reconnaissance-aircraft wind observations made in Pacific typhoons. From this mean pattern he was able to compute the inflow of moisture into the storm, and by using other known facts about the hurricane circulation, he determined the rainfall rates for various sectors of the storm. These rates were such that if a hurricane center passed directly over a rain gauge while moving in a straight line, there would have been an accumulation of about eleven inches in a period of forty-eight hours. This gives an estimate of the rainfall occurring while the center of the hurricane is still at sea, since all the data used by Hughes were taken within storms at sea.

The rainfall rate over land may be quite different. Whenever all or a portion of the storm is over land, where surface friction is greater than it is over the water, the winds tend to be retarded and blow more directly across the isobars toward the center of the storm. This increases the low-level convergence, and the rate of rainfall is also greater. This increase in convergence and the removal of the hurricane from the warm waters of the oceans over which it was spawned, however, are the first steps in the dissipation of the storm, and the increased rainfall rate will be temporary, unless some other factors enter into the situation to prevent a decrease. If the path of the storm carries the remnants of the hurricane over higher terrain, the added orographic lifting may greatly increase the original ascending motion due to convergence about the center of the storm, and rainfall rates will remain high or actually increase. When a hurricane impinges on a mountain range or moves along a line parallel to a mountain range, torrential rains occur. Twenty to thirty inches are not at all unusual. Heavy rainfall may also persist when hurricane moves to a northerly latitude and the moisture-laden tropical air is forced to ascend over a dome of cold air behind a cold frontal surface.

It is interesting to note that for heavy rains to persist for any length of time, there must be a continued flow of moist air into the center of the storm or along the upslope of a mountain range, frontal surface, or other mechanism for lifting the air. For example, in connection with hurricane Diane (1955), Mook [65] has shown that if all the precipitable water over the New York–New England area on August 18 had fallen at one time, only 2.88 inches of rain would have resulted. Some sections within this area received more than twelve inches during the twenty-four-hour period on the eighteenth, which proves that additional moisture was continually being funneled into the area. This was brought in by the southerly winds which were present to the east of the dying but still dangerous Diane. This renewal of the moisture supply is, of course, necessary for any prolonged rainfall, however produced, and is not restricted to tropical cyclones alone.

The total accumulation of rain at a given locality is greatly dependent upon the forward speed of the hurricane, simply because in slower-moving storms the rain lasts a longer time. A good example occurred

TABLE 14

Some Heavy Rainfall Totals in Connection with Tropical Cyclones

Inches	Date	Place
40.8	June 14, 1876	Cherrapunji, India — may not have been tropical storm. Averages 426 in. per year.
21.4	June 15-16, 1886	Alexandria, Louisiana
26	Feb. 15-21, 1896	Pamplemousse, Mauritius
47	Feb. 15-21, 1896	Reunion, Mauritius
41	Feb. 15-21, 1896	La Marie, Tamarind Falls, and l'Etoile, Mauritius
63	Date unknown	Mt. Malloy, Queensland, Australia, in 3 days
96.5	Nov., 1909	Silver Hill, Jamacia, in 4 days
46	July, 1911	Baguio, Philippine Islands
88	July, 1911	Baguio, Philippine Islands, in 4 days
81.5	July 18-20, 1913	Funkike, Formosa, in 3 days
22.22	July 14-15, 1916	Altapass, North Carolina
23.11	Sept. 9-10, 1921	Taylor, Texas
29.60	Sept. 13-14, 1928	Adjuntas, Puerto Rico
19.76	Aug. 6-10, 1940	Crowley, Louisiana, 33.71 for 5-day period
31.66	Aug. 6-10, 1940	Abbeville, Louisiana, for 5-day period
29.65	Aug. 6-10, 1940	Lafayette, Louisiana, for 5-day period

in hurricane Ione (1955), which moved only forty-five miles in ten hours across eastern North Carolina, depositing 16.63 inches of rain at Maysville and 13.04 at New Bern.

Some of the heaviest rainfalls in connection with tropical cyclones are shown in Table 14. All amounts are for a twenty-four-hour period unless otherwise noted. At the other extreme, as an illustration of the individuality of hurricanes, the center of a storm passed thirteen miles south of Miami on October 6, 1941. It was attended by winds of 123 mph at Dinner Key, but only 0.35 inch of rain fell. Considerable damage was reported to crops, tropical vegetation, and shrubbery from salt spray blown many miles inland. Ordinarily the heavy rains attending a hurricane will immediately wash off the salt and it will do little damage to plants. Extremely light rain was also noted when this storm passed Nassau in the Bahamas. There is no known similar case among all our hurricane records. The hurricane of October 12, 1947, was attended by high-intensity rainfall in Miami, with 1.32 inches falling in ten minutes and 3.60 inches in one hour at the Weather Bureau Office. At a United States Geological Survey gauge at the Hialeah water plant over 6 inches fell in seventy-five minutes.

Some representative storm totals and twenty-four-hour amounts for hurricanes [90] entering the United States at various points along the Gulf and Atlantic coasts are shown in Figures 54 through 60. These

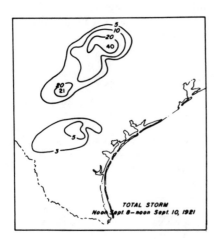

Fig. 54. Rainfall Totals for the Texas storm of September, 1921.

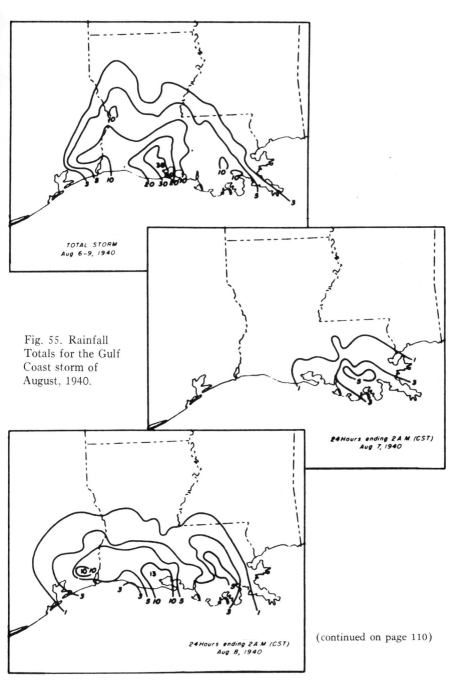

TOTAL STORM
Aug 6-9, 1940

Fig. 55. Rainfall
Totals for the Gulf
Coast storm of
August, 1940.

24 Hours ending 2 A M. (CST)
Aug 7, 1940

24 Hours ending 2 A M (CST)
Aug 8, 1940

(continued on page 110)

(continued from page 109)

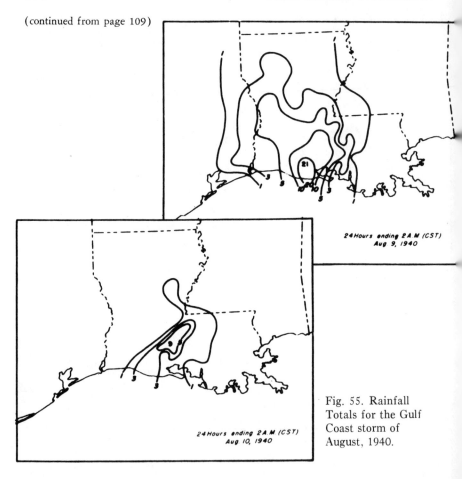

24 Hours ending 2 A.M. (CST)
Aug 9, 1940

24 Hours ending 2 A.M. (CST)
Aug. 10, 1940

Fig. 55. Rainfall Totals for the Gulf Coast storm of August, 1940.

illustrate the apparent lack of any correlation between the intensity of the storm, i.e., the strength of the winds, and the intensity of the rainfall. The September, 1921, storm entered the coast of Mexico, then moved north across the Rio Grande, and by the time it reached Texas, it scarcely could be identified as a cyclonic circulation. Yet Taylor, Texas, recorded 23.11 inches of rain in 24 hours, and nearly 40 inches was measured near Thrall during the period of the storm. The August, 1940, storm (Figure 55) followed a very unusual course, moving southwestward across northern Florida on the second, then across the northern Gulf and inland near Cameron, Louisiana, on the seventh.

 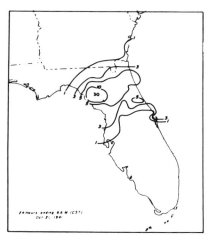

Fig. 56. Rainfall Totals for the Florida storm of October, 1941.

It was barely of hurricane intensity, the highest wind being 82 mph at Port Arthur, Texas. The width of the hurricane winds was only about twenty miles. This storm moved very slowly, and both Figures 55 and 58 illustrate the huge rainfall totals that can result from slow-moving storms. The storm of October, 1941, Figure 56, was never of hurricane intensity; yet it dumped a maximum of thirty-five inches on Trenton, Florida, over a three-day period. The twenty-four-hour totals reached about thirty inches (see bottom of Figure 56).

The storm of August, 1928, Figure 57, entered the Florida coast near Melbourne on the seventh and turned northeastward east of Apalachicola on the ninth. It continued on a generally northeastward course and finally passed off the Maryland coast on the twelfth. The orographic effect of the eastern slopes of the Appalachians was reflected in the general rainfall pattern, which showed the axis of the heaviest rains to be to the west of the path of the storm. On the eleventh and twelfth a cold front approached the hurricane from the northwest, causing the remnants of the center to turn to a more easterly course and also providing additional lifting for the moisture-laden air, thereby contributing to the rainfall maximum over northeastern Virginia and Maryland. The rains of Connie and Diane (1955), are shown in Figures 59 and 60. These are included primarily because of their importance to the disastrous floods which they produced. These will be discussed in more detail in Chapter 12.

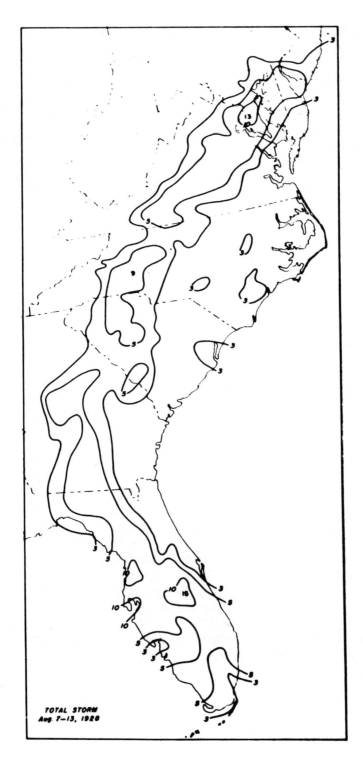

Fig. 57. Rainfall Totals showing the influence of mountains on rainfall distribution, August, 1928.

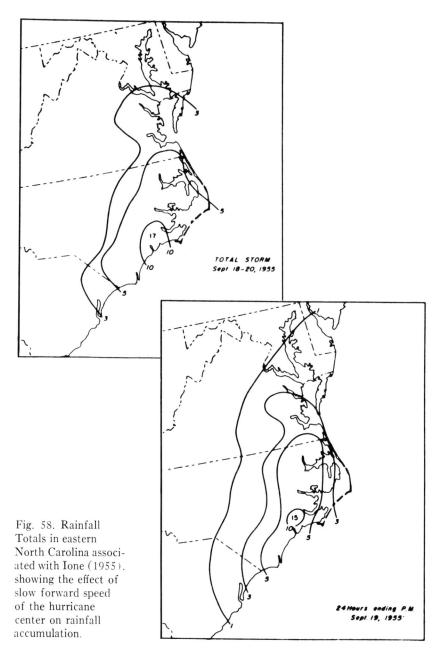

Fig. 58. Rainfall
Totals in eastern
North Carolina associ-
ated with Ione (1955).
showing the effect of
slow forward speed
of the hurricane
center on rainfall
accumulation.

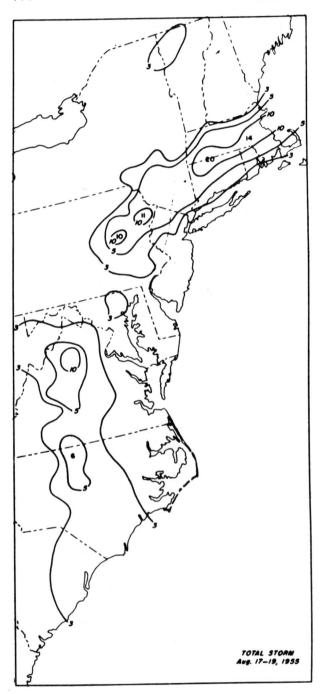

Fig. 59. The Rains of Diane (1955), called "The Billion Dollar Hurricane." This is the pattern of the heavy rainfall area in its relation to the path of the storm.

TOTAL STORM
Aug. 17–19, 1955

Midnight to midnight
Aug. 18, 1955

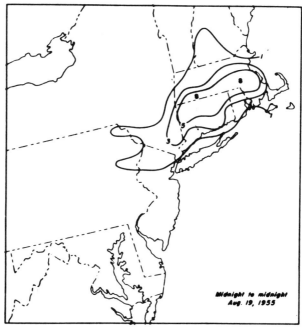

Midnight to midnight
Aug. 19, 1955

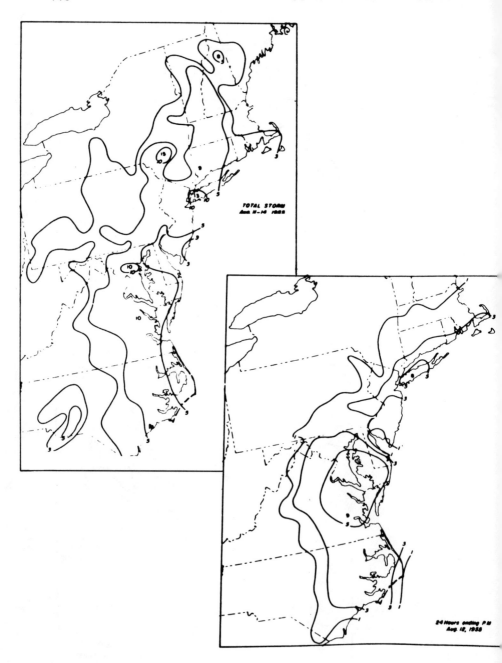

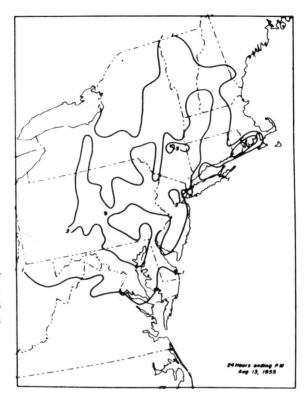

Fig. 60. The Rains of Connie (1955) showing excessive rains from North Carolina to New England.

The distribution of rainfall around the hurricane has been the subject of much interest among meteorologists. The conclusions one draws seem to be similar to the blind man's interpretation of the elephant. It all depends upon where the storms are observed, the stage of development, the speed of motion, and the degree of recurvature the storm has undergone.

Cline [8] found the amount and area of rainfall distributed quite asymmetrically around the storms along the Gulf coast, if the hurricane center was moving. In these cases the area of greatest intensity was found sixty to eighty miles in front of the cyclone center and mostly to the right of the line along which the cyclone was advancing. Relatively little rain fell in the rear half. Cline offered the explanation that convergence is produced by winds of high velocity moving through the right rear quadrant, while winds in the right front quadrant were of lesser velocity, causing the air to ascend; and that momentum carries the ascending air forward into the front of the cyclonic area, expanding and cooling as it reaches the higher levels. This was responsible for the heavier rain in the forward portion of the storm. In the hurricane of October 10-12, 1909, for example, 12.04 inches fell on Key West before the center and only 0.24 inches after.

However, Cline also examined three hurricanes which had ceased to move forward appreciably after the center moved inland, and he found the distribution of precipitation in this class of cyclones to be materially different from that in a traveling storm. There is as much or more precipitation in the rear half of the stationary cyclone as in the front. In contrast, the theoretical study of Hughes [40] showed rather a symmetrical rain pattern around the center for moving storms. More recently Schoner [89] has investigated the areal distribution of rainfall around the centers of hurricanes which moved inland on the Texas coast. He concluded that the heaviest rainfall is most likely to occur in the right front quadrant, which substantiates the earlier work of Cline.

Other observations made in the vicinity of storms at more southerly latitudes reveal a different pattern. The last three Puerto Rican storms are typical. In the San Felipe storm of September 13, 1928, 3.03 inches of rain fell at San Juan in the first half and 7.85 inches in the last half of the storm; this was a mature Cape Verde type of storm. In San Ciprian, September 27, 1932, 1.17 inches fell before and 1.59 inches after the center passed. This was a relatively immature storm and the center passed very close to San Juan. On September 19, 1931, in San Nicolas, 0.71 inches was recorded before the calm center and 1.15 inches after. This was another immature storm and it came and went in two hours, which accounts for the small amount of rainfall. These observations indicate greater symmetry of the rainfall pattern than either Cline or Schoner found to be the case for Gulf storms.

It appears that Cline's analysis for Gulf storms is correct, and that the pattern is actually different for storms at lower latitudes. Many of the hurricanes studied by Cline were in an advanced stage of recurvature and some may have been assuming nontropical characteristics. In general it appears that as hurricanes reach more northerly latitudes and begin to recurve or to pass overland, differences in friction, air masses, and the wind flow in which the storms are imbedded all tend to reduce the symmetry of the pressure field, the wind circulation, and the rainfall distribution.

1 <.005	2 .01	3 .01	4 .04	5 .05	6 .05	7 0	8 0	9 0
10 .01	11 .02	12 .03	13 .06	14 .03	15 .01	16 <.005	17 0	18 <.005
19 .03	20 .04	21 .05	22 .06	23 .08	24 .08	25 .03	26 <.005	27 0
28 .06	29 .07	30 .11	31 .13	32 .18	33 .12	34 .04	35 .03	36 .01
37 .05	38 .07	39 .14	40 .26	41 .26	42 .10	43 .05	44 .02	45 <.005
46 .02	47 .04	48 .07	49 .14	50 .11	51 .06	52 .02	53 .01	54 0
55 .01	56 .01	57 .02	58 .04	59 .06	60 .02	61 .01	62 <.005	63 .01
64 .01	65 .01	66 .01	67 .01	68 <.005	69 .01	70 .01	71 <.005	72 .01
73 <.005	74 .01	75 .01	76 .02	77 .01	78 .01	79 .01	80 <.005	81 .01

Fig. 61. Mean Hourly Rainfall relative to the center of a hurricane. Arrow at left indicates the direction of movement of the center. Numbers in upper left identify the square. Hurricane is at the center of square 41. Sides of the square are one degree of latitude. Rates in inches per hour.

At the latitude of Florida, where both orographic and extratropical influences are at a minimum, a detailed analysis of the hourly rainfall rates around sixteen hurricanes shows that the rates ahead of the center are greater than those to the rear, but that the differences between the right and left sides are not large. The results of this analysis [62] are shown in Figure 61.

Recent radar photographs of the rainfall distribution in northerly latitudes have shown that whenever the cyclone center becomes stationary, the rain shield around the eye shows a tendency to become more or less circular, but that when the center is advancing, the heaviest amounts are concentrated in the forward half, as shown in Figure 62.

A brief summary of the known facts about the distribution of rainfall around the center of a hurricane follows:

1. About immature storms, storms observed at low latitudes, and stationary storms even when they are at northerly latitudes (provided they are

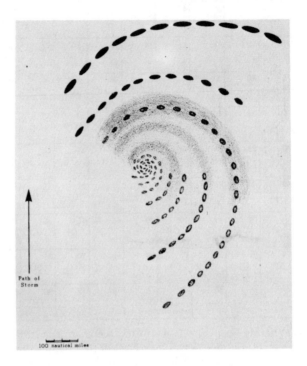

Path of
Storm

100 nautical miles

Fig. 62. Composite of many Radar Photographs of hurricanes, showing the average distribution of rainfall about a moving hurricane at a northerly
latitude. (After Rockney)

not assuming nontropical characteristics), the rainfall distribution is more
or less symmetrical, although there is some evidence that the maximum
occurs to the rear of the center.

2. In storms undergoing recurvature, in those observed at latitudes as
far north as the Gulf coast, and in those assuming nontropical features,
the rainfall maximum is usually shifted to the front portion of the storm.
This is usually to the right of the line along which the center is advancing, but other features such as mountain ranges and advancing cold fronts
may cause the maximum to be on the left, as in Hazel (1954) and Diane
(1955).

It has long been known that the uncontrollable fury of a hurricane
is not an unvarying phenomenon, even near the wall cloud surrounding the eye. Periods of extreme gustiness are interspersed with comparative lulls in the wind's violence. Reconnaissance flights have shown

that cloud density is also extremely variable: heavy cloud bands in which torrential rains are occurring alternate with periods of light rains, or none at all, and a minimum of cloudiness. However, it was not until radar came into use during World War II that a definite pattern could be assigned to these variations.

Radar observations of the precipitation around a tropical storm have established that the rainfall is concentrated within a series of bands. Some of the bands can be observed hundreds of miles from the center of the storm. These concentrations of rainfall are known as the "spiral bands." They are long and narrow and vary in width from three to eight to as much as twenty miles [113]. Figure 63 shows a radar photograph of the spiral-band structure of hurricane rains. The number of bands varies from one to several, and the width and the spacing between the bands increases as one goes from the center of the hurricane outward. Between the bands almost no rain is observed.

Fig. 63. Hurricane Detection by means of radar. Note circular motion on radar-scope.

The radar bands are the lines along which low-level convergence is concentrated. The general shape of the bands is very close to that of a logarithmic spiral, and in fact logarithmic curves have been fitted to the spiral bands, which are [91] useful in locating the eye of the storm by radar, but this will be discussed in more detail in Chapter 9.

The spiral-band structure of hurricane rains is unique and almost as remarkable as the eye. Its discovery was quite accidental, awaiting only the development of radar. Perhaps the most amazing feature of the spiral bands is that no one, either from theoretical considerations or from examinations of numerous rainfall records from countless storms, even suspected that the rain bands might assume a spiral character. They have since, however, provided one of the most useful means of tracking the progress of the hurricane, particularly when the center is within two hundred miles of land-based radar installations.

6

THE ENERGY OF THE HURRICANE

VARIOUS COMPUTATIONS [40, 62] HAVE INDICATED THAT from 2.0 to 6.0 x 10^{26} ergs per day are liberated in the form of heat within the area of the average hurricane. The larger figure (and even that may well be exceeded in some mature cyclones) is equivalent to approximately sixteen trillion kilowatt-hours per day! For comparative purposes, the total electrical power generated within the United States is of the order of two billion kilowatt-hours per day. The efficiency of the hurricane as an engine for converting heat into mechanical energy is very low, probably less than 3 per cent [84]. Even if the 3 per cent of the total heat released by a hurricane could be converted into electricity a hurricane could in one day provide more than six months' supply of electrical power for the entire United States.

Scientists have given us some energy comparisons between weather phenomena and atomic detonations. An ordinary summer afternoon thunderstorm has the energy equivalent of thirteen atomic bombs (Nagasaki type). An average hurricane will squeeze out about 20,000-000,000 tons of water in a twenty-four-hour period. This represents an energy equivalent to 500,000 atomic bombs. An atomic detonation lifted 10,000,000 tons of water in Test Baker, but a hurricane poured 2,500,000,000 tons of water on the island of Puerto Rico within a few hours, and this was only a fraction of the total rainfall throughout the area of the cyclone. Another calculation has a hurricane 500 miles in diameter releasing latent heat energy at the rate of ten trillion horsepower and maintaining this rate for as long as ten days.

Sources of Energy

The principal source of energy of the tropical cyclone is the release of the latent heat of condensation. The process of adding water to the atmosphere requires heat, which is supplied directly or indirectly by the sun. As the warm, moisture-laden air overlying the tropical oceans flows into the hurricane circulation, principally at low levels, the air begins to ascend. This ascent cools the air as it is allowed to expand against the reduced pressures of the higher elevations. The air soon reaches saturation and some of the moisture is forced to condense; heat is now released and added to the surrounding atmosphere. Several factors limit the amount of energy released by the ascending air, large though it is. These are the pressure, temperature, and relative humidity of the air at the time ascent began, and the prevailing lapse rates within the atmospere surrounding the cyclone. The temperature and moisture content of the surface air are closely related to the temperature of the underlying water surface. In this way the ocean temperature limits the amount of energy available for both hurricane formation and maintenance.

Essentially the hurricane is a heat engine, which implies the existence of a heat source and a cold source. It was pointed out in an earlier chapter that the interior of a hurricane is warmer than its environment. This warm core of the hurricane is the heat source. Air flows into the storm at low levels (moving from lower to higher temperatures) and ascends from near the surface of the ocean to the upper atmosphere, where it is removed from the region of the cyclone. It then mixes with the surrounding atmosphere and gradually sinks. In this type of circulation, ascent takes place at higher temperatures than does descent. This results in the production of kinetic energy, i.e., wind. *This transformation of heat to kinetic energy can take place only when temperatures increase toward the cyclone center.*

Clearly then the heat of condensation must be released and removed from the hurricane in such a manner that some regions are maintained at lower pressures relative to others. In the vicinity of tropical cyclones the atmosphere is usually undisturbed at elevations of about 100 mb. Since cold air is heavier than warm air, in areas of extensive warming of the air columns extending from the surface to the upper atmosphere, the sea-level pressures will be lower in areas with warm columns than they will be in cold regions. Thus pressure gradients are established by differential heating of the air columns. Pressure gradients set air in motion and are therefore the connecting link in the transformation of heat to kinetic energy.

It follows that the production and maintenance of the warm core is the vital cog in the process of converting the heat of condensation to the mechanical energy of the winds of the hurricane. It would appear that the most warming might occur in the areas of greatest rainfall (greatest amount of latent heat released), but such is not necessarily the case. The picture is further confused by recent aircraft observations [99] which have shown that frequently the rain areas are denser than their surroundings, thereby being unable to convert heat into kinetic energy.

As air rises, the maximum amount of heat energy will be released (for a specific surrounding atmosphere and its temperature distribution) whenever there is no mixing between the rising air and its environment. Such ascent is known as "parcel ascent," and it rarely occurs on a widespread scale. In actuality the rising air mixes, or "entrains," with the surrounding air. This entrainment effectively reduces the buoyancy of the rising air and also results in lower rain-area temperatures than would be realized following parcel ascent. Much of the entrainment, however, takes place along the outer edges of cumulonimbus towers, and recent studies by Riehl and Malkus [57] have indicated that the inner cores of these towers are effectively protected by the outer edges of the clouds so that no unsaturated air reaches the inner portions of the cumulonimbus clouds. Hence, parcel ascent is really taking place in the cores, and it is within these cores that the largest net ascent in convective clouds actually occurs. At significant distances from the center of the cyclone the percentage of the total area in which parcel ascent is taking place within the cores of these cumulonimbus towers is small, but as the wall cloud is approached [55] these rapidly rising towers (which are shielded from entrainment[1]) become highly concentrated, thereby carrying air of high heat content to great elevations. These factors partly explain the temperature field observed around the cyclone.

Even if completely undiluted subcloud air possessing the temperature and moisture content of the mean tropical atmosphere were lifted from sea level to the elevation of 100 mb, the resulting temperature field aloft would be warm enough to produce a cyclone of barely hurricane intensity. The addition of heat and/or moisture to the subcloud air from the ocean surface increases the equivalent potential temperature of the converging air and permits the ascent of the air at warmer tem-

---

[1]Air flowing through the cyclone at mid-tropospheric levels may at times result in cooler or drier air entering the inner portions of the storm, thus inhibiting hurricane development. Termed "ventilation," this process will be discussed in Chapter 11.

peratures, thus leading to warmer air columns from the surface to, say, 100 mb. Malkus [55] has calculated that the surface pressure will be decreased by about 12.5 mb per 5° increase in the equivalent potential temperature of the ascending air. Her calculations also show that the increase in heat transfer from water to air necessary to maintain a hurricane of moderate intensity is within acceptable limits. Above-normal sea-surface temperatures will obviously make a substantial contribution to such heat increase.

Increasing the equivalent potential temperature of the subcloud air and the subsequent warming aloft as air ascends to higher elevations can probably account for much of the pressure fall observed in weak and moderate hurricanes. Still another mechanism (descent within the eye) must be postulated in order to obtain temperatures warm enough to account for severe hurricanes. Descent within the eye has already been discussed in Chapter 4.

The Energy Budget

Radial inflow occurs principally within the lower few thousand feet. As air spirals inward toward lower pressure and higher temperatures, kinetic energy is produced. A large percentage of this kinetic energy is generated near the hurricane core where pressure gradients are the steepest. At higher levels hurricanes are frequently characterized by anticyclonic circulations, although a small cyclonic circulation may still be present inside the surrounding anticyclone. Net outflow occurs here, although the outflow is not symmetrical around the center. Outflow within the cyclonic region consumes kinetic energy, and within the anticyclonic circulation kinetic energy is again generated. The latter is, however, small in comparison with that generated at the lower levels.

A portion of the kinetic energy is dissipated by surface and internal friction. Some is exported to the environment by the strong upper-level outflow, which may at times occur in jets with velocities exceeding 60 knots [85]. Heat is also exported to the surroundings, where a large portion is dissipated by radiation. The energy exported by the hurricane is available to drive other portions of the general circulation of the atmosphere [84].

In some instances, however, the characteristic high-level anticyclone is not well developed and the resulting outflow may be very weak. Thus little or no kinetic energy can be exported by the system. Outflow takes place at mid-tropospheric levels, and much of the kinetic energy generated within the lower levels is dissipated by *cyclonic outflow against the pressure gradient.*

It has been possible here to touch only briefly on the energetics of the hurricane, much of which is still not clearly understood. The reader who wishes to pursue the subject further is referred to the many excellent works on the subject [55, 57, 76, 82, 84, 85].

Hurricane Modification

The United States Weather Bureau in the course of each year receives many suggestions for hurricane prevention or elimination from well-intentioned persons who are appalled by the annual death and destruction which these severe cyclones cause. Since many proposals have been made and all so far have been impracticable, it is evident that most people have little realization of the energy generated and consumed in an average hurricane. Thirty years ago the suggestion most frequently made was to send naval ships out to bomb and to destroy hurricanes. This was comparable to lighting a match to heat a barn with the temperature 40° F. below zero. Nowadays the majority of the letters recommend the use of atomic bombs or seeding with dry ice or silver iodide.

Weather Bureau scientists state that although modern thermonuclear weapons still release less energy than even an incipient hurricane, they are no longer insignificant when compared to the energy of such a storm. If the use of an atomic bomb is practicable at any time it would have to be at an early stage of development. However, since hurricanes form over warm ocean waters, usually far from land, they are frequently not detected at this stage. Initially the unsettled area covers several thousand square miles with several weak circulations, one of which eventually becomes dominant. This large, indefinite area adds to the difficulty of locating the proper place to detonate the bomb. The energy for the storm's intensification comes from the release of energy in the form of heat (latent heat of condensation) during the precipitation process and, possibly, a nuclear explosion would only add more energy to the developing storm. The Weather Bureau concludes that it is not known at the present time whether a nuclear detonation would dissipate, intensify, or leave unchanged the characteristics of a tropical storm in the formative stage.

Once the storm is completely developed, even the energy of the latest bomb falls far short of competing with the energy of the hurricane. Even if it were possible to slow the winds down to a calm, the energy released by the formation of rain could restore the winds to full hurricane force within fifteen minutes.

Finally, of course, because of cost, only those hurricanes approaching the coast would be bombed. Hurricanes only approach the coast when the air stream in which they are imbedded is also moving toward the coast. This air stream would be contaminated with radioactive poison from the nuclear explosions with consequent possible serious health hazards to areas over which this current passed. This could easily be far more dangerous to life than the hurricane itself.

Malkus [56] has recently speculated on the possibilities of modifying intense hurricanes by saturating the eye. The amount of water needed to cause such saturation is greatly in excess of the amount that could be carried by aircraft, but not vastly greater than the total raised by an underwater atomic explosion. To quote Dr. Malkus: "The Bikini lagoon test raised about a thousand billion grams; evaporation of one hundred times this much water could saturate the eye of a typhoon like Marge. Unfortunately, cooling of this air to its wet-bulb temperature would only raise the central pressure in the eye from 890 mb to about 930 mb, which is still in the intense (cyclone) range. Saturating the eye of a more moderate hurricane . . . (which has higher original humidity) could raise the central pressure by 10-12 mb at most. Thus introduction of water into the eye does not appear to be a promising possibility for hurricane modification."

The Weather Bureau does not take the position that the possibility of man's eventually finding some way to modify hurricanes is completely hopeless. Rather, at the present time, lack of knowledge of the physical processes of the hurricane and lack of any means for definite determination of any possible effects of nuclear weapons make it too dangerous to attempt such experiments. The possibilities of hurricane control by means of cloud seeding, which has the advantage of not resulting in radioactive fallout, will be discussed in the final chapter.

FORMATION

THE EXACT NATURE OF THE PHYSICAL PROCESSES INVOLVED in the formation of hurricanes is not yet definitely known, but any hurricane-producing mechanism must supply (1) low-level convergence strong enough to dissipate the normal trade-wind inversion and lift the moist layer, (2) high-level divergence to remove the accumulated air from the system and permit the pressure to fall at the surface, and (3) sufficient energy to maintain the circulation.

It is definitely known that tropical cyclones originate (1) in easterly waves, (2) in the intertropical convergence zone, and (3) in the trailing southerly portions of the old polar troughs. Palmén [75] has found hurricanes will develop only over comparatively warm water, 79° F. and higher, although there have been a few exceptions. Below-normal sea-surface temperatures correlate well with subnormal hurricane frequencies, but above-normal sea temperatures are not invariably accompanied or followed by above-normal hurricane frequencies. Since in 1890 and 1914 there was only one tropical storm and in several years only two or three were noted, it is apparent that a very special and unusual combination of circumstances is necessary for hurricane development.

The convection theory of hurricane formation was first advanced many years ago and was generally accepted until the early 1930's. It was believed that the calm, moist air of the doldrums or the intertropical convergence zone (ITC) was favorable for convection because of the surface heating or the high moisture content or both. As the heated air began to rise, numerous cumulonimbus clouds, widespread showers, and thunderstorms developed. Then the pressure mysteriously began to fall, the cumulonimbus gradually coalesced, and if the area were far enough away from the equator for the Coriolis force (which causes moving air to turn to the right in the Northern Hemisphere) to be effective, a cyclonic circulation was initiated. The development of

129

the circulation continued until full intensity was reached through release of the latent heat of condensation. It is true that small hurricanes may appear to be one huge convective cloud and there is no doubt that the hurricane is essentially a convective mechanism, but the convective theory of formation left many questions unanswered. Among them are: What is the starting mechanism? What causes the initial fall of pressure? Why are there so few hurricanes? This is not meant to belittle the role of convection in the process of formation, since it is vitally important and plays a necessary role. But convection alone is not enough.

Some attempts were made during the early 1930's to apply Norwegian air-mass methods to tropical-weather analysis. The ITC between the northeast and southeast trades or, in some cases, the boundary between the trades and the ITC was considered as a front along which cyclonic disturbances could develop in a manner analogous to the formation of an extratropical cyclone along a front in the Temperate Zone. This theory provided an energy source as a starting mechanism. However, many tropical storms start in the trade-wind region and not in the vicinity of the so-called tropical front. Neither in the trades nor in the ITC is there any temperature or density discontinuity, since the air is essentially homogeneous. And there are other serious objections to the frontal theory of hurricane formation.

Thus the problem of formation is obviously a very complex one. By far the most comprehensive and probably the most realistic and currently accepted hypothesis has developed as a result of contributions from many meteorologists but principally from Dr. Herbert R. Riehl of the Department of Meteorology, University of Chicago. Riehl [82], as have many others, compares the hurricane to a man-made engine and lists five stages of development:

1. The main energy input is latent heat produced from water vapor.

2. A suitable wind arrangement acts as the starting mechanism. The kinetic energy of these winds furnishes the initial independent energy.

3. Condensation during ascent is the means by which latent heat is converted to sensible heat. The starter must therefore be able to produce such ascent. High level outflow and compensating lower inflow develop, i.e., kinetic energy of radial motion is generated. This circulation in the vertical must be arranged to survive influences that tend to destroy it.

4. Coriolis and centrifugal forces convert radial to tangential kinetic energy; after some time tangential energy predominates.

5. High tropospheric currents provide the cooling system which carries away the excess heat to other regions outside the hurricane area.

A pre-existing disturbance, and one or more are always present in the tropics, forms part of the starting mechanism. The second part of the starting mechanism is the arrival of some outside influence which acts to intensify the initial disturbance. This intensification takes place throughout any wave trough in the easterlies. Several vortices frequently form, and usually the northernmost becomes dominant, perhaps for two reasons: (1) the Coriolis force is increasingly important with latitude and (2) a greater cyclonic wind shear is always present to the north. This intensification increases the rate of organized ascent inside the disturbance and increases the pressure gradient.

To further the formation process interaction between the low-level disturbance and the upper atmosphere takes place. The initial low-level disturbance provides a region into which air from the surrounding area can converge, or flow. This convergence increases the convection already going on inside the disturbance, it becomes better organized, and large quantities of air are lifted to high levels. On a nonrotating globe the convergence would soon cause the initial disturbance to fill, but the rotation of the earth causes a cyclonic circulation to be set up. However, even on a rotating earth there is a component of wind flow across the isobars into the center of the incipient disturbance, and it would eventually fill without the influence of the circulation at higher levels. Since air is flowing into the disturbance at the bottom, it must flow out again at the top. If more air flows in than out, the disturbance will die out; if the upper outflow exceeds the lower inflow, the cyclonic circulation will grow.

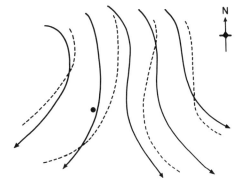

Fig. 64. Model of Streamlines (solid) and Contours (dashed) at 200-mb during the early phases of deepening of tropical cyclone (black dot). (After Riehl)

The initial fall in pressure at the surface is not easy to explain. To date, all efforts to explain the falls from low-level considerations have failed. For a starting mechanism Riehl [81] introduces a northerly current within the 30,000- to 40,000-foot layer, which acts upon the existing low-level disturbance. Deepening (fall in pressure) takes place when the high-level flow is anticyclonic or changes from cyclonic to anticyclonic. This can occur when a high-level ridge lies to the west of the surface disturbance and a high-level trough to the east, as shown in Figure 64. The wind patterns above 30,000 feet in the tropics do not reveal the same constancy of direction that the lower trade winds do; instead they become variable with alternating cyclones and anticyclones more or less drifting about. It is when one of the anticyclones becomes superimposed over the lower-level disturbance that air at high levels is pumped outward· from the region of the storm and deepening takes place. The mechanics of pressure falls are beyond the scope of this book, and the reader is referred to Riehl's [82] textbook on tropical meteorology.

The interaction between the lower and higher levels can produce a fall in the pressure at the surface, although the initial fall may also be caused by the advection of vorticity or be due to an overall lighter air column resulting from warming by organized release of latent heat. Low-level convergence and the resulting lifting of the air from the surface to high levels sets up the vertical circulation shown in Figure 65. This vertical circulation produces kinetic energy, since the air is lighter in the region of ascent than in the surroundings. It is maintained by continuous advection of polar air at the left of the upper current and moist adiabatic ascent at the right, looking downstream. This circulation cell increases the efficiency of the convective activity associated with the original disturbance in producing kinetic energy. The air that rises is pumped out from the area of the disturbance and

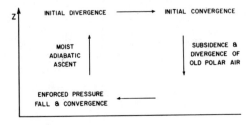

Fig. 65. Model of Vertical Circulation during early stages of hurricane formation. (After Riehl)

transported a considerable distance away before it sinks, thus permitting the circulation to continue. Furthermore, this circulation will be accelerated if the temperature of the rising air is greater than that of the descending air. Condensation is responsible for this temperature gradient, i.e., the air in the rain area is less dense than that in the surrounding area. Otherwise the circulation would soon die out.

It has been possible here to present only a very abbreviated and incomplete sketch of Riehl's logical and comprehensive theory of hurricane formation. However, he would be the last to say that it is a complete and final answer. It is not known what is the main trigger nor just exactly how some outside influence acts to intensify the initial disturbance, nor is it definitely established that the high-level divergence is the correct explanation for the initial pressure fall. Many of the data and measurements required for full evaluation of this theory are not normally available. Like a man-made engine which will not run if any of the parts work improperly or if gas or oil are lacking, a hurricane will not form if temperature, moisture, or instability fail to meet certain sensitive and rather delicate requirements. The gross weather situation which would seem to meet the specifications for hurricane formation occurs very frequently, perhaps somewhere in the tropics every day during the hurricane season. Yet the number of tropical cyclones is small. This suggests that the mechanism misfires, stutters, and perhaps usually fails because all the numerous ingredients involved rarely reach the critical values simultaneously.

Events during the past several hurricane seasons, however, have pointed to one possible trigger and one brake on hurricane formation. Riehl [85] has prepared detailed analyses of two situations that occurred in the Gulf of Mexico in 1957, one in June and the other in September. Most of the significant synoptic features normally expected to lead to hurricane development were present in both cases. Yet one resulted in the devastating Audrey and the other remained a relatively weak tropical storm. Riehl calculated the transports of mass, heat, moisture, and kinetic energy across the boundaries of the Gulf for both cases. The energy transports were very nearly equal in both cases, but the mean ageostrophic flow was much greater during Audrey and it persisted for a greater length of time. In other words, the low-level inflow and high-level outflow were larger in the June hurricane than in the September storm. The resulting acceleration in the circulation around Audrey was quite large, and Riehl suggests that mechanical forcing by the surrounding disturbances triggered the severe cyclone. The hypothesis will, of course, have to be tested further before its validity can be fully accepted.

National Hurricane Research Project flights into Carrie (1957) and Daisy (1958) have shown air flowing through the cyclones at mid-tropospheric levels, thus mixing air that has ascended from the subcloud layer with that advected laterally into the hurricane. This flow, termed "ventilation" by Riehl and Simpson [98], keeps importing relatively cool, dry air from the outside and acts as a definite brake on hurricane development. There are unquestionably other constraints to hurricane formation as well as other triggering mechanisms. All necessary and sufficient conditions for formation are not fully understood [86], but research in the future will most likely be directed toward discovery of additional triggers and constraints.

While understanding of the mechanics of hurricane formation are of great interest and importance to the meteorologist, day-to-day weather conditions that lead to formation are perhaps of more vital interest to the hurricane forecaster. Namias and C. Dunn [71] have discussed hurricane formation from the standpoint of "planetary waves." An examination of an upper-level chart for the Northern Hemisphere will reveal that winds in the prevailing-westerly belt seldom follow a straight path eastward. Instead the wind flows in a wavelike, or sinusoidal, pattern, with the wave length varying from 50° to 120° of longitude. These are the long waves, or planetary waves, of the atmosphere. Superimposed upon these planetary-wave patterns are the short-wave motions associated with frontal systems and traveling cyclones. The east-west component of the winds is referred to as the "zonal motion" and the north-south component as "meridional flow." To quote these authors:

> In the case of hurricanes Connie and Diane (1955) two climatological factors bearing on their formation and course appear highly pertinent:
>
> 1. The planetary zonal wind systems during the two months preceding their formation were appreciably farther north than normal, and
>
> 2. The regions in which zonal wind systems were displaced farthest north were eastern North America, the eastern Atlantic and Europe and the west central Pacific. . . .
>
> Since the sub-tropical Atlantic anticyclone was well north of normal and associated with a compensating deficit of mass in the lower latitudes,

it is perhaps not surprising that the Atlantic hurricane season got under way early with the detection of hurricane Connie on August 4. . . .

While hurricane Connie was first reported on August 4 at about 16.6°N and 48.0°W, there is some indication that it developed off North Africa some time earlier. At any rate planetary wave forms over the North Atlantic evolved in a manner which the authors have come to associate with tropical storm formation.

Thus in late July the ridge in the Azores upper level anticyclone thrust strongly northeastward into Europe, thereby introducing a northeasterly flow which, through vorticity (the tendency for rotary motion) flux, led to an anomalously sharp and deep trough extending along the Spanish and African coasts. It is probably at the base of this trough that Connie developed — its formation encouraged by the injection of cyclonic vorticity from the north and by associated vertical destabilization processes as discussed in an earlier report. If this hypothesis is correct, the frequency of tropical storms of the Cape Verde type may well depend upon the degree of development or suppression of the protruding Azores ridge to the north. . . .

This prevalence of upper level anticyclones gave Scandinavia one of its finest tourist seasons in terms of sunny, rainless weather.

That these ideas are not wholly new is illustrated by the explanation of Garriott [26] for the above-normal frequency of hurricanes in 1906 when he wrote: "Tropical storm development was exceptionally active in American waters during September 1906. In seeking the causes of this activity we find an apparent contributory condition in the distribution of atmospheric pressure over the region of observation. In the West Indies and adjacent waters barometric pressure was unusually low, while in the more northern latitudes of the Atlantic, and more especially from the Azores over the British Isles, the barometer averaged above normal, and after the 17th, was remarkably high."

A number of earlier writers have pointed out the apparent development of hurricanes following intrusions of cold air into the subtropics, and the apparent requirement of a warm water surface has been mentioned earlier. Namias [68] ties these two together as follows:

Although variations in water temperatures over tropical oceans undoubtedly occur from one year to another, it appears more likely that variations in vertical stability, which affect the likelihood of tropical cyclone formation, are brought about chiefly by variations in mid-tropospheric temperature. The logical instrument for bringing about these mid-tropospheric temperature variations are planetary waves which perform the function of periodically interchanging the tropical and polar air masses. Thus deep and meridionally extensive troughs in the westerlies deploy deep cold currents into the tropics, thereby bringing about variations in thermo-dynamic stability. . . . The organization of thunderstorm cells into hurricane vortices may be favored also by the injection of cyclonic vorticity from the troughs of the westerlies into the tropics. Thus, the two factors, cold air aloft leading to instability, and a general field of cyclonic vorticity incident to the penetration of westerly troughs into low latitudes, bring about a favorable climate for tropical cyclone formation.

It does not seem likely data will be available to confirm or disprove the hypotheses of Namias for some time. The ideas of Namias are not contradictory to those of Riehl.

Obviously so far little has been described of immediate practical use to the short-range weather forecaster. The principal conditions favorable for hurricane formation are:

1. The existence of subnormal pressure in low latitudes and above-normal pressure in high latitudes [2].

2. An existing disturbance of some sort in the tropics.

3. Easterlies decreasing with height above the normal inversion level but extending to 30,000 feet or higher.

4. The location of the surface disturbance under 200-mb streamlines in accordance with Figure 64.

5. Movement of the disturbance at less than 20 mph and preferably less than 15 mph.

6. Norton [72] suggested that high-pressure areas from the temperate latitudes moving out into the Atlantic and reinforcing the semi-permanent Azores-Bermuda anticyclone play a role in hurricane formation. These cause a line of wind shear or surge in velocity in the trade-wind belt, either at the surface or aloft or both. When such a surge comes into contact with an easterly wave, it may be changed quickly from a stable wave to a tropical storm. A sharp increase in the vertical wind shear east of the wave may produce a similar effect.

7. Riehl [81] found that whenever an easterly wave (moving westward) approaches a trough in the westerlies (moving eastward at a higher latitude) both trough and wave intensify. They weaken, however, as they separate, unless a closed cyclonic circulation has developed on the wave, in which case the wave does not show a tendency to fill. This superposition of trough and wave may be one process whereby stable easterly waves are changed into unstable ones.

8 | THE HURRICANE-WARNING SYSTEM

THE PROGRESS OF HURRICANE FORECASTING HAS BEEN VERY slow and gradual and beset with difficulties, since these storms are born and spend most of their lives at sea. Until the advent of radio it was almost impossible to obtain observational data in oceanic and tropical areas. Throughout the first decade of the present century, detection was a most difficult problem. When a message was received by cable indicating the presence of a hurricane, warnings or a hurricane alert were frequently issued for extensive portions of the United States coast line. On one occasion during the first years of the twentieth century a message was received in Washington, indicating that a hurricane was approaching the Antilles. During the ensuing week hurricane warnings were displayed at one time or another from Charleston, South Carolina, to Brownsville, Texas, only to have the hurricane eventually show up at Bermuda. As late as 1909 hurricane warnings flew from Mobile, Alabama, to Charleston, South Carolina, in connection with a hurricane which eventually affected only extreme southern Florida. Not until about 1920 did forecasters begin to make a serious attempt to try to actually forecast hurricane paths.

History and Development of Hurricane Forecasting in the Atlantic

The first mention of the type of storm now known as a hurricane occurs in the logs of the voyages of Christopher Columbus. He uses the same terminology to describe the severe storms of both winter and summer. It seems very likely that most of the winter storms encountered by him were not true hurricanes. Tannehill [102] believes Columbus first encountered a hurricane in the region of Santo Domingo in October, 1495, and other sources mention one in about the same

137

area in 1494. In 1502, Columbus writes about another also in the vicinity of Santo Domingo. A wealth of historical information on these early hurricanes can be found in a recently published book, *Hurricane,* by Marjory Stoneman Douglas [12].

1743   Several of the milestones in the development of meteorology ocurred in connection with tropical cyclones. One such was the more or less inadvertent discovery by Benjamin Franklin that storms moved progressively from one place to another and that they were not steered by the surface wind. Franklin, who was living in Philadelphia, had made arrangements with a friend in Boston who was also interested in astronomy to make simultaneous observations of a lunar eclipse scheduled one evening in September, 1743. A northeaster developed in Philadelphia and Franklin was unable to make any observations. Since the wind was northeast he expected that his friend in Boston would also have the same difficulty. He was very much surprised to learn by mail a few days later that the weather had been fine in Boston at the time of the eclipse and that the storm had arrived there the following day. He then proceeded to gather additional details on the storm from other sources and learned that it had once been a hurricane and that it had moved northeastward off the coast against the surface winds observed at coastal points. It is questionable whether he inferred much about the circulation of the storm, but he did discover that the storm system moved and that this movement was not controlled by surface wind.

1819   It was also a hurricane which Professor Farrar of the University of Cambridge, New England, now Harvard University, was describing in an account of the Boston storm of September 23, 1815, printed in the *American Philosophical Transactions* and reprinted in the *Quarterly (Brandes) Journal of Science* in 1819, page 102. In this article he used the following remarkable expressions (for the time): "I have not been able to find the center or the limits of this tempest. It was very violent at places separated by a considerable interval from each other, while the intermediate regions suffered much less. Its course through forests in some instances was marked almost as definitely as where trees had been cut down for a road. *In these cases it appears to have been a moving vortex and not the rushing forward of the great body of the atmosphere.*" He then goes on, according to Piddington [77], to describe the extent of the storm, the veerings of the wind, and its turning in opposite directions at Boston and New York, as well as the difference of time between the maximum violence at the two places, so as to leave no question about this storm's having been a true cyclone.

1831   William C. Redfield published in the *American Journal of Science* an article stating that storms of the American coast were whirl-winds; moreover, they were progressive whirlwinds moving forward on curved tracks at a considerable rate and were traceable from the West Indies and along the coast of the United States till they curved off to the eastward between the Bermudas and the Banks of Newfoundland. During the following two decades Redfield published a number of articles on hurricanes, some giving many excellent practical rules for navigation so as to avoid the strongest winds and also valuable remarks on the barometer as a guide.

Redfield was probably the first United States citizen to make a sub-stantial contribution to our knowledge of hurricanes. He was born in Middletown, Connecticut, March 26, 1789, and died in 1857. Accord-ing to Humphreys [41], Redfield obtained only a rudimentary common-school education but became a notable philosopher, meteorologist, and Naval engineer. His attention was first drawn to the subject of storms in 1821, when he examined the position of trees prostrated by the great September gale (hurricane) of that year. Noting the direction in which trees and other objects fell and comparing times when storms reached different places, he conceived the idea that this hurricane was a progressive whirlwind. A long series of essays on rotary storms followed.

1831   Lieutenant Colonel William Reid of the Royal Engineers, London, became greatly interested in hurricanes while rebuilding gov-ernment structures destroyed in the severe hurricane of that year on the island of Barbados when 1,477 persons lost their lives in a seven-hour hurricane. He was able to develop more fully the theory of circulation and movement of hurricanes, and he collected detailed information on a considerable number of storms during his sojourn there. Reid pub-lished a book in 1838 which is still held in high esteem as a book of reference. In it he formulated his "law of storms," including rules for mariners to maneuver so as to avoid the most dangerous quadrants. In 1847, he established a hurricane warning display system (the first of which we have record) when the barometer indicated the approach of a storm.

1839   About this time Henry Piddington was investigating tropical storms in India. He coined the word "cyclone," from the Greek word

"Kyklos," meaning "coil of the snake," to describe all rotary storms. When squall lines are observed on radar pictures of hurricanes, one marvels at how apt was the derivation of the word "cyclone." In 1851, Piddington published *The Sailor's Hornbook,* which is the source of much of the preceding information on these early hurricane investigators.

1844   In any history of the development of forecasting, whether middle or low latitude, mention should be made of the invention of the telegraph. The first telegraph line was completed in this year between Washington and Baltimore. Any system of weather forecasting requires the rapid collection of observational data, and the invention of the telegraph provided meteorology with the necessary rapid method of communications.

1870   This year was notable for several important developments. A Federal Weather Service was established in the United States under the Army Signal Corps and the first United States government weather forecast was issued, although some weather "probabilities" had been distributed the previous year by the Cincinnati Chamber of Commerce.

The Observatory of the College of Belén had been established by the Jesuits in 1857 in Havana, Cuba, and from the beginning the priests there maintained a considerable interest in weather, particularly in hurricanes. In 1870 the Reverend Benito Viñes became director of the college and immediately and energetically began to think about the hurricane problem in Cuba.

Viñes was a true scientist, making a significant contribution both to hurricane theory and to the art of forecasting hurricanes. He probably deserves the foremost position among all meteorologists in the Western Hemisphere who up to and through the nineteenth century contributed to our knowledge of tropical cyclones. He was born September 19, 1837, in Poboleda, Spain, and died July 23, 1893, in Havana, Cuba. Shortly after he became director of the Belén Observatory, he defined the problem that he set himself to solve, which according to Drumm [14] was (1) to find some sign or group of signs that would invariably prove the existence of a cyclone while it was yet at a great distance from the observer; (2) to get his bearing in regard to the whirlwind, i.e., to determine from what part of the horizon it was coming; (3) to locate the trajectory or curve along which the cyclone would move, and to do this in time for the observer to take himself to a safe distance from it; and (4) to determine the distance of the hurricane from the observer, its intensity, area, and velocity. He carried out a considerable amount of work on barometry and later on clouds, particularly the forecast value of cirrus and cirrostratus. In 1877 he published one of his more famous papers, "Apuntes Relativos a los Huracanes de las Antillas," later incorporated into the *Anales de la Academia de Ciencias de la Habana.* Willis L. Moore, Chief of the Weather Bureau, wrote in *Colliers Weekly,* October 6, 1900, that probably the Reverend Benito Viñes gave more intelligent study to the investigation of tropical cyclones than any other scientist (up to that time). His earliest known printed forecast was September 11, 1875. He wrote some fourteen special treatises and reports.

In the several decades preceding 1900 and for a decade or so thereafter, the influence of the Reverend Benito Viñes was dominant. If there was evidence of a tropical cyclone, its location with reference to the observer was based on surface winds and cloud directions in accordance with the ideas of Viñes. Thus the storm had to be sufficiently close to the observer for the winds at all levels to be influenced by the storm's circulation, or, as a rule, in latitude 25° N, within 300 to 500 miles. Cirrus clouds were thought to radiate directly out from the center of the hurricane, especially in the front semicircle. Viñes [110] claimed to have detected the existence of a hurricane three to four days before its arrival from plumiform cirrus.

Viñes developed a law which associates latitude of recurvature with season as well as averages of direction and twenty-four-hour amounts of movement based on latitude and season. His results were surprisingly similar to those of Mitchell [64] and Colón [9] years later.

1873 — August 6 The Signal Corps of the United States Army began obtaining reports from Havana on this date and from Kingston, Jamaica, and Santiago de Cuba shortly thereafter. On August 23 of this year, the Signal Corps issued cautionary signals from Cape May, New Jersey, to New London, Connecticut, which was probably the first hurricane warning. However, the storm moved offshore, and it is likely that by this time it had become extratropical. The Signal Corps weather map issued for September 28, 1874, is the first containing a hurricane, which was located off the coast between Savannah, Georgia, and Jacksonville, Florida.

1875 — September 11 Viñes issued his first authenticated hurricane warning on this date, although it is possible he may have issued one earlier. During the subsequent years, he was the first to forecast a hurricane from the upper clouds and to state that the place of formation and direction of movement changes with the season.

1880 — October 1   The organic act creating the United States Weather Bureau was approved, and shortly thereafter the transmission of West Indian reports to the United States was discontinued because of some doubt about the legality of spending money for weather stations outside the United States. The following year the legality of such a procedure was firmly established and six stations throughout the Antilles began reporting.

1888 or 1889   The network of stations was extended to Puerto Rico and Antigua. On July 7, 1889, Congress passed a bill authorizing the United States Weather Bureau to establish and operate observing stations throughout the West Indies and along Caribbean shores.

1898   The Spanish-American War began and the Hurricane Warning Service underwent its first reorganization during this year. Previously warnings had been issued only to United States coastal areas but now a more extensive system was set up to include warnings for shipping and the military. At Kingston, Jamaica, was established a forecasting center, which was transferred to Havana on February 1, 1899, and all areas in the West Indies were given the benefit of the hurricane-warning service.

1900   The first serious study of tropical storms by the United States Weather Bureau was published in this year, *West Indian Hurricanes* by E. B. Garriot. Garriot's main contribution was bringing hurricane statistics up to date; otherwise the publication contained an extensive series of quotes from Redfield, Viñes, and others, with hurricane tracks for about the preceding twenty-five years.

1902   The United States Hurricane Warning Service was transferred to Washington, where it was concentrated until 1935. Wireless telegraphy was invented by Marconi about this time and became available for use by ships at sea. On December 3, 1905, the first marine weather report was radioed from a ship at sea, and on August 26, 1909, the SS *Cartago*, near the coast of Yucatan, radioed the first ship report indicating the existence of a hurricane. The weather-reporting program from ships was steadily expanded until by 1935 more than 21,000 ships' observations were received from the hurricane area of the Atlantic during the six months which constitute the hurricane season.

1912   A study entitled *Hurricanes of the West Indies* by O. L. Fassig was published. It contains some statistics and some research on hurricane characteristics and hurricane swells. Oliver Lanard Fassig was born in 1860 and died in 1936. He is most widely known for his comprehensive treatment of climate and weather of Baltimore, of Maryland and Delaware, and of Puerto Rico. He was graduated from Ohio State University and entered the United States Weather Service in 1883. He specialized in aerology and climatology. He was stationed in San Juan, Puerto Rico, from 1909 to 1912 and in 1919 returned to organize the Caribbean weather and climate service of the Weather Bureau. He established a hurricane-forecast center in San Juan for Puerto Rico and contiguous areas. He published seventy-five or more papers, including a number on hurricanes and Caribbean climatology [20].

1922   Edward H. Bowie published an article on the formation and movement of West Indian hurricanes in which he formally stated for the first time that the movement of the hurricane is in accordance with the general motion of the air surrounding it and that hurricanes move clockwise around the periphery of the Atlantic anticyclone.

1924   C. L. Mitchell in this year published *West Indian Hurricanes and Other Tropical Cyclones.* Mitchell tracked all tropical storms from 1887 through 1923, developing statistics on frequency, place of origin, and normal rate and direction of movement. This was the most exhaustive study up to this time, and 30 years later most of his statistics and conclusions are still recognized as valid. Charles L. Mitchell, recognized for many years as one of the United States Weather Bureau's most brilliant forecasters, was born in Dunningsville, Pennsylvania, in 1883. He entered the United States Weather Service in 1904 and became district forecaster in 1915. He published a number of papers, the most important of which were those on hurricanes. He is now retired and living in Pennsylvania.

1926   In this year, I. M. Cline published *Tropical Cyclones,* which was the first authoritative book in the United States on the subject of hurricanes. It contained considerable original work on rainfall distribution around hurricanes, tides, and swells, particularly as observed in the Gulf of Mexico area.

Isaac Monroe Cline was born in 1861 and died in 1955 at the age of ninety-four years. He entered the weather service in the Signal Corps in 1882 and became best known for his hurricane-warning and river and flood work. He was officially commended for his "Heroic devotion to Duty" during the famous Galveston hurricane in 1900, which devastated that city, killing some six thousand people including his wife. Cline again distinguished himself in 1927, during the great Mississippi Valley flood, and for this he later received a special commendation from President Herbert Hoover. Cline was the author of a multitude of meteorological papers and books, of which the most noteworthy was the one on tropical cyclones.

1935 The second major reorganization of the United States Hurrican Service was effected by E. B. Calvert and I. R. Tannehill when the service was decentralized in 1935. Centers were established in Jacksonville and New Orleans, continued at Washington, and re-established at San Juan. A twenty-four-hour hurricane watch during the hurricane season was instituted, and a hurricane teletype system was set up between Jacksonville, Florida, and Brownsville, Texas. Ships and coastal observations were increased to four a day and advisories were issued at six-hour intervals or more frequently when required. Decentralization of forecasting and increase in the observational program plus the development of a more adequate upper-air observational network led to a marked improvement in the hurricane-warning service. The number of fatalities per unit damage decreased from 161.0 during the period 1926 to 1930 to 2.7 during the last decade.

1937 A radiosonde network was established. The radiosonde together with pilot balloons now began to provide the forecaster with upper-level steering data.

1942 Ivan Ray Tannehill published *Hurricanes — Their Nature and History,* the second authoritative book in the United States on this subject. Particularly from the standpoint of a statistical compilation of hurricanes since the beginning of the sixteenth century and their paths since 1900, the book has become a classic.

Tannehill was born in McConnelsville, Ohio, March 13, 1890, and died on May 2, 1959. He obtained a Bachelor of Science degree from Denison University and entered the Weather Bureau in 1914. He was in charge of a number of offices in Texas and sections in the Central Office in Washington, D.C. and became Assistant Chief of the United States Weather Bureau in 1954. He was president of the International Commission on Projections for Meteorological Charts in 1946 and served on the International Commission for Synoptic Weather Information in 1947. He was a prolific writer on meteorological subjects, principally drouths, hurricanes, and solar-weather relationships.

1943 Colonel Joseph P. Duckworth made the first intentional plane reconnaissance into the eye of the hurricane and proved that aircraft hurricane reconnaissance was feasible. The following year [1] hurricane reconnaissance by aircraft was begun by the United States Air Force and Navy on a routine basis.

Grady Norton has been the outstanding hurricane forecaster produced by the United States Weather Bureau. He was born in 1894 in Alabama and died on October 9, 1954. He entered the Weather Bureau in 1915 and established the Hurricane Forecast Center at Jacksonville in 1935 under the general direction of Walter J. Bennett, Meteorologist in Charge. While his written contributions to hurricane forecasting were comparatively few, he stimulated and inspired the work of many of his colleagues. Norton, in February of 1949, received the Department of Commerce Silver Medal for Meritorious Service in recognition of his outstanding hurricane work. The following is extracted from the citation given him on this occasion: "His effective manner of instilling confidence in the civilian population of coastal areas during storms and storm threats by his issuance of accurate and timely hurricane warnings has resulted in a tremendous reduction in the loss of life due to hurricanes. During the 10-year period from 1936-45, the number of hurricane fatalities for each unit of ten million dollars property damage was decreased by 87 per cent."

No doubt, there have been many investigators and writers on the subject of hurricanes and forecasters in the Caribbean area of whom little note has been taken in the United States. It is indeed sad but true that most meteorologists in the United States show little inclination for the translation of meteorological articles written in foreign languages. However, several worth-while articles have appeared in United States publications from Caribbean writers, such as Maxwell Hall and J. F. Brennan in Jamaica and Serge Frolow in Martinique, now in Madagascar, and no doubt there are numerous others who deserve mention.

So far, mention has been made of only those meteorologists who are active in this field no longer. Probably among those still active (1960), José Carlos Millás has had the longest service. Millás, Director of the National Observatory, Havana, Cuba, was born January 22, 1889, in Havana. He received the degree of Civil Engineering at the University of Havana and did postgraduate work in science at the University of Chicago. He was Assistant Director of the National Observatory from 1913 to 1922 and has been Director since that time. He is the representative from Cuba to the World Meteorology Organization (WMO) and is a member of the Havana Academy of Sciences and the American Meteorology Society. As a tropical meteorologist, he has been through and studied forty-eight hurricane seasons. He is the author of some sixty meteorological papers, but unfortunately many of them have never been translated into English.

No attempt has been made, in this brief history of hurricane forecasting in the Atlantic area, to mention the many younger contemporary workers in this field. But since their pre-eminence in this field is so well established, this discussion should not conclude without a brief mention of Herbert Riehl, Clarence E. Palmer, and Robert H. Simpson.

Riehl was born in Munich, Germany, March 30, 1915. He came to the University of Chicago as Associate Professor in 1942 and is currently Professor of Meteorology in the Department of Meteorology there. He was Director of the Institute of Tropical Meteorology at the University of Puerto Rico, Rio Piedras, in 1947. He has been a civilian officer or technical consultant in various capacities with the United States Air Force, Navy, and Weather Bureau since 1944. He has been an outstanding and prolific contributor to meteorology in the field of the upper atmosphere, the jet stream, and in tropical meteorology. His recent book, *Tropical Meteorology* is the only authoritative book, in the United States at least, covering this entire field. While Dr. Riehl would be the last to claim that he has solved the problem of hurricane formation or perhaps any of the other principal hurricane problems, he has been the outstanding worker in this field for the past ten or fifteen years; more than any other individual, he has been responsible for the remarkable progress in tropical meteorology during and since World War II.

Clarence E. Palmer has made many notable contributions, not so much in regard to hurricanes, but rather in the broad field of tropical meteorology. Born in New Zealand and Chief of the New Zealand Forecast Service for several years before World War II, Palmer was the first Director of the Institute of Tropical Meteorology at the University of Puerto Rico. During the past few years he has been specializing in tropical meteorology at the University of California at Los Angeles and in the Hawaiian Islands for the Geophysics Directorate of the United States Air Force. The most notable of his many valuable contributions in this field is that of the analysis of the field of motion in the tropics, or the streamline-isotach technique. Within the next few years this may become the standard method of analysis in the tropics. For a description of this method the reader is referred to Report Number 76 of the Air Force Surveys in Geophysics, entitled, "The Practical Aspect of Tropical Meteorology," September, 1955.

During the past few years the most indefatigable worker in the field of hurricane research has been Robert H. Simpson, Director of the National Hurricane Research Project (NHRP) at Miami, Florida. Simpson was born in Corpus Christi, Texas, in 1912, and entered the United States Weather Bureau in 1940. His meteorological interests have been centered principally in synoptic meteorology, forecasting, and administration. He has specialized in tropical meteorology and has flown into more tropical cyclones than any other civilian meteorologist. Following the disastrous series of hurricanes in the early 1950's, he designed the NHRP, the largest and most imaginative meteorological research project yet planned and carried out. The results so far are described in other sections of this book.

The Hurricane-Warning System of the United States Weather Bureau

The hurricane-warning service of the United States Weather Bureau has three principal functions: the collection of the necessary observational data, the preparation of forecasts and warnings, and the rapid and efficient distribution of advices and all other pertinent hurricane information to the public.

The necessary observational data include both surface and upper-air reports. In general, six-hourly surface reports are received from a representative network in the eastern and southern United States, Mexico, Central America and islands in the Antilles, Bermuda, and rather irregularly the Azores and the Cape Verde Islands. These are supplemented by several hundred ship reports. Upper-air information is obtained from pilot balloons, radiosondes, and aircraft. Pilot balloons provide the forecaster with wind directions and velocities up to 25,000 to 30,000 feet when there are no clouds to obscure the balloon or no winds too strong to take the balloon quickly out of the field of observation. A balloon is filled with hydrogen or helium to the extent which will permit it to rise at some predetermined ascensional rate. The balloon is observed by means of a theodolite, which in some ways resembles a surveying instrument. The azimuth and elevation angles on the theodolite are read every minute. The direction and rate which the balloon moves each minute can be computed by trigonometry, which will give the wind direction and velocity during each minute of ascent. These winds are known as PIBALS (abbreviation for "pilot-balloon observation").

The radiosonde came into general use about 1935. The instrument, which will measure the pressure of the atmosphere, the temperature, and the humidity, is sent aloft attached to a large balloon filled with helium. The instrument sends back these data by means of radio signals to a recorder on the ground. The balloon rises until it bursts at 60,000 to 100,000 feet above the surface. A parachute attached to the radio-sonde permits the instrument to float gently back to earth and, if found and renovated, it can be used again. The radiosonde balloon can be followed by radio direction-finding equipment or by radar, and high-level wind observations can be secured even during bad weather. The wind data are known as "rawins" (radio winds). From all these data, constant-level or constant-pressure maps high into the atmosphere can be constructed and the steering current obtained.

Vital upper-air information is obtained from airplane reconnaissance, and this will be discussed in Chapter 9. Considerable weather data of value are received from in-flight reports from commercial aircraft. Much more information would be available if pilots could be persuaded to transmit it to the forecaster.

To aid in the distribution of hurricane forecasts and warnings, during the hurricane season a special hurricane teletype circuit is installed connecting all Weather Bureau city and airport offices on the Gulf and South Atlantic coasts from Brownsville, Texas, to Charleston, South Carolina. A second teletype circuit serves all other offices along the Atlantic coast from Miami to Portland, Maine. All stations on these circuits receive, instantaneously, all observations and forecasts placed on the line by any other station. In addition to the regular network of surface- and upper-air-reporting stations on the continent, there are available to forecast and local offices other regular and special reports furnished through the co-operation of various agencies and governments. Included are observations from Coast Guard stations, lighthouses and mobile units, oil rigs and other private sources, national-defense installations, and special observations from Mexico, Central and South America, the West Indies, and the Bahamas and Cuba. Of great importance also are the observations from ships at sea which are received regularly by radio every six hours and special reports rendered at more frequent intervals at the request of the forecaster.

Aircraft reconnaissance and radar reports, whether military, private or from the Weather Bureau, go on the hurricane teletypes. These special teletype circuits are in operation from June 15 through November 15.

The several types of warnings issued in connection with hurricanes are:

1. *Hurricane watch* — issued to alert the public that the hurricane may endanger a locality or area in some way (tides or winds) within thirty-six hours, although indications are not yet sufficiently definite to justify a hurricane warning. *The issuance of a hurricane watch is not a hurricane warning.*

2. *Gale warning* — issued to warn the public and maritime interests that within twenty-four hours winds of Beaufort force 8 (39 mph) or higher are expected either on the coast or over waters adjacent to the coast or that there is a possibility of the wind's attaining a velocity sufficiently high and sustained for a period long enough to interfere with safe operation of seagoing vessels. This form of warning is frequently the *first warning* issued in connection with a hurricane, although a hurricane watch may have been issued earlier for the same portion of the coast. A gale warning may be issued when only the fringe effects of the hurricane are expected to be felt in the area.

3. *Hurricane warning* — issued to warn the public that within the next twenty-four hours winds of Beaufort force 10 (55 mph) or higher are expected and either there is a possibility of increase to full hurricane intensity or the accompanying waves or tides or other conditions justify emergency action.

The hurricane-forecast centers and their respective districts are: Boston for the New England coast and adjacent waters; Washington for coastal and marine areas from Cape Hatteras, North Carolina, north to New York and Long Island; Miami for the western Caribbean, for the extreme eastern Gulf of Mexico, for the the Atlantic coast south of Cape Hatteras, and for the Atlantic Ocean south of latitude 35° N eastward as far as reports are available; San Juan for the Caribbean sea and the islands east of longitude 75° W and south of latitude 20° N; and New Orleans for the western and central Gulf of Mexico (Figure 66).

Warnings and advisories are prepared and distributed by these centers as soon as a tropical storm or a hurricane is discovered and for as long

Fig. 66. Hurricane-Forecast Districts of the United States and Atlantic areas.

as it remains a hurricane or a threat to life or property south of latitude 50° N and west of longitude 35° W. The messages contain position of the storm, its intensity, direction, and rate of movement, a description of the area of strong winds and a twelve- to twenty-four-hour forecast of movement and sometimes of intensity. When the storm is over the open sea, cautionary advices are given vessels, and when it is approaching or likely to affect any land area, details on when and where it will be felt and data on tides, floods, and maximum wind are included.

Normally during the progress of a hurricane, advisories are issued every six hours, at 5:00 and 11:00 a.m. and p.m. EST. Occasionally rapid developments or the receipt of later reports will require the issuance of interim advisories. After hurricane warnings have been issued for some section of the coast line, bulletins may be issued as often as one every hour or as often as the public interest is served.

Widespread and rapid distribution is given these warnings, advisories, and bulletins by all available means of communication, including the hurricane teletype systems which make them immediately available to Weather Bureau offices in all cities simultaneously. Each local office then gives the warnings intensified distribution by radio, telephone, newspapers, television stations, and other means in its area of responsibility. Arrangements are made with local radio stations for immediate broadcast, often from microphones located in Weather Bureau offices. All of these hurricane advices are also immediately sent from the forecast center to the press associations, which give them the highest-priority distribution to all interested sections.

The purpose of the Weather Bureau's hurricane-warning service is to enable all individuals and interests in areas affected by these storms to receive advance warnings and advices in sufficient time to make all practical preparations for safeguarding of their lives and property. Persons in these areas interested in additional information regarding distribution of hurricane warnings in their area should make the necessary arrangements with the nearest Weather Bureau office before the hurricane season. Obviously, in practice, the small local Weather Bureau offices cannot solve the hurricane problem for each individual. The local forecaster will keep newspapers, radio and television stations informed, and the public should rely on these sources for their hurricane information.

9

LOCATING AND TRACKING THE HURRICANE

DURING THE EARLY YEARS OF THE TWENTIETH CENTURY IT was not uncommon for a tropical cyclone to develop and remain undetected for days; even after the existence of a hurricane was established its exact location was frequently very uncertain. In the Atlantic area this is no longer true. Travel over the oceans, both in the air and on the surface, has increased greatly, but there are still large areas of the tropical Atlantic relatively untraversed by sea and air lanes. Additional weather stations have been established in and around the periphery of the hurricane belt and radar has been added to the equipment of some of the old as well as the newer stations. Most important of all has been routine aircraft reconnaissance.

The Area of Suspicion

Several times during the course of the average hurricane season newspapers and other news media carry a short statement that the Weather Bureau is keeping a close watch on a "suspicious area" somewhere in the tropics or subtropics. Such stories indicate the existence on the weather charts of one of those disturbances in which hurricanes usually form. It further indicates that the disturbance is more "unstable" or stronger than normal. By "unstable" meteorologists imply that the amplitude of the disturbance is increasing and that conditions are becoming more favorable for tropical-cyclone formation.

Just what constitutes an area of suspicion? If complete surface and upper-air observations were available over the tropical oceans, the forecaster could simply examine the charts and pick out regions where the upper-level divergent mechanism is superimposed upon a low-level disturbance in the manner described in Chapter 7 and label these as potential hurricane spawning grounds. Unfortunately, however, such detailed analyses are not available (and possibly never will be); there-

152

fore, meteorologists have been forced to develop a set of simple and easily applied empirical rules that make use of weather, pressure changes, etc., which enable them to locate areas of suspicion quite readily, if surface observations are available. Some of the more important rules will be described and, where appropriate, the physical processes behind them.

The atmospheric pressure in the tropics is relatively stable and varies within narrow limits, with the net twenty-four-hour change being less than the normal diurnal variation. This is not true, however, when traveling disturbances are present. Associated with the steady progression of easterly waves from east to west are areas of falling and rising pressures of irregular extent and relatively slight magnitude. Most of of the twenty-four-hour pressure changes are of the order of 0.0 to 2.0 mb (0.00 to 0.06 inch), which are not considered significant if the weather is normal. However, if there is any unusual squalliness or deformation in the wind field, even these waves should be carefully watched for possible development. Whenever the twenty-four-hour pressure fall reaches the order of a tenth of an inch (about 3.4 mb) or more (if localized in areal extent), development of a tropical storm is indicated. Similarly pressure values 5 mb or more below normal, i.e., to around 1,008 mb or 29.77 inches indicate probable cyclogenesis.

Over the tropical regions, large-scale vertical motions are much smaller than they are in more northerly latitudes. This is due in part to the small horizontal temperature differences normally observed within the tropics. Consequently rainfall occurs mostly out of cumuliform clouds as showers and scattered thundershowers, with little or no middle or high cloudiness usually observed. A variation in this regime in the form of solid altostratus or cirrostratus clouds or heavy or steady rainfall (as distinguished from showers) at several adjacent stations indicates that upward motion is well organized at intermediate levels and over a wide area, which leads the forecaster to suspect that a tropical storm has formed.

The winds also might naturally be expected to furnish clues to possible storm formation, and such is the case. The trade winds blow steadily over the oceans, from a direction between northeast to southeast at about 15-20 mph, and an increase in wind speeds by as much as 25 per cent (except where local influences such as the sea breeze reinforce the normal flow) indicates that a potential disturbed condition is developing. More important, if a wind with a westerly component of

10 mph or more is observed within the trade-wind belt, a storm has already developed. This may be in the form of a closed vortex in an easterly wave or the ITC. Many of the latter do not develop into hurricanes; frequently the deciding factor is just how far away from the equator the ITC has moved.

The distribution of the weather and temperature around an easterly wave also gives valuable information about possible storm formation. In most stable easterly waves the greatest concentration of cloudiness and showers occurs behind (to the east) of the wave (Chapter 2). Whenever strong convective activity and squalliness is found to the *west* of the trough line the wave is becoming unstable. Showers and thundershowers may extend as far as 400-600 miles ahead of the surface position of the wave, with an abundance of cloudiness at all elevations. To the rear of the wave, thick middle and high cloudiness predominates. Experience has also shown that warming at intermediate levels north or east of any wave that has shown other signs of becoming unstable may be regarded as potentially dangerous. This warming relative to the environment indicates that the vertical circulation postulated by Riehl [82] is operating efficiently and that enough heat of condensation is being transported upward to transform the original cold core of the wave into a warm vortex. Hubert [37] has pointed out that this warming can be the result only of large-scale ascent of air initially located near the surface of the oceans. An increase in the meridional wind components around a wave usually indicates that a closed cyclonic circulation is forming.

In the absence of any other direct information swells (Chapter 5) which are generated by a hurricane and outrun the center may point to the existence of a distant tropical cyclone. Such swells may arrive at the coast from a direction other than that of the prevailing wind, and they will have a longer period and wave length than the normal trade-wind swells. In the Atlantic the normal frequency of swells is eight to ten per minute and in the Gulf of Mexico about fourteen per minute. In an average hurricane the number of swells will decrease to five or six per minute and in a severe hurricane to only four per minute. Above-normal tides may also indicate the presence of a hurricane offshore. Both tides and swells, however, should be used with caution in any attempt to locate the exact direction of the storm from the observer.

Ship Reports

In order to apply the empirical rules which enable the forecaster to establish the existence of a suspicious area, frequent weather reports from the entire hurricane area are needed. Land stations around the periphery of the hurricane-forming regions supply much valuable information, but frequently by the time the incipient storm is well developed enough to be detected by clues derived from these stations it is so close to a coast line that the usual early warnings cannot be issued. For this reason extensive use is made of ships' weather reports. All of the rules listed in the previous section (except those pertaining to the state of the upper atmosphere) can be applied to ship reports as well as to those received from land weather stations. Currently in the Atlantic about one half the total storms observed are initially detected by ships.

Aircraft Reconnaissance

Once the existence of a suspicious area has been established, the next step is to dispatch a reconnaissance flight to the area. The objectives of the flight are to determine the intensity and exact location of the storm. Many flights discover that the suspected area does not contain a storm at all, and occasionally the same area will be reconnoitered several days in a row before the expected development takes place. Many of the potential storm areas remain weak and finally dissipate without ever reaching even storm intensity.

Great reliance is placed on aircraft reports. High-level wind and pressure data obtained by the Air Force planes are very useful in forecasting direction and rate of movement.

Most of the world's shipping follows certain well-recognized and well-traveled routes such as New York to the Gulf of Mexico ports, New York–Canal Zone, or New York–Capetown routes. There are other oceanic areas where very few or no ships travel. To fill in one of these gaps during the hurricane season, the United States Air Force flies a regular predetermined triangular track from Bermuda to a point to the east of the Antilles, thence westward and then back to Bermuda.*
Usually half of the flight is flown at approximately 10,000 feet (700-mb surface) and the remainder at 18,500 feet (500-mb surface). This

---

*A curtailment of this program began in 1959.

regular flight serves both as a detection technique and as an aid for the construction of upper-air charts.

The first flight into a hurricane was made by Colonel Joseph B. Duckworth of the United States Air Force off Galveston, Texas, on July 27, 1943. As the single-engined plane flew into the main portion of the hurricane, it encountered increasing turbulence of the choppy or bumpy type and a few updrafts widely separated and not as severe as in the ordinary thunderstorms. The air became steadily more choppy, and bumps, which were occasionally severe, were encountered as the wall cloud of the eye was approached. Colonel Duckworth made a second flight into the storm later the same day and reported that neither flight through the hurricane was as uncomfortable as through a good rough thunderstorm. However, considerably more severe conditions than those described by Colonel Duckworth are often encountered.

A weather officer on a reconnaissance flight into the Great Atlantic hurricane of 1944 estimated winds at 140 mph and reported turbulence so great that the pilot and copilot together could not keep the plane under control. Several times it was feared the plane would be torn apart or crash out of control. When it returned to base it was found 150 rivets had been sheared off on one wing alone. Personnel in Navy planes have suffered severe injuries in several instances. And in hurricane Janet in 1955, Lieutenant Commander Windham and crew never returned from reconnoitering this severe hurricane. Several hurricane-reconnaissance planes have also been lost in Pacific typhoons.

Regular hurricane reconnaissance was begun in 1944 and is now jointly performed by the Air Force and the Navy. The Air Force hurricane-hunting squadron is located at Bermuda and the Navy squadron at Jacksonville. The total area covered by these reconnaissance planes is approximately a million and a half square miles. As a rule at least two flights a day are made into or near the storm's center. In one area all flights are made by Air Force planes, in another all are made by Navy planes, and in still a third area flights are made by both services. During the hurricane season of 1955 weather planes on hurricane reconnaissance spent more than one month of flying hours in the air.

The aircraft are fitted with the latest meteorological instrumentation for weather observing. Temperature, pressure, humidity, wind, and cloud data are obtained. Navy weather observers, and on certain occasions Air Force observers as well, estimate the wind velocity from the surface of the sea. Photographs have been taken of the sea surface over deep water under measured wind velocities from altitudes of 400 to 600 feet at approximately the same angle.

At over 100 mph it is difficult to distinguish the torrential rain of the hurricane from the flying spray and foam of the sea, and the sea and atmosphere seem to mix. A Captain Burmeister describes the state of the sea as he observed it in a hurricane on October 19, 1924, in about latitude 23.8° N and longitude 84.2° W: "The whole sea was a boiling, seething mass. It appeared as if the surface was covered with a mass of turbulent steam. The sea was breaking in such a manner that it was impossible to tell whether the water in the air was rain or sea water."

The sea method of wind estimation is unsuited for Air Force requirements; its planes usually fly at high levels and the sea is often not visible. The appearance of the sea varies greatly with the amount of light present. New-type wind indicators are now installed in most Air Force reconnaissance planes and these are very accurate. However, experienced observers feel that winds can be estimated from the sea surface within an accuracy of 10 per cent. Estimates of wind speeds from elevations of 2,000 feet or more will vary greatly with cloud thickness and must be regarded as much more subjective than the ± 10 per cent mentioned previously.

The key person in the eight- or ten-man reconnaissance crew is the weather officer, or aerologist, who sits in the nose of the plane. Here he observes the clouds, the visibility, the weather, and the surface of the sea, if visible. The navigator of the aircraft guides the flight into the vicinity of the storm and into the eye, if that is desired, with the assistance of the radar operator, who keeps constant watch on the radarscope and advises the navigator where the more intense rain bands are and where weak spots in the turbulent and violent inner core of the storm may be found. The pilot and navigator will endeavor to take the plane into the center from the weaker side. After penetration into the eye (which is comparatively calm and serene) the aircraft may spend several minutes or even hours recording data.

While in the eye the low-level flights can obtain a reasonably accurate measurement of the central sea-level pressure. The higher-level flights, by use of a dropsonde (a small radio transmitter, dropped by parachute, which as it falls radioes back to the plane temperature, pressure, and relative humidity data) can obtain the heights of the 500-, 700-, and 850-mb surfaces as well as the surface pressure. Normally, within the

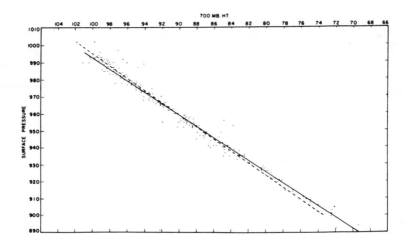

Fig. 67. *A*, Relationships between 700-mb Heights and Surface Pressures within the eye of a hurricane; *B*, for 500-mb Heights. (After C. Jordan)

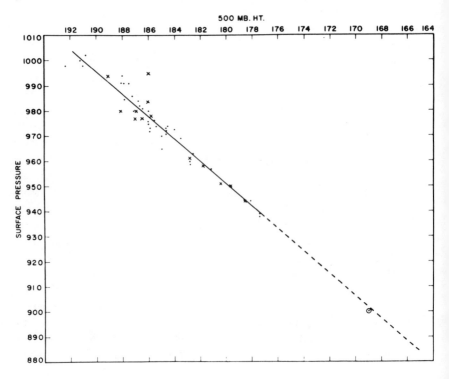

tropics these pressure surfaces are observed at elevations of about 19,000 10,000, and 5,000 feet, respectively. Within the eye of the hurricane, however, these heights are greatly lowered. Jordan [44] has correlated these heights with the sea-level pressures and found that by the use of the 500- and 700-mb heights the surface pressures within the eye can be determined with an accuracy of 3 to 5 mb, sufficient for most practical forecasting purposes. The relationships are very nearly linear and are shown in Figure 67.

The central pressure is important because it is closely related to the maximum winds of the storm. Fletcher [22] has developed the following formula:

$$V_{max} = 16 \sqrt{P_n - P_o}$$

where V_{max} is the maximum wind in knots, P_n and P_o are the pressures in millibars along the periphery and at the center of the storm, respectively. The outside pressure can be selected from the surface chart by adding 2 or 3 mb to the value of the last closed isobar around the storm, or in most cases a constant value of P_n of 1,010 mb can be used with good results. The formula usually produces as accurate an estimate of the maximum winds as can be obtained by any other means, although some meteorologists believe it overestimates the sustained wind and more closely approximates gusts. Thus the importance of Jordan's formula (Figure 67) becomes apparent. Aircraft flying at high levels can measure the heights of the 500- or the 700-mb surfaces by use of dropsondes (or if they are flying near one of the constant-pressure surfaces, the heights may be determined by use of radio altimeters), and these may be used to estimate the sea-level pressures; then by use of Fletcher's formula the maximum surface winds can be reliably estimated. This may eventually make it possible to make all hurricane-reconnaissance flights at high levels, thereby eliminating the more hazardous low-level flights.

Reconnaissance reports are not, of course, confined to determining the maximum winds and the central pressures within hurricanes. Continuous observations of wind, pressure, and other weather elements are made both during penetration and while returning to the aircraft base. These give the forecaster the radius of the hurricane-force winds, the areal extent of storm winds (40 mph), as well as the distribution of the various weather elements about the center. Usually at least two fixes on the center position per day are obtained, from which the forecaster can determine the direction and speed with which the storm is moving.

Two records of reconnaissance flights into a severe hurricane off Puerto Rico in 1950 are shown in Figures 68 and 69. These are plots of the data made by the aerologist during the flight. The wind speed is plotted at the base of the arrows, which fly with the wind. To the right of the black squares marking the location of the aircraft are plotted: the sea-level pressure in whole millibars, the altitude of the plane, the time of the observation, the past weather (in symbolic form), and the state of the sea and the direction of the swells. Cloud data are plotted above and below the squares, and visibility, current weather, and degree of turbulence are plotted to the left. The sketches indicate the locations of the principal rain bands. Note the pronounced spiral structure. This was one of the few hurricanes that have been labeled "impenetrable" by the hurricane hunters.

Most reconnaissance flights are made during the day. However, whenever a hurricane threatens coastal areas, night flights are frequently made. These are always high-level flights, and no attempts are made to penetrate the center of the storm. The planes remain on the periphery and keep the hurricane under continuous surveillance by means of air-borne radar. These aircraft fixes are supplemented by those of land-based radar installations as soon as the storm moves into range of the latter.

Too much credit cannot be bestowed upon the intrepid Air Force and Navy fliers who deliberately and routinely probe the secrets of these mighty monsters. Without the information they supply, present-day hurricane forecasting would be dealt a crushing blow. Tannehill [103] has paid a high tribute to these men, and those who are interested in knowing more details about their exploits are referred to his *Hurricane Hunters*.

One quite inadvertent reconnaissance of the hurricane of October 11-12, 1947, was made by Mr. and Mrs. Eddie Jones and thirty-four other passengers on a flight from Havana to Miami. Eddie Jones, for many years Chief of the Associated Press Bureau in Miami and best-known hurricane reporter in the United States, had been in Havana covering the Mee murder trial and was a passenger aboard a Pan American plane which flew directly into the middle of the hurricane. Here is his story:

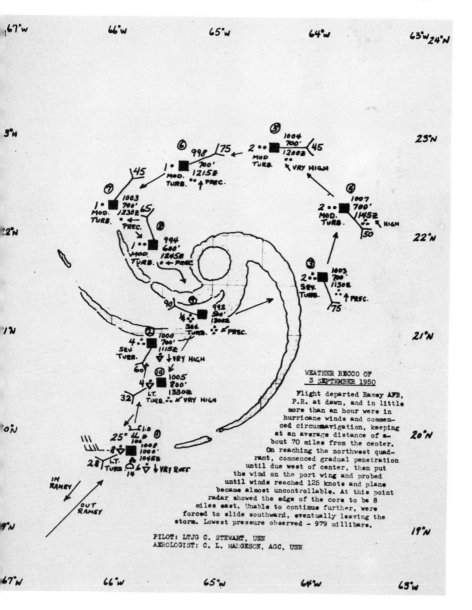

WEATHER RECCO OF
3 SEPTEMBER 1950

Flight departed Ramey AFB,
P.R. at dawn, and in little
more than an hour were in
hurricane winds and commenced circumnavigation, keeping
at an average distance of a-
bout 70 miles from the center.
On reaching the northwest quadrant, commenced gradual penetration
until due west of center, then put
the wind on the port wing and probed
until winds reached 125 knots and plane
became almost uncontrollable. At this point
radar showed the edge of the core to be 8
miles east. Unable to continue further, were
forced to slide southward, eventually leaving the
storm. Lowest pressure observed - 979 millibars.

PILOT: LTJG C. STEWART, USN
AEROLOGIST: C. L. MANGESON, AGC, USN

Fig. 68. Weather-Reconnaissance Observations made in the hurricane of September 3, 1950.

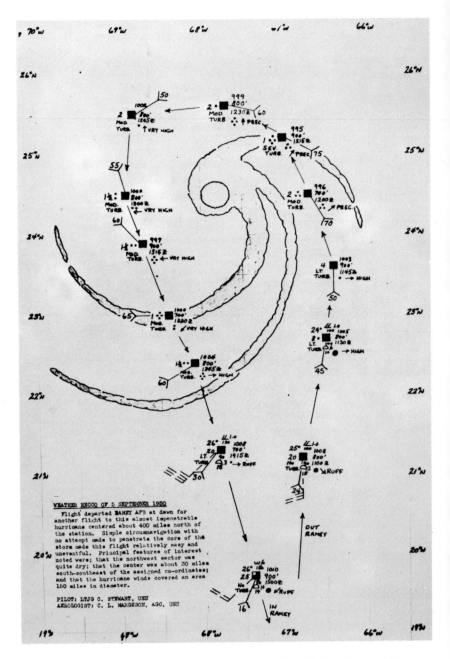

Fig. 69. Weather-Reconnaissance Observations made in the hurricane of September 5, 1950.

Air Force and Navy hurricane hunters can welcome a couple of Cuban grandmothers, a bride and groom and 32 other passengers into their ranks after a wild ride through the hurricane by a four-engined passenger plane Saturday night.

The Pan American Airways DC-4, en route to Miami with 40 persons on board, went on a hurricane-hunting jaunt entirely unintentionally and, as far as passengers are concerned, unwillingly.

Through some fault in weather information, the crew left Havana believing they would follow the storm into Miami. Instead, the plane virtually passed through the eye of the vicious disturbance southwest of Miami. No group of air passengers ever received a wilder ride.

Seven passengers passed out cold from fright. Others dripped cold sweat, and all agreed later that prayers had been said. Mrs. Jones and I can testify to the cold sweat. We were aboard.

The group left Havana at 5:45 p.m. Saturday in a torrential downpour and sped out over the Florida Straits. They witnessed a colorful sunset above the clouds — and nosed into the storm. The big airplane was tossed about like a feather. Vertical air blasts sometimes threw it straight up 1000 feet or more, sometimes dropped it sickeningly as great a distance. Lightning, brilliant and blinding, flickered around the plane constantly and once a ball of St. Elmo's fire leaped across the wing.

Rain in such torrents that only the nearest of engines could be seen, hammered against the fuselage, flooded into the pilot's cockpit, and dripped down the cabin walls. Twice the plane ran through hail and the sound was like the wings being torn off.

The wildly bucking and weaving plane twisted so that the cabin door leading out of the plane flew open. Steward F. S. Yado unbuckled his safety belt and, held by Stewardess A. A. Brady, caught the door and pulled it shut again. So wild was the ride that to unbuckle one's safety belt was to invite a tossing from end to end of the cabin.

Capt. L. R. Shaw and Co-Pilot Hal Wildman found Miami and made passes at the airport, but gales and unbelievably heavy rains blanked it out time after time. Miami was circled for an hour and a half after the storm already had been fought for half an hour. Finally, the pilots fought clear and headed for Nassau where the plane was landed for the night. But troubles were not over. After an early morning takeoff with the same passengers, the plane arrived over Miami's International Airport Sunday — and a landing gear signal indicated one wheel could not be located. Passengers who already felt they had stared death in the face were given crash instructions while the plane circled the airport for an hour. Badly frightened, all were too weak to repeat a rousing ovation and backslapping they had awarded the pilots after the safe landing at Nassau.

The bride and groom who received these unexpected thrills on their honeymoon were Mr. and Mrs. Peter J. Pricone of Wethersfield, Connecticut. An Englishman, P. G. Smyrk of London, saw the United States for the first time while being tossed by the hurricane. Joseph Wallem, Jr., of Vincennes, Indiana, expressed most passengers' views by saying: "Hereafter, the Air Force and Navy can do all my hurricane hunting."

Radar

Radar, a powerful new tool for detecting and tracking hurricanes, came out of World War II. Produced for the purpose of detecting enemy aircraft and for other military purposes, radar has already demonstrated great value for varied meteorological uses [87]. Briefly, the radar apparatus transmits a pulsed radio wave which is transmitted into space in the form of a beam, which, upon striking a target (precipitation), is reflected back into the transmitter, where it can be detected by a receiver. The target can be displayed much as a television picture and is called an "echo." Thus reflected electromagnetic waves from water droplets in thunderstorms, tornadoes, or squall lines within hurricanes appear on the radarscope as echoes. Since the squall lines are usually wound in spiral bands around the hurricane center, or eye, the position of the eye can be located on the radarscope and over a finite period of time the rate and direction of movement of the center can be determined. Current radars have a range of 150 to 200 miles but it is hoped that within the near future this range can be extended to 200 to 250 miles.

The Weather Bureau in 1955 installed a modern radar at Hatteras, North Carolina, and all three hurricanes which affected the United States that year passed within range of this radar. By 1961 the Bureau plans to have all the coastal regions of the United States from Eastport, Maine, to Brownsville, Texas, under constant radar surveillance during the hurricane season. In 1955 the hurricane picture as it appeared on the Hatteras scope was transmitted by radio-photograph to the hurricane-warning center at Washington, and the forecasters there were able to watch visually the progress of the hurricane. Upon completion of this project there would appear to be no reason why there should not always be some warning for every hurricane approaching any portion of the coast line of the United States, although many of the rapidly accelerating New England storms will reach the coast within a short time after the center appears on radar.

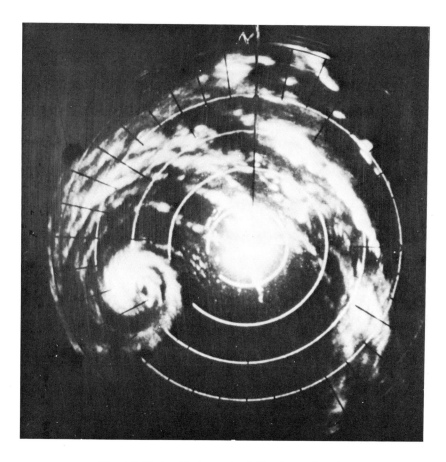

Fig. 70. Radar Photograph of Hurricane Connie.

A radar picture of hurricane Connie taken at 11:32 a.m. EST on August 12, 1955, by the radar at Cape Hatteras, North Carolina, is shown in Figure 70. The radar is, of course, located at the center of the polar co-ordinate grid. Distances between the circles are twenty miles. The azimuth angle is measured clockwise from the north. The eye of the hurricane can be seen approximately at 62 miles 244° WSW. The strong spiral bands extending outward from the wall cloud around the eye are clearly visible as well as the weaker spiral bands to the north of the main vortex. The much larger precipitation area in the forward

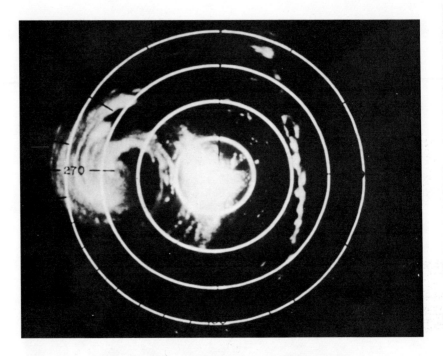

Fig. 71. Radar Photograph of Hurricane Ione.

semicircle of the advancing hurricane is typical of tropical cyclones in the more northern latitudes. A somewhat similar radar picture of hurricane Ione on September 19, 1955, is shown in Figure 71. Others are pictured in Figures 72 and 73. Note the cellular structure of the more solid echoes in the upper right-hand portion of the pictures. This is a characteristic phenomenon and it is in these more typical thunderstorm echoes that tornadoes occasionally occur on the forward fringes of the hurricane.

The banded structure of precipitation as seen in these two figures is characteristic of all tropical cyclones. They are most symmetrically distributed around the eye in the mature and late immature stages of the hurricane and less so in the developing and decaying stages. The weather bands are evident on the surface by heavy bursts of precipitation, increases in wind of sometimes 50 per cent, a wind shift usually but not always (if some observations are to be taken at face value),

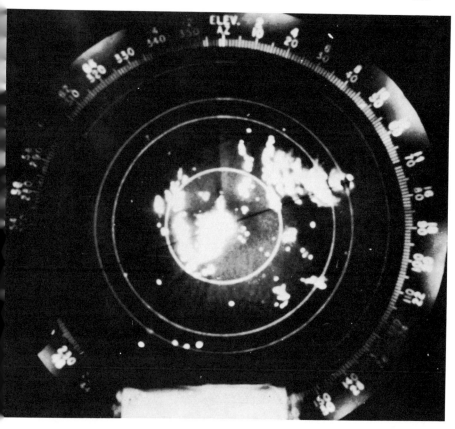

Fig. 72. Radar Photograph of Hurricane Betsy made at a range of 233 miles. (United States Navy Photograph)

wind veering rather than backing, and, if a very large-scale barograph is used, by some irregularities in the pressure. The width of the bands is very variable.

Wexler [113] has endeavored to explain the squall lines in hurricanes by starting with the well-known parallel array of cloud bands frequently noted in the tropics. These cloud bands are attributed to the combination of vertical wind shear and thermal instability. If a circular vortex, according to Wexler, is introduced into a region of the cloud streets originally oriented along the wind, these streets will become circular and, in case of a hurricane vortex, will spiral inward toward the center.

Fig. 73. Radar Photograph of Hurricane Helene as seen by Hatteras radar. Time
should read 1805E. (United States Weather Bureau Photograph)

Ligda [52] made a detailed study of the radar bands of the hurricane
of August 23-28, 1949, and found:

1. There was little or no actual rotation of the spiral bands as a
whole around the eye.

2. Individual small precipitation echoes did move along the outer
spiral bands in toward the center.

3. Protuberances on the bands and small precipitation echoes between the bands near the eye move along or parallel to the bands.

4. Precipitation continuously forms on one end of the band and disappears on the other.

5. There is some evidence that the precipitation pattern (away from the eye) seemed to rotate in a clockwise manner.

Airplane reconnaissance would indicate that the main concentration of rain bands in various quadrants of well-developed hurricanes varies from day to day, being found in the right rear on one day, the right forward quadrant on the next, etc. There is no generally accepted explanation for this apparent rotation, and it is unknown whether the rotation, if it exists, is clockwise or counterclockwise, continuous or discontinuous. As Ligda concludes, further research on the radar weather bands should lead to a considerable increase in our basic knowledge of the structure and behavior of hurricanes.

Until quite recently it was thought the spiral rain bands were produced within the forward semicircle, particularly in the right front quadrant, where the most severe convergence within the hurricane normally occurs. It was believed the rain bands tended to spiral inward toward and eventually to wind themselves around the eye, constantly replenishing the wall cloud.

Recent work by Senn [92] of the University of Miami indicates that many spiral bands are born at the storm center and propagate radially outward. The rain bands maintain a quasi-conservative position relative to the quadrants in which they are formed with respect to the storm center. Individual echoes appear to have their origin in the outward-propagated wave and are not pre-existing elements which assume a spiral shape. Preliminary evidence indicates the eye of the hurricane is defined by a wall cloud made up of one or more spiral bands in process of generation. Tepper [104] suggests an atmospheric gravity wave as a mechanism for the development of rain bands.

All radar fixes between latitudes 32° and 36° N from Cape Hatteras and the Navy and Air Force reconnaissance planes have been plotted for hurricane Connie, August 11-12, 1955, as she approached and crossed the North Carolina coast, Figure 74. The Hatteras radar-eye fixes became reasonably accurate at a range of 140 nautical miles for this hurricane. The cyclonically curved movement of the apparent eye as indicated by aircraft radar from 0330 to 0500 EST can be seen as well as the two

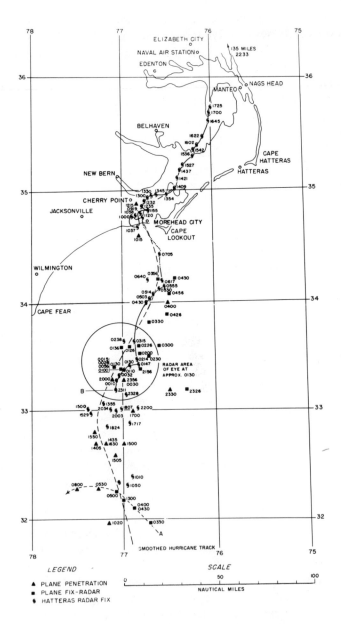

Fig. 74. Track and Radar Fixes, Hurricane Connie, 1955.

eye penetrations at 0550 and 0800 EST, and then the next eye position at 1020 EST to the south of the previous position indicated by "A" at the bottom of the Figure 74. Compare the radar-indicated path during this period with the smoothed track of the hurricane. The plane may have been following a parasitic circulation — a false eye. Anticyclonically curved cusps (B) can be noted from 2311 EST on the eleventh to 0147 EST on the twelfth and from 0147 to 0555 EST and perhaps another from 0555 to 0705 EST. It is not known whether the hurricane center actually took such a course and, if so, what the explanation is of the apparent anticyclonic curvature.

The eye of Connie as observed by radar was unusually large, and its relative size at 0130 EST on the twelfth is indicated by the circle on Figure 74.

Another feature of interest, Connie moved at the rate of 5.7 mph from 1100 on the ninth to 1700 EST on the eleventh. After this time Connie began to accelerate, but temporarily slowed as the center approached and crossed the North Carolina coast line. The center curved to the left just as it crossed the coast and made one or more loops, remaining quasi-stationary west and north of Morehead City for about three hours. The curve to the left, slowing, and looping occurred in all three North Carolina hurricanes in 1955, and this decrease in forward progress is often noted in hurricanes as they cross a coast line.

Radar has become very useful in hurricane forecasting and research. However, at this time (1960) the forecaster is not quite certain what the observer sees on radar and what the general relationships are in regard to radar, cloud precipitation, pressure and wind eyes, or centers, and the physical processes which go on in each with time. Certainly at this time hurricane radar reports require expert interpretation, and no forecast should be based on one individual radar fix.

Hurricane Betsy, 1956, was perhaps the outstanding example to date of what radar tracking can accomplish. This storm was under continuous radar surveillance from the time it approached Puerto Rico until it recurved northeastward off the coast of Florida. Radar stations located at the Weather Bureau in San Juan, the chain of guided-missile tracking stations in the Bahamas, the United States Navy ground installation at the Fleet Weather Central in Miami, plus the air-borne radar of the reconnaissance aircraft assisted in the tracking. About one third of the numerous fixes are shown in Figure 75a. Although this tracking

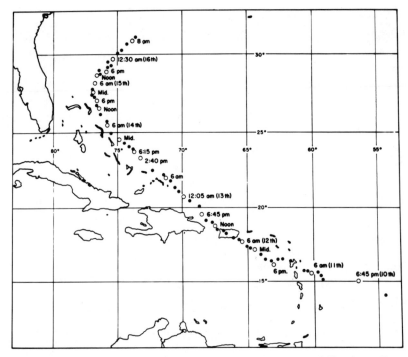

Fig. 75a. A Few of the Radar Fixes obtained on the center of Hurricane Betsy, 1956.

was somewhat fortuitous in that the hurricane came within range of the guided-missile radar-tracking stations, it shows the tremendous value of radar in following the course of storms. During the 1958 season coastal radar stations from Miami to Nantucket did an even more remarkable job of tracking hurricanes Daisy and Helene.

Satellite

A new vista in hurricane spotting was opened in April, 1960, when Tiros I, the experimental television weather satellite, made meteorological history by photographing a fully developed hurricane, or typhoon, which had not previously been reported (Figure 75b). Existence of this tropical storm, located about 800 miles east of Brisbane, Australia, was later confirmed by the Australian Meteorological Bureau.

United States Weather Bureau scientists at the receiving station at

Fig. 75b. Fully developed Typhoon first detected by the U. S. television weather satellite, Tiros I.

Ft. Monmouth, New Jersey, early on the morning of April 10 discovered the typhoon when they analyzed photos taken on the 125th orbit of Tiros.

"What this means," Dr. F. W. Reichelderfer, Chief of the United States Weather Bureau, said, "is that hurricanes spawned anywhere over the vast oceanic areas can be detected much earlier than ever before possible. It also gives hope that with future weather satellite camera systems man will be able to solve the tornado observation problem in 'Tornado Alley' of the United States."

10

TECHNIQUES FOR FORECASTING HURRICANE MOVEMENT

FORECASTING THE MOVEMENT OF A HURRICANE IS AT THE same time one of the most difficult and one of the most rewarding tasks the meteorologist has to face. During the past two decades significant progress in this field has been achieved. This has been due largely to the increase in the number of upper-air stations both in the middle latitudes and in the hurricane area, which has lead to a better understanding of the responses of the basic hurricane-steering current to changes in the planetary-wave systems. Better methods of detection and tracking, notably routine aircraft reconnaissance, have also made outstanding contributions to the solution of the forecast problem. However, only the most optimistic consider the problem solved, because so much depends upon precision in forecasting the storm track.

Simpson [97] has summarized the problem in these words:

> For example the City of Miami requires a full 12 to 18 hours notice to prepare adequately for a hurricane, and does so at a cost of more than three quarter million dollars. A difference of only a few degrees in storm heading over a 24-hour period can mean that these expensive precautions will be made uselessly. Or, consider the individual case of the Dow Chemical Company on the highly industrialized Texas coast. This company's large plastics plant is vulnerable to high water from hurricanes. As little as ten miles variation in the track of a storm can spell the operational difference between this plant having to close down or remain open. To close the plant costs the company more than $900,000. Finally consider the case of hurricane Carol, which in late August of this year (1954) formed in the Bahama Islands. This storm moved stealthily and with indecision slowly northward off the Capes of North Carolina before surging suddenly ahead and roaring across the Long Island and New England coasts with a destructive intensity equalled on only two previous occasions in historic times. The last 400 miles of its movement over water was covered in a little more than 12 hours. The forecast problem in this case

was especially critical. If the storm, during the last 12 hours of movement, had followed a heading less than 10 degrees to the right of its actual path, New England would have escaped virtually unscathed. In 50 years at least 54 other storms approached the North Carolina Capes along the same general path as Carol, yet failed to affect New England seriously. . . .

Fortunately the hurricane usually moves forward at a rather leisurely rate, normally about 12 mph, thus providing time for warning and preparation. When tropical cyclones recurve, however, they tend to accelerate as they are picked up by southerly and westerly winds, and, infrequently, by the jet stream. Both the New England hurricane of 1938 and Carol of 1954 accelerated to a forward speed of about 60 mph as they approached New England. Accelerations pose a very difficult problem for the forecaster, but fortunately the rapidly moving storm is subject to less erratic changes in direction than are the slow ones.

Current methods of forecasting hurricane motion make a judicious use of climatology, extrapolation of the past motion of the storm, an evaluation of the basic steering current in which the storm is embedded, and the changes this current is expected to undergo in response to the long-wave (or planetary-wave) patterns. Various techniques for applying these principles have been developed, among which are the Riehl-Haggard system and the use of numerical weather forecasting by utilizing a high-speed electronic computer. These techniques, along with certain empirical rules that have stood the test of the years, will be discussed in this chapter.

Climatology

Hurricanes forming within the same general area and at the same time of the year show a tendency to follow preferred paths as indicated by an examination of hurricane tracks [102]. Naturally there are numerous exceptions; otherwise the forecasting of hurricane movement would be a relatively simple process. A knowledge of the climatology of hurricane tracks does, however, furnish one of the most useful tools in forecasting motion. In fact when a hurricane is first detected in the Atlantic area between the Lesser Antilles and the coast of Africa (where upper-level wind observations are missing) climatology provides one of the most reliable considerations upon which to base the initial forecast.

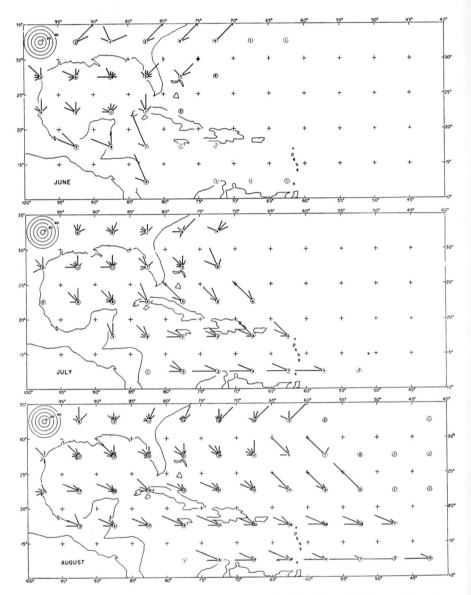

Fig. 76. Percentage-Frequency Distribution of the Direction of Motion of Tropical Cyclones by 5° squares. Number in the inner circle represents the number of cyclones observed in each square. Length of the vector gives

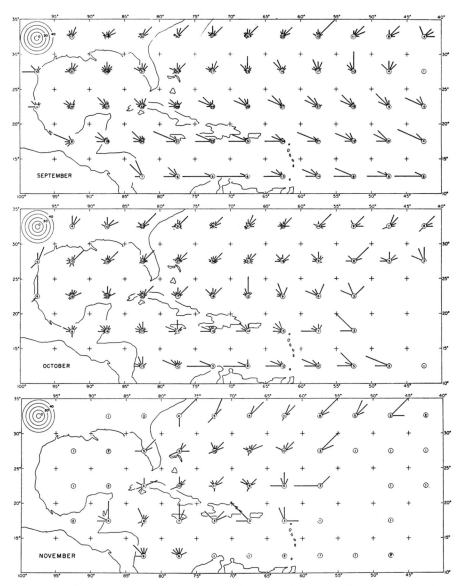

the percentage frequency of cyclones moving in 22.5° sector centered
at that direction. Scale at upper left. (After Colón)

José A. Colón, now at the National Hurricane Center in Miami, Florida, and formerly with the Department of Meteorology, University of Chicago, has produced some excellent work on the climatology of hurricane tracks for forecasting purposes [9]. Using some of Mitchell's data [64], Colón calculated the percentage-frequency distribution of the direction of motion of tropical cyclones, and these are shown in Figure 76. The most probable direction can be determined from Figure 76 by inspection, as well as the probability of the storm displacement in other directions. The number of storms used in determining the percentages is shown inside the circles; where this number is small, no great reliance should be placed on the direction of movement. Colón has suggested a number of ways in which these charts can be used. These ways may be summarized as follows:

1. The number of cases is sufficiently large to make hurricane displacement probabilities quite reliable in many sections, especially during the months of August, September, and October, which make up the heart of the hurricane season.

2. In August, for example, no storm of record in the area south of 25° N and east of Florida has moved east of north or south of west, and it would be quite illogical to predict such abnormal movement without the most cogent of reasons.

3. In some areas, such as the Gulf of Mexico, good modes (the most frequent occurrence) hardly exist. This absence reflects the variability of the flow patterns aloft.

4. The application of climatology has the most value in the early stages following detection. It can be used with the greatest confidence in the lowest and highest latitudes and with the least confidence between latitudes 20° N and 30° N. Unfortunately this region is the area within which the forecast problem is the most critical for other reasons, notably the threat that hurricanes located here offer the United States coast line.

The median speeds of hurricane motion, also calculated by Colón, are shown in Figure 77. In the principal hurricane months of August and September a belt of minimum speeds will be noted between 20° and 30° N, with belts of considerably greater average movement to the north and south. In October, the third main hurricane month, the belt of comparatively slow movement is located farther south in the Caribbean and southern Gulf of Mexico, with the average speed increasing everywhere to the north. This corresponds to the southward shift of the belt of the polar westerlies during this month.

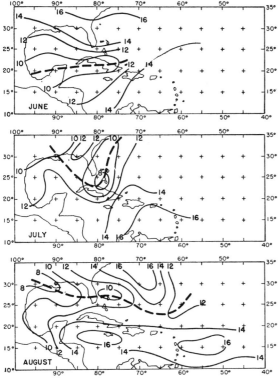

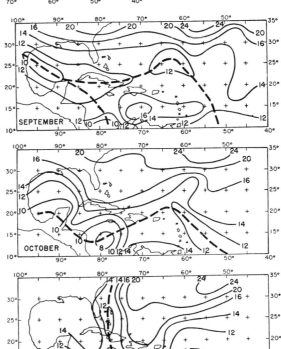

Fig. 77. Median Speed
of Hurricane Move-
ment (miles per hour)
by months. (After
Colón)

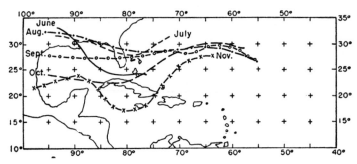

Fig. 78. Modal Latitude of Recurvature of Hurricanes by months. (After Colón)

One of the most difficult parts of forecasting hurricane motion is the anticipation of the point of recurvature, or change in the track from a generally northwesterly direction to northeasterly. It is also of vital importance, because it can mean the difference between a hurricane moving inland over the eastern coast of the United States or moving harmlessly out to sea. Colón has also prepared some data on the modal latitude of recurvature by months. These are shown in Figure 78. It will be noted that October and November hurricanes recurve at much more southerly latitudes than do those in other months. This is a reflection of the mean monthly position of the subtropical ridge, which is also farther south during the later months of the hurricane season. The southward shift of the subtropical ridge is accompanied by a similar shift in the polar westerlies.

A judicious use of these climatological aids improves the accuracy of forecasts of hurricane motion, but they are not intended to serve as the basis for the final forecast. They are of the greatest value when other data are missing. No hurricane forecaster would think of leaning heavily on climatology when he has a wealth of upper-air data in which he has full confidence, and it would be foolhardy for anyone to forecast the climatologically most probable path when there are clear indications, based on the current synoptic situation, that the future course of the storm will not follow climatology.

Continuity

Extrapolation of the past movement of an atmospheric disturbance is widely used in all branches of forecasting today. This continuity has long been recognized as a valuable tool in hurricane

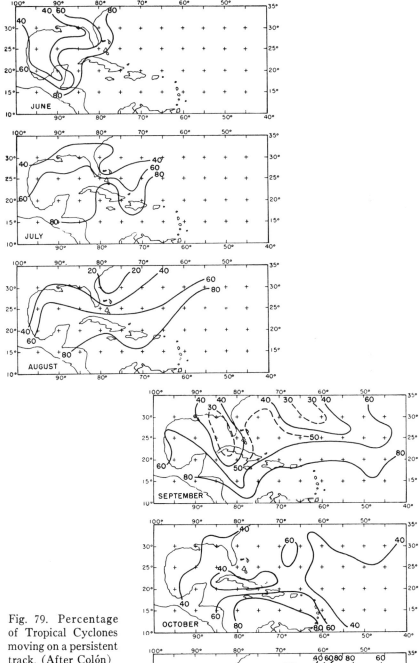

Fig. 79. Percentage of Tropical Cyclones moving on a persistent track. (After Colón)

forecasting. Colón [9] has investigated the usefulness of persistence in forecasting the motion of tropical storms. His results, which show the percentage of storms which moved on a persistent track, i.e., the path for the next twenty-four hours was within 10° of the track for the previous twenty-four hours, are shown in Figure 79. Extrapolation usually gives satisfactory results in the conservative easterly trade-wind belt, especially south of 20° N, where persistence verifies about 80 per cent of the time. However, this technique fails rapidly in the latitude of normal recurvature, where the influence of either the easterlies or the westerlies may predominate. Even farther north, following recurvature and especially north of 35° N, storms are subject to rapid acceleration, and persistence often fails to yield a satisfactory forecast.

The success of extrapolation deserves a word of explanation. After the motion of the hurricane has been established, it gives an indication of what the steering forces have been. Insofar as these forces remain unchanged, past motion can be used as a guide to the future course of the storm. This continuity of the upper-air flow is much more likely to be observed in the lower latitudes, in the region of the deep easterlies, than it is farther north, where small oscillations in the position of the subtropical ridge may bring the storm under the influence of either the easterly current to the south of the ridge or the westerly flow to the north. This is in agreement with the findings of Colón.

Steering

The movement of a tropical cyclone is to a large extent determined by the direction and speed of the basic current in which it is embedded. Much of the emphasis in hurricane forecasting has been directed toward an evaluation of this basic, or "steering," current. Over the years a number of forecast methods have been developed which make use of various concepts of steering. Some have given generally good results, but there have been serious failures in all of them. A number of difficulties are evident, both in determining the basic current and in relating this precisely to storm movement. The storm circulation both horizontally and vertically obscures the basic current over a considerable area. Even if the basic undisturbed flow could be determined, there still exists the question of what part of the motion is due to the actual carrying along of the storm by this current and what part represents the "dynamic" component, which is due to internal forces within the storm and asymmetry in the field of horizontal divergence around the storm.

Elizabeth Jordan [42] in 1952 made an intensive study and on the basis of a rather limited number of cases found that in the mean, tropical storms move in the direction and with the speed of the steering current, if the latter is defined as the pressure-weighted mean flow from the surface to 300 mb and extending over a band 8° latitude in width and centered on the storm. On the other hand, Sherman [93], using a much smaller number of cases, tentatively concluded that the steering current accounted for only a little more than half of the observed variability in the direction of movement. More recently, Miller [61] in 1957 extended the work of E. Jordan, using almost eight times the amount of data. His best estimate of the average steering current was the layer from 6.0 to 12.5 kilometers, about 500 to 200 mb, integrated over a doughnut-shaped ring extending from 2° to 6° from the center. He examined every layer from the surface to 16 kilometers, and the mean motion of the storm was faster than the mean flow throughout all layers, with the exception of the 12.5-16.0 kilometer layer, in which the mean wind was faster, but in the latter case the direction of the mean wind deviated greatly from the direction of the storm travel. Thus evidence is mounting that the hurricane is not like a cork bobbing along in a stream, but that air is flowing through the storm circulation in a complicated manner and its motion may be faster than that of the basic current. At present opinion among meteorologists is divided, but the influence of internal forces is likely not insignificant. It is expected that the National Hurricane Research Project now under way will resolve this difference of opinion within the next several years.

When sufficient data are available it has been found that the use of streamline analysis of successive winds-aloft levels usually gives indications of hurricane movement for as much as twenty-four hours in advance. Since upper-wind observations are usually few near a hurricane, the analysis of these charts is somewhat subjective. However, Grady Norton, who was the Weather Bureau's Chief Hurricane Forecaster for many years (and the chief proponent of the steering technique), was very successful in using the steering concept and stated that it seldom failed to give dependable forecasts when data were available to high levels near the storm.

The users of "high-level steering," as the principle is usually called, do not contend that the winds aloft at any single level are responsible for the motion of the hurricane, but rather that the winds at the steering level represent the mean flow of the atmosphere from that level down to the surface, which various investigators have attempted to show controls the motion of the storm. The steering level is defined as the height at which the cyclonic circulation of the hurricane has virtually disappeared. It coincides with the top of the warm hurricane vortex and will vary in height with different stages and intensities of the storm. It may be located as low as 20,000 feet in a weak, poorly developed storm and as high as 50,000 feet in a large, mature cyclone. Once the steering current has been determined (and this is not often easy to do since winds aloft are seldom available at high levels near the region of the hurricane), the center is forecast to move about 10° to 20° to the right of the indicated steering and at 60 per cent to 80 per cent of the wind at the steering level. The high-level steering technique has been applied principally to hurricanes moving in westerly and northwesterly directions, since after recurvature storms in the Atlantic seldom offer a threat to the United States coastal areas. Present indications are that for northeastward-moving storms the deviation of the storm movement will be to the left of the steering current, which suggests that the deviation of the storm track from the steering current may be due to some internal force which causes the storm to move northward even in the absence of any steering current. This will be discussed later in this chapter.

The Riehl-Haggard System

A more elaborate scheme for making use of the steering principle has been developed by Riehl and Haggard [83] and others associated with Project AROWA (Applied Research: Operational Weather Analyses) of the United States Navy. Recognizing difficulties in obtaining mean-wind data through a deep layer around the storm, which would be needed to test the operational significance of the steering layer as defined by E. Jordan [42], they chose the 500-mb chart as an approximate representation of the mean-wind flow from the surface to approximately 300 mb. Recent tests made by Miller [61] indicate that the 500-mb chart does frequently provide a good estimate of the mean wind through a deep layer.

The Riehl-Haggard system differs from the older high-level technique in the following respects:

1. No attempt is made to determine the winds at the top of the hurricane vortex. The steering level is assumed to remain constant (at 500 mb, or about 19,000 feet) throughout the life cycle of the storm.

2. Winds are computed from the contour gradients at 500 mb and actual winds aloft are not used.

3. The forecast is relatively objective in nature, once the analysis of the 500-mb chart is completed.

4. The meridional (north-south) and zonal (east-west) displacements are computed separately. These are then combined to obtain the final forecast position.

In applying the Riehl-Haggard technique, a grid 15° longitude in width and 10° to 15° latitude in height is placed over the surface position of the hurricane, and 500-mb heights are read from the analyzed 500-mb chart at various grid points. The meridional component is determined first. The mean 500-mb height differences between the meridians is determined. This can be converted into a geostrophic wind component.

After the meridional displacement has been calculated, the grid is shifted northward by an amount equal to the forecast meridional movement. The zonal displacement is computed by taking the average height difference between the two parallels located 5° south of the initial position of the hurricane and 5° north of the final storm position. This is then converted into a twenty-four hour east-west movement in degrees longitude.

In forecasting the meridional motion second and third approximations are sometimes made, depending upon the indicated movement obtained from the first computation. This is done in an attempt to measure the forces that will likely influence the motion of the hurricane during the twenty-four hours of the forecast period. The grid is shifted prior to making the zonal calculation for the same reason. Thus to a somewhat limited extent the Riehl-Haggard system has built into the grid some slight measure of acceleration that may be expected during the next twenty-four hours. The use of this technique has given some good results, and it is now employed in routine operational forecasts at all the major hurricane-forecast centers.

Success or failure of the system depends upon the accuracy of the 500-mb analyses, to which the computations are extremely sensitive, since small systematic errors in an analysis can result in large errors in the forecast position of the cyclone. Obviously an accurate upper-air analysis over the oceans is very difficult to obtain, but the expansion of the upper-air network and supplementary data from aircraft reconnaissance at the 500-mb level have made it practical to perform rather detailed analyses over much of the hurricane area west of about 60° W longitude, which is the area of primary interest to the forecaster. Without the aircraft data, however, the success of the Riehl-Haggard technique could not be possible.

Recently Miller and Moore [63], working at the Hurricane Warning Center at Miami, Florida, have applied a technique similar to the Riehl-Haggard to the 700- and 300-mb levels and to a mean of the 700-, 500-, and 300-mb charts in an effort to determine the best level for forecasting hurricane movement. They conclude that the 700-mb level is equally as good as 500 mb and that both are better than 300 mb. This is encouraging since in the tropics (given the same amount of data) the 700-mb chart is usually easier to analyze than the 500-mb level. Twelve-hour persistence was combined with the geostrophic components to obtain a twenty-four hour forecast scheme which can be used instead of the Riehl-Haggard system whenever reconnaissance aircraft fly at 700 mb instead of at 500 mb, which is often the case. Operational use during the 1958 season gave promising results, but further rigorous testing is needed before the 700-mb system can be adopted for routine use.

Synoptic Climatological Prediction

The use of the upper-air data for forecasting hurricane movement is sound from a physical standpoint since the various techniques now in use attempt to approximate the steering current acting on the vortex by evaluating the basic flow at more than one level or by the selection of the one level that is most representative of the mean flow from sea level to the top of the hurricane circulation. However, in many cases upper-air data are incomplete or missing altogether, so that it is necessary to depend upon the less representative surface data.

Veigas and Miller [109] have derived a series of multiple-regression equations for hurricane prediction, using surface data exclusively. The data sample was divided into two categories according to the initial latitude of the center (either north or south of 27.5° N); data from a total of 347 hurricanes were used in formulating the system.

They also used a grid system, but the grid was much larger than that used by the Riehl-Haggard technique, extending over a longitude of 60° and a latitude of 30°. The grid computations result in an estimate of the steering derived from sea-level pressures. Combined with twenty-four hour persistence, the Veigas-Miller technique, which was used operationally by the Weather Bureau in 1958, produces forecast results comparable to those obtained by other standard forecast methods. The forecasts prepared by this method may also be expressed in terms of probability that the hurricane will be within a specified area at the end of the forecast period.

Effect of the Long-Wave Patterns

None of the steering techniques are immune to the effects of changes in the broad-scale flow patterns. These include acceleration and marked changes in the direction of movement. The possibilities of radical deviations from steering current indications should always be borne in mind even for periods of less than twenty-four hours, and in all cases must be considered when a longer-range prediction is made. This means that the forecaster must consider the wind patterns over an area of the order of one half a hemisphere. For example, cyclogenesis in the Pacific [47] and its influence on the long-wave pattern downstream played an important part in determining the movement of the September, 1947, hurricane, which after curving northwest to the northern Bahamas, stalled and was then deflected to the west-southwest to pass near Miami and later New Orleans.

For a while a storm moves westward or west-northwestward under the subtropical ridge of high pressure (steered by the influence of the easterlies). Even so, minor troughs passing eastward over the northern side of the subtropical ridge alter the intensity of the ridge and contribute to the acceleration or deceleration of the westerly-moving hurricane, since changes in the intensity of the ridge change the basic steering current. The most critical period for changes in both direction and speed occurs when a hurricane approaches a long-wave, or major, trough in the westerlies.

Minor waves (also referred to as short waves) in the westerlies are constantly moving through the long-wave position. The minor waves intensify as they approach the long wave and weaken as they pass through it. Whether or not there is sufficient break-through in the sub-tropical ridge to permit movement toward the north is a question of the amplitude resulting from the superimposition of the long- and short-wave troughs at the time the hurricane is at the longitude of the trough. The problem is further complicated by the fact that a hurricane has a tendency to build and extend a ridge downstream in the right quadrant. This is brought about by the outflow at high levels from the region of the storm of great masses of warm air that have been lifted from the surface of the ocean. If the trough which the hurricane is approaching is weak (possessing small amplitude) there is always a strong possibility that this anticyclogenesis will result in filling of the southern portion of the trough, and the hurricane will continue on westward or at most be deflected only temporarily from its westward track. A rapidly moving trough in the westerlies may also bypass the hurricane, and recurvature does not occur.

Riehl [82] describes as follows a sequence of events which shows the interaction between a storm and a trough:

A storm moving on a track toward the west-northwest may meet several smaller troughs before it encounters the main trough. Long and short wave troughs are superimposed at first and the amplitude of the composite flow is large. Then the short wave trough moves on, and in the middle latitudes, the amplitude of the westerlies decreases. The storm at first is intercepted and starts to recurve. Then as the short-wave trough weakens and the ridge in the east recovers, it executes a hump or cusp and once again propagates westward. Meanwhile a new trough from the northwest has reached the long-wave position, assumed to be stationary for this illustration. The amplitude of the flow is large again, and a second attempt at recurvature soon begins. Since the relative distance between storm and long wave trough has decreased, this attempt may well succeed unless a fundamental rearrangement of the middle-latitude flow pattern occurs.

More specifically, typical flow patterns associated with recurvature are:

1. Large-amplitude troughs, extending southward from the westerlies and located within a few hundred miles to the west of the center. If the trough is stationary or moving slowly, the storm will remain well to the east of the trough and be steered by southerly winds ahead of the trough. The existence of pronounced wave amplitude upstream as well as in

the trough immediately to the west of the storm is also favorable for recurvature. Such upstream amplitude tends to ensure preservation of the amplitude of the trough which is influencing the motion of the hurricane.

2. Well-marked low-latitude trough building northward into the westerlies. Occasionally a hurricane is associated with a large-scale trough in the subtropics, and the storm will recurve in the general vicinity of the trough as it opens up toward the westerlies. Such troughs are sometimes referred to as "inverted" troughs.

3. Weak trough between two separate subtropical high cells. In some cases hurricanes move northward through very weak breaks in the subtropical high. These are usually difficult to predict. Elongated subtropical highs will frequently break into smaller cells as the westerlies to the north decrease in intensity and vorticity effects tend to favor a shorter wave spacing.

Flow pattern associated with nonrecurvature include:

1. A strong subtropical HIGH to the north of the storm, with the major trough in the westerlies located far to the west of the longitude of the storm. In effect this is the flow pattern which steers the hurricane westward over the oceans. An accompanying characteristic of this pattern is that the westerlies are shifted far to the north of their normal position.

2. Westerlies flat, i.e., waves having very small amplitude, and at latitudes at or north of normal. A narrow subtropical ridge separates the westerlies from the tropical trough. This is very similar to number 3 of the recurving type, and the two are very difficult to separate. In such cases an examination of a higher level, e.g., 200 mb, may lead to clues indicating whether or not recurvature will occur.

This period, when the storm oscillates between the influence of the easterlies and the westerlies, is the most critical one. Essentially the forecaster is faced with the problem of determining the changes in the current in which the storm is embedded and from this making subjective corrections in the indications of the usual steering methods. This requires forecasting both the progression and the changes in the amplitudes of the waves or troughs, in the westerlies. This is not a a simple procedure, and it is not the intention of this book to discuss the techniques used in the preparation of such prognoses. The National Weather Analysis Center, Washington, D.C., employs a group of well-trained meteorologists who are specialists in the preparation of both surface and upper-air prognostic charts. These charts are prepared several times daily for periods ranging from thirty to seventy-two hours in advance and are transmitted by facsimile circuits to the weather stations all over the United States. A few prognoses prepared by high-speed electronic computers are also now transmitted over the facsimile network. Thus the hurricane forecaster has at his fingertips not only his own knowledge and experience but the efforts of the best available thinking from other specialists in the field. It is the responsibility of the hurricane forecasters to combine all these features into the best possible forecast.

The rearrangement of the long-wave patterns frequently results in spectacular changes in the movement of hurricanes. The example of the September, 1947, hurricane has already been mentioned. Some outstanding northward accelerations have occurred, among which are the New England hurricane of 1938, the Great Atlantic hurricane of 1944, and more recently Carol and Hazel of 1954. Such rapid accelerations are responsible for some of the worst forecast failures (although it is not meant to imply that the forecasts of the above hurricanes were failures). Extreme acceleration is always preceded by strong deepening, or increase in amplitude, of a trough over the eastern or central United States, which results in the establishment of an unusually strong southerly or southwesterly flow off the eastern seaboard coincident with the arrival of the hurricane there. Such deepening can frequently be anticipated. A southeastward-moving pool of cold air through the Great Lakes, or the advection of cyclonic vorticity into the region where the hurricane is advancing, the strong building of a ridge of high pressure off the east coast of the United States, or some combination of these features may result in strong acceleration. Since all will result in rapid and marked changes in the steering pattern, even if the acceleration is fully forecast, the exact path of the hurricane is difficult to define twenty-four hours in advance. Sometimes these marked accelerations are attributed to the jet stream's picking up the hurricane, but the presence of the jet is merely a manifestation of either the cold pool or the moving area of strong cyclonic vorticity.

Numerical Forecasting

Predictions of hurricane locations have appeared on routine prognostic charts produced by the JNWP (Joint Numerical Weather Prediction Unit) since the 1955 season. These forecasts are prepared by means of high-speed electronic computers. Current data, usually the 500-mb chart, are fed into the machine. The rate of change, or time derivatives, of the initial data can be expressed as a spatial derivative (in the form of finite difference), provided the time interval is not too large. The advection of vorticity is the element usually forecast. The time interval is usually one to one and one-half hours. The forecast chart (a one-hour prognosis) then replaces the initial data in the memory units of the machine, and the process is reiterated until forecast of the desired time interval, usually twenty-four to seventy-two hours, is obtained.

Until 1960 the forecasts of hurricane motion were not very satisfactory. Numerical prediction is based on the assumed atmospheric models, and three different ones have been tried. Each model, while representing the true atmosphere in certain respects, contains some assumptions which are not strictly valid. It is probably these deficiencies in the models which result in a good part, though not all, of the error in hurricane forecasting.

The initial barotropic model generally underestimated the motion of the storm. One of the major sources of error as far as hurricanes are concerned is the truncation error, i.e., the small errors made in approximating the derivatives of the height field by finite differences accumulated throughout the iteration process. In addition, the spacing between the grid points was too large, about 260 nautical miles, relative to the size of the hurricane circulation. The grid spacing has now been reduced to 165 nautical miles, which may reduce the errors somewhat.

Other models neglect the effects of latent heat of condensation, which is of great importance in forecasting hurricane motion. No divergence is assumed for the 500-mb level, which may be very damaging. Not the least of the errors (as applied to hurricanes) are caused by "boundary errors," or lack of data from much of the hurricane belt. Also the forecast chart is always smaller in area than the initial chart, with the result that the forecast is not very reliable over much of the hurricane belt (usually south of about 25° N).

Numerical-prediction models are being improved and will continue to be improved. Currently some excellent 500-mb prognostic charts are being prepared for much of the temperate latitudes, and these are being transmitted by the National Meteorological Center via the facsimile networks. Some very good hurricane forecasts have been prepared. Unfortunately this has not been universally true, but the same can be said of the forecasts made by all the other techniques now in use. With the intensive research now being carried on by the various universities (notably the University of Chicago), it may reasonably be assumed that within the foreseeable future numerical methods will yield the best predictions available to the hurricane forecaster.

Miscellaneous Forecast Methods

A number of efforts have been made to correlate the motion of a hurricane with the thermal pattern. Sufficient data have seldom been available from the area of the storm to apply such methods except in a very subjective manner. However, when a storm is in an area where the preparation of accurate 700- to 500-mb thickness charts is possible, Simpson [94] has suggested the use of a "warm tongue" analysis, based on the difference in heights between the two surfaces.

Even at relatively low levels air flows out ahead of a hurricane, as both E. Jordan [42] and Miller [60] have shown. Since the core of a tropical cyclone is warmer than its surroundings, this outflow produces a pronounced belt of warm air ahead of the storm. The orientation of this warm tongue may be used as an indicator of the storm's movement for the next twenty-four hours. The tongue is at times displaced to the right of the path of the storm, and in this case the indicated motion is parallel to the major axis of the warm tongue. The mean virtual temperature of a layer determines the thickness of the layer. Thus the thickness of the 700-500 mb layer delineates the warm tongue.

Usually the warm tongue is very difficult to locate, and for this reason its use in forecasting has not become a routine practice. A clue to the positioning of the warm tongue can sometimes be derived from observations of the shields of altostratus and cirrostratus ahead of the storm. These clouds also result from outflow from the region of the storm. Simpson believes that sudden and rapid reorientation of this cloud shield may indicate a change in the course of the storm.

The asymmetry of the wind pattern around a hurricane has also been used to forecast movement. Moore [67] developed an equation for the movement of a hurricane, using the winds (based on reconnaissance data) just above the surface. He used the differences between the winds measured at equal distances from the storm's center. The wind to the north of the center minus the wind to the south, and the wind to the east minus the wind to the west gave a relationship which appeared to give good twenty-four hour forecasts in the Pacific. It has not proved to be of much value in the Atlantic, probably due to the fact that the winds cannot be measured with great enough accuracy. An error in the winds of 5 mph, for example, results in a very serious error in the final forecast position. Winds in a hurricane cannot be measured with an accuracy even approaching an average of 5 mph, and it appears unlikely that Moore's method will come into routine use.

Occasionally the forecaster has to contend with the problem of forecasting the motion of two hurricanes located relatively close together, although this is a rare occurrence. In September, 1950, for example (Figure 25), three hurricanes were in progress in the Atlantic and the Gulf of Mexico at the same time. The forecast is then complicated by the tendency of pairs of vortices to rotate about a common center, located on a line joining the two storms. If the hurricanes are of equal intensity, the point of rotation will be midway between them. Otherwise it will be displaced toward the storm of greatest intensity. The rotation is, of course, counterclockwise. The storms rotate about each other and are mutually attracted. As they come closer together, influence on each other grows and the relative motion increases. This motion is sometimes called "Fujiwhara effect" after the Japanese meteorologist who first studied it.

As tropical storms reach great diameters comparable to the dimensions of the middle-latitude cyclones, they present to the forecaster the problem of determining how much the path will vary from that indicated by steering and other external forces. That such variation exists is indicated by the equation for the meridional motion derived for the Riehl-Haggard [83] technique, which is:

$$C_n = 0.8 + 1.2G_n$$

where C_n is the meridional component of the storm motion and G_n is the meridional flow component at 500 mb. All units are in degrees of latitude per day. This equation indicates that even when G_n is zero (no meridional steering component present) the hurricane will, on the average, move northward about 0.8° of latitude in twenty-four hours. This corresponds to a speed of about 2 knots.

This movement is apparently due to internal forces produced by the hurricane itself. Rossby [88] attributes this force to the variation of the Coriolis parameter across the latitude of the storm (the Coriolis parameter increases as one goes northward). This same force exists in anticyclones and tends to drive them southward. It apparently varies with the size of the storm. The two knots indicated by the Riehl-Haggard equation represent an average. For very large storms it may be as much as 1° to 3° of latitude per day. For very small storms it becomes almost negligible.

Another internal force has been described by Yeh [116], who believes that instead of following a smooth, curved or straight-line path a hurricane oscillates about the mean position in a sinuous fashion. The oscillations vary in both amplitude and period, from 0.5° in twelve hours to 2.0° in forty-eight hours. Prediction of these oscillations is not possible except on a persistence basis. However, even this could be important, as the size of the oscillation (as a hurricane approaches a coast) could determine the region where the maximum winds and the greatest damage would occur.

Very little emphasis has been placed on the effects of surface friction on the movement of hurricanes, although the increase in friction as the hurricane moves inland is believed to play an important part in changing the direction in which the center moves. G. E. Dunn and collaborators [19] in their discussion of the 1955 hurricane season attribute a turn to the left by Connie, Diane, and Ione to the frictional differential between a portion of the storm over land and a portion over water. With increased friction over land and a resultant greater cross-isobar flow, there was an increase of mass and a relative increase of pressure in the right front quadrant, which deflected the center of lowest pressure to the left. As soon as the greater portion of the hurricane moves over land, the frictional differential decreases, and the hurricane resumes its normal course.

The relative importance of surface friction on the motion of hurricanes usually depends upon the speed at which the storm is moving and whether or not a new source of energy is available. A slow-moving storm would be under the influence of this frictional differential for longer periods of time, whereas the direction of a rapidly moving center should show little change. If the hurricane encounters a new source of energy (usually in the form of colder air entering the circulation), the deviation is less pronounced due to increased asymmetry and to acceleration, but usually some brief slowing of the forward motion is evident. The angle with which the hurricane center approaches the coast is also a factor in determining the effects of friction on the subsequent path of the storm.

These then are the tools with which the hurricane forecaster has to work. It is evident that he is dealing with an erratically moving phenomenon. Only a few storms pursue a smooth trajectory from beginning to end. They slow, speed up, and slow again. They move toward the west, turn to the northwest or north for a day or so, resume a westward course, make right-angle turns, loop the loop, and do all the things a good broken-field football carrier will do. The famous hurricane of October, 1909, [27] is one of the best examples. It formed in the western Caribbean, moved north-northwestward into the Gulf of Mexico. Two or three days later barometers began to fall again over western Cuba, at Sand Key, and at Key West. It was thought that a second hurricane was approaching. It was not until ship reports were received by mail and plotted that it became evident that a single storm had looped in the southeastern Gulf.

Few of the techniques used to forecast the motion of hurricanes are completely objective. The knowledge, experience, and skill of the hurricane forecaster still play an important part in the forecast, which must be considered more of an art than an exact science. It is, however, the aim and the hope of all those connected with hurricane forecasting to develop more objective methods so that all forecasters at the various hurricane-forecast centers will arrive at approximately the same solution to any specific hurricane-forecasting problem. This is still far in the future, but the efforts of the National Hurricane Research Project, the promise of the eventual success of numerical weather prediction, plus the efforts of the various research forecasters at the hurricane-warning centers, coupled with the many research efforts at universities and other privately sponsored activities, will undoubtedly in time bring about the desired goal.

11

INTENSIFICATION AND DISSIPATION

A TROPICAL CYCLONE IS BORN IN THE WARM, MOIST AIR overlying the tropical oceans. Initially the disturbance is small, wind velocities are not more than 15 to 20 mph, and the pressure at the center is lowered only a few millibars below the normal. Within a matter of days this tiny infant may grow into a rampaging monster, packing the wallop of 150-mph winds, and the pressure at the center may now be as much as 10 per cent below that of the surrounding atmosphere. Fortunately, however, the life of the beast is relatively short, usually a matter of days, although on rare occasions one may live as long as a month. It is a schizophrenic sort of creature, however, and even as it is being born it begins to display suicidal tendencies. At every opportunity it seeks to move northward away from the tropics where warm air and water fed it so well during both birth and growth. This northward motion begins to sow the seeds of its own destruction; it weakens and dies, or undergoes a complete metamorphosis, in which phoenix-like it changes into a nontropical storm with renewed vigor and starts off on a new life which may greatly outlast its span as a hurricane. What are the processes that cause these developments?

No completely objective techniques for forecasting intensification of a tropical storm have so far been developed. A few empirical rules which verify fairly well in the Atlantic are:

1. An unstable easterly wave moving forward with a speed of 15 mph or less is favorable for intensification.

2. Forward progress in excess of 20 mph is unfavorable. It should be stressed that these rules apply to only the incipient stage of development. Once the storm has reached hurricane intensity, no such correlation between speed of movement and intensification has been noted. In fact, there is evidence that the reverse is true, i.e., acceleration of the hurricane center is frequently accompanied by intensification. Hazel (1954), Janet (1955), and Audrey (1957) were hurricanes of this nature.

3. Storms developing in the Gulf of Mexico and along the Atlantic coast in September and October on an old, diffuse frontal zone or shear line will not usually become intense.

4. Between June 15 and November 1, if a tropical depression has increased to Beaufort force 6 (25 mph), it will usually increase to hurricane intensity provided (a) no drier or cooler air enters the system, (b) it does not pass inland over a large land mass or reach a high mountain range, and (c) it is located south of 25° N latitude. These rules verify best in the Caribbean, the Antilles, and the Bahamas, but not quite so well in the Gulf of Mexico and in the Atlantic north of the Antilles and east of the Bahamas.

Influence of the High-Level Circulation

The efficiency of the hurricane as a machine for converting heat into kinetic energy is very low. Obviously then any factor or combination of factors which act to increase this efficiency of the engine will result in intensification without any necessity for increasing the energy input, which is partly determined by the water temperatures. The circulation features surrounding the storm are most important factors in determining the efficiency of the hurricane as an engine and consequently must take precedence over other elements in the intensification process.

The process of hurricane formation (Chapter 7) is essentially an intensification of the initial disturbance, and the same general circulation patterns that lead to formation, if continued long enough, will result in further intensification of the storm even after it has reached hurricane intensity. Most tropical meteorologists examine the 200-mb level for indications of intensification. It is near this level that the major outflow from the region of the storm is concentrated. The outflow is an indication of the pumping away from the storm of air that has been lifted from the surface.

The United States Navy Project AROWA (Applied Research: Operational Weather Analyses) at Norfolk, Virginia, has made the intensification of hurricanes the subject of special study [107]. Circulation patterns most favorable for intensification are described as follows:

1. If the hurricane lies under the influence of a cyclonic circulation at 200 mb, the storm will not reach great intensity (barely hurricane force).

2. For moderate intensity (average hurricane), the surface position of the storm will be located under a 200-mb HIGH. The latter possesses

relatively small size, and outflow from the storm is blocked by troughs that lie to the northwest and northeast.

3. For extreme intensity (hurricane of 150 knots or more), the surface cyclone lies under a large HIGH that makes contact with the westerlies of the middle latitudes. This permits the lifted air to flow away from the region of the hurricane into the middle latitudes. It dissipates the excess heat and removes the accumulation of air in the upper levels.

Miller [59] has also studied the 200-mb flow pattern most favorable to intensification. His results are similar in some respects to those of Project AROWA, but there are some differences. A 200-mb chart which Miller believes results in maximum intensity is shown in Figure 80; it has the following features:

1. A large HIGH is located to the east of the center.
2. A secondary and somewhat smaller HIGH is located to the southwest.
3. There is a trough of low pressure to the northwest. In large and intense hurricanes there is still evidence of a cyclonic circulation at 200 mb, but its diameter is unknown and it may be much smaller than that shown in Figure 80.

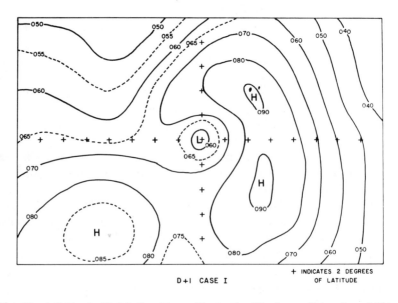

Fig. 80. A 200-mb Circulation Favorable to the Maximum Intensity of Hurricanes. Heights in tens of feet plus 40,000.

TABLE 15
Per cent △D(Relative to 900 mb) Contributed by Layers
(After Malkus)

Pressure, mb	Daisy Eye, Aug. 27		Wet Adiabat = 360°A	
	%	Acc. %	%	Acc. %
100				
	23		13	
200		23		13
	29		29	
300		52		42
	14		19	
400		66		61
	10		14	
500		76		75
	9		10	
600		85		85
	6		7	
700		91		92
	5		4	
800		96		97
	4		3	
900		100		100

If the outstanding features of Figure 80 are responsible for intensification (and it is by no means certain that they are), they apparently perform the following functions: The combined action of the HIGH to the east and the trough to the northwest furnishes an efficient outflow mechanism for removal of the vast quantities of air that have been lifted from the surface. The HIGH to the southwest apparently causes air entering the area from the west to be diverted around its borders to the southwest, i.e., it does not enter the hurricane circulation.

Perhaps it should be emphasized that the high-level circulation can serve only as a means for removing the air that has been lifted from the surface. Such removal is necessary because it prevents accumulation of heat within the upper levels of the cyclone, thus permitting continuation of the convection process, without which there could be no hurricane. The high-level circulation may (by producing net divergence) cause the initial fall in pressure inside the incipient disturbance. However, the bulk of the pressure fall at the surface is caused by warming the air columns in and around the hurricane core.

Malkus [55] has calculated the relative contributions of the various layers (by 100-mb intervals) to deviations from the tropical standard atmosphere ($\triangle D$) at and above the 900-mb level for hurricane Daisy on August 27, 1958. These departures (essentially the percentage contribution each layer makes to the fall in pressure at the surface) are shown in Table 15. It will be noted that about 75 per cent of the pressure fall at the surface can be explained by warming above the 500-mb level and that about one half is the result of warming above 300 mb.

Mid-tropospheric Ventilation

The vertical temperature structure within a hurricane is in large measure governed by the sensible and latent heat content of the subcloud air [59], but recent aircraft data obtained by the National Hurricane Research Project indicate that temperatures in the rain area are usually somewhat colder than would result following moist adiabatic ascent of undiluted subcloud air. These lower upper-air temperatures reduce the intensity of the hurricane.

Additional aircraft measurements of mid-tropospheric wind data in hurricane Carrie (1957) and Daisy (1958) have shown a movement of environmental air *through* the core of the cyclones. Figure 81 shows the relative inflow-outflow through Carrie at 14,000 feet. Note that air is entering the front quadrant and leaving through the rear.

This movement of outside air through the cyclone has lead Simpson and Riehl [98] to postulate that the vortex is being ventilated by the invading cold air and that by this process temperatures in the interior of the hurricane are being lowered, thereby reducing the efficiency of the heat engine which maintains the hurricane circulation. In other words this mass flow through the cyclone acts as a throttle which governs the intensity of the hurricane. This is an important new concept which may go a long way toward explaining some phases of the intensification process.

External Forcing

A recent comparison between the low-level inflow [50], based on surface observations of winds made by ships, and the central pressures of some mature Atlantic hurricanes revealed an inverse linear relationship between the two. Large mass inflow was associated with

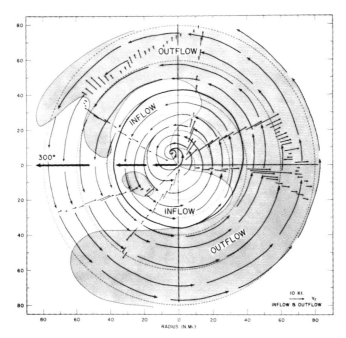

Fig. 81. Relative Motion through Hurricane Carrie at 14,000 feet, September 15, 1957, showing the "ventilation" of the hurricane core. Individual arrows representing radial components of winds scaled to represent speed. (Courtesy National Hurricane Research Project)

very low central pressures. However, the data did not indicate which was cause and which was effect.

In the case of hurricane Audrey (1957), Riehl [85] has demonstrated that the increase in low-level inflow occurred prior to the acceleration in the circulation, and he has proposed mechanical forcing by the neighboring disturbances as one triggering mechanism leading to intensification. A similar forcing has been noted in connection with hurricane Janet (1955).

External forcing is also suggested by Figure 17 (Chapter 3), which shows a great concentration of cyclones reaching hurricane intensity in the very heart of the trade-wind belt. This is where the kinetic energy of the trades reaches a maximum, and the increased low-level inflow as an incipient disturbance moves across the trade-wind belt may well result in intensification of the cyclone by the process described by Riehl [85]. The foregoing observations tend to confirm an old rule of thumb used by Norton [72] to forecast hurricane development. He noted that when the Azores-Bermuda HIGH was strengthened and a surge in the trade followed, an easterly wave could be transformed into a hurricane with great rapidity. It appears highly probable that external forcing was the mechanism responsible for the cyclogenesis.

Influence of the Sea-Surface Temperatures

It has been stated that a tropical cyclone once having reached hurricane intensity will never dissipate over the tropical oceans. With a few exceptions this is true. There have been a few instances of hurricanes dissipating in the Gulf of Mexico. As hurricanes move northward into the Atlantic the number that dissipate over water increases.

In the absence of mid-tropospheric ventilation the vertical temperature structure of the hurricane core is determined by the heat and moisture content of the subcloud air. The latter is closely related to the temperatures of the underlying water surfaces. Although not subject to positive proof, there are indications [59] that the presence of abnormally warm ocean temperatures probably contributes to the intensification process. Some specific examples include Janet (1955), which passed over waters having an average temperature of about 86° F. just before it reached maximum intensity. There were some indications that Carrie (1957) reached great intensity, then passed over cold water and weakened, and later moved into an area of warm water and intensified again. Also in 1957, Audrey intensified rapidly as it approached the Louisiana coast where the water temperatures were highest. None of these examples are conclusive proofs, however, since in both Audrey and Janet external forcing may have been the predominant factor in the deepening process.

That hurricanes tend to decay as they move over colder waters can hardly be questioned. The speed with which the decay of a tropical circulation occurs depends upon the size of the cyclone and the temperature of the water over which it moves. Small hurricanes off the coast of Lower California, for example, degenerate very rapidly when they move over the cold waters of the eastern Pacific, whereas the huge hurricanes of the Atlantic may travel for days over the relatively cool waters north of 30° N latitude, with only a gradual cooling of the core and a resultant loss in intensity.

This loss in intensity is due to the removal of the hurricane from its surface heat source. Air spiraling into the center of a hurricane should be cooled by adiabatic expansion. (The transfer of air from the outer edges of a mature hurricane into the center where the pressure is in the order of 28.00 inches is equivalent to lifting a parcel of air almost 2,000 feet.) Such cooling does not occur, and this is due to the transfer of sensible heat to the air from the ocean surface. If this warming, which is in addition to that supplied by the release of the latent heat of condensation, did not occur, the tropical cyclone would have a tendency to develop a core with much lower temperatures, and this would reduce the intensity of the hurricane circulation. As the center of the hurricane moves over colder waters, the amount of sensible heat transferred to the subcloud air is reduced, leading to loss in intensity.

The removal of the surface heat source (as apart from the heat of condensation) applies to storms that move inland, and storms fill over land almost twice as fast as the increased friction alone would indicate they should. This occurs in spite of the fact that rainfall associated with a hurricane moving over land frequently continues undiminished, and may even increase and spread over a wide area due to orographic lifting of the moisture-laden air. Thus the latent heat of condensation is still present to provide the energy necessary to maintain the storm. However, since the surface air is not warmed by contact with the warm ocean waters, the core of the cyclone cools and eventually loses its tropical nature.

Frictional Influences

As the winds blow strongly over a water surface, the air exerts a frictional drag that sets the water in motion. As the wind gains velocity the roughness of the water increases and the frictional drag mounts rapidly. However, friction over water never approaches that over land. The mean angle of inflow, for example [35], is 23° over water and 38° over land.

This increased angle of inflow as the center of the hurricane moves inland brings into the central area more air, which, if uncompensated by increased outflow at higher levels, causes increased pressure and filling of the center. The speed of filling depends upon the roughness of the terrain and the length of time the center remains over land. Many storms move over relatively flat country such as the Yucatán and Florida peninsulas, weaken only slightly, and then regain their original intensity after moving once again out over warm ocean waters. Mountainous terrain, such as the Dominican Republic, causes great distortion of the surface center, rapid filling takes place, and the most intense hurricanes are reduced to small storms within a few hours. However, the circulation aloft decreases much less rapidly, and many storms regain hurricane velocity after moving out into the open sea again.

Hubert [36] concluded that friction alone is not enough to dissipate a hurricane within a few hours after the center moves inland. He thinks that a hurricane should fill a little less than twice as fast over land as it did over water. He also believes that 10 per cent per three hours is an average rate of gradient decrease near the center for several hours after landfall. This would result in a decrease of only about 15 per cent in the wind velocities after ten hours over land. Storms actually fill faster, on the average, than this. Factors other than friction contribute to filling over land, and it appears likely that the faster rate is due to these causes. One such cause was mentioned in the last section.

Transformation into an Extratropical Cyclone

Many hurricanes which move into temperate latitudes transform into or combine with extratropical cyclones. When hurricanes encounter the polar front and the associated trough aloft, they frequently begin to intensify in response to the usual middle-latitude effects such as the advection of cyclonic vorticity into the area of the hurricane. During the transformation the storm center becomes located in the band of strong thermal gradient, and the circulation of the storm expands. In most cases the transformed storm becomes a major feature of the circulation. Even though the storm takes on many extra-tropical features, it may still retain for some time such tropical characteristics as intense winds near the center, traces of an eye, and heavy rainfall.

Many of the major storms which have affected the east coast of the United States were in the process of transforming into extratropical cyclones as they moved up the coast. Notable among such storms were the two major New England hurricanes of 1938 and 1944, and Carol, Edna, and Hazel of 1954. All of these storms maintained or even increased their intensities even after they had been moving over colder coastal waters or over land for some time. Each of the three major storms of 1954 moved northward along the east coast at a time when a long wave trough was increasing in amplitude between the Mississippi

Valley and the east coast. These trough intensifications not only affected the motions of the storms, but also provided new sources of energy for extratropical-cyclone development which served to maintain the storms against the dissipative effects of friction and the weakening oceanic heat and moisture sources. In the case of Hazel, for example, the strong new source of energy in the form of a pool of very cold air and the associated cyclonic vorticity would have produced a severe storm even if the hurricane had never been present. Hazel was transformed from a severe hurricane into a very vigorous extratropical cyclone within a matter of hours.

Some tropical cyclones weaken, however, upon reaching the polar front. This is most likely to occur when the flow aloft over the front is anticyclonic or a weakening cyclonic type. If the storm is moving slowly, it is especially susceptible to weakening as cold air enters the circulation near the surface. This allows the cold air to sweep rapidly around the center at low levels, thereby cutting off the source of tropical air, which is necessary for the maintenance of a true tropical cyclone.

12

THE DESTRUCTIVE FORCES

A RECENT TELEVISION-FILM PRODUCTION WAS DEVOTED TO the atmospheric processes that create the weather. It was called "The Unchained Goddess" (Frank Capra Productions), because man's most boastful efforts at destruction, and these include the H-bomb, cannot begin to match the fury of nature on the loose. The hurricane cannot match the concentrated and almost total destructive power of the tornado. Nor can it begin to approach in size or total energy the huge extratropical cyclones of the middle latitudes, which at times may spread gale-force winds over half an ocean. However, the tornado is small and its life span is usually merely a matter of minutes, or occasionally perhaps a few hours at most. The extratropical cyclone may live for days or even weeks, but it spreads its less destructive forces over a wider area than does the hurricane. That leaves the hurricane as the most spectacular and the most destructive of the "Unchained Goddesses."

Tides and Surges

Because of the recent catastrophic losses from sea action in the North Atlantic and in the Middle Atlantic States, interest in this phase of the hurricane problem has developed rapidly during the past few years. However, our understanding of this problem is still primitive, and as one might expect, a considerable confusion has arisen in the definition of terms. The rise of the ocean level induced by meteorological conditions should not, strictly speaking, be called a "tide," as that term implies a periodic rise and fall of the level of the sea. Since it seems likely that the term "storm tide" will continue in popular usage for many years to come, both it and the more correct terms will be used more or less interchangeably in subsequent discussions. The following are some of the other most commonly used terms.

Forerunner is sometimes used to mean the slow rise of the tide produced by swells from the storm while it is still some distance from the coast, and occasionally this rise takes place even though the local winds may be offshore and opposing a rise in the water level.

The surge (hurricane or storm surge) is a rapid rise in the water produced by onshore hurricane winds and falling barometric pressures.

Meteorological tides are departures from normal astronomical tides due to the abnormal action of meteorological elements. Normal meteorological effects are included in the predicted tide stages published by the United States Coast and Geodetic Survey. "Storm tides" and "hurricane tides" are used synonymously with "meteorological tides."

The water level is generally defined as the mean height the water would reach if there were no waves, i.e., it is the average elevation between wave crests and troughs. In other words it is the "still-water" level. A tide forecast of nine feet above normal refers to such a water level, upon which may be superimposed huge waves whose crests may be expected to rise considerably higher.

There are a number of hurricane phenomena which may affect the water level, and among the most important are the barometric effects, the forerunners, the storm surge, and the resurgencies. Each of these appear to have a somewhat different physical basis; each may act independently or all may be superimposed or combined. Together they produce the hurricane tide.

Over the open ocean the rise in the mean water level (not to be confused with the wave heights, which may be tremendous) is usually small. The rise is due primarily to the low pressure in the hurricane and is sometimes known as the "inverted-barometer wave." If the water surface were allowed to reach hydrostatic equilibrium with the atmospheric pressure, a change in the elevation of the sea surface would occur, with the water rising approximately one foot for each inch the barometer falls. Thus the maximum effect of the low barometer on the sea surface should not exceed three or four feet at the most. However, due to the motion of the storm, the influence of the waves, etc., such hydrostatic equilibrium is seldom if ever reached. Therefore, the actual change in the water level due to the inverted-barometer effect is not definitely known. There have been numerous instances of surges much higher than four feet on isolated islands in both the Atlantic and the Pacific. Some of these have occurred on Bimini and other islands in the Bahamas, Bermuda, Apia, Samoa, and others. However, shallow water

near a coast line may tend to amplify the rise in the water level created
by the inverted-barometer effect, and it is believed that there may be
sufficient shallow water around the islands just mentioned to account
for the abnormal rise in the water level.

Such amplification is due to resonance, and it occurs only when the
inverted-barometer wave moves into shallow water or into a partially
enclosed bay, sound, estuary, or the like. Hubert and Clark [38] cite a
theoretical example of a hurricane whose central pressure has fallen two
inches, and the center of the storm is moving toward the coast at a

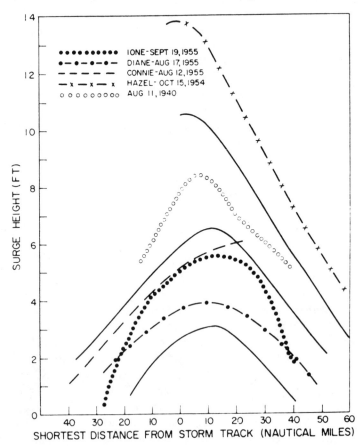

Fig. 82. Surge Profiles of hurricanes which have entered the coasts of North
Carolina, South Carolina, and Georgia. (After R. Hoover)

speed of 15 knots. The rise in the water level due to the low pressure would be about two feet. As this moved into water 140 feet deep the rise would be amplified to 2.4 feet and then increase to 2.8 feet when a 70-foot depth was reached. Fortunately the time during which significant resonance can exist is usually of the order of a few hours at most.

The other case involves a partially enclosed bay, which it can be shown possesses one or more natural modes of oscillation. The hurricane winds could initiate a seiche (an oscillation of the surface of a semilandlocked body of water) which would be amplified if the following hurricane surge were impressed upon the bay with the correct timing and frequency. Thus the wave amplitude could increase rapidly as a result of resonance between the natural frequency of the body of water and the moving hurricane surge.

The gradual build-up of the hurricane tide ahead of the hurricane (the forerunner) has been attributed by Cline [8] to the transport of water by the swells which run well out in advance of the storm center. However, this effect is difficult to evaluate. The force of the wind on a water surface does produce some transport of water, but this is restricted to the surface layers. Over the open ocean, i.e., in deep water, there is no significant pile up of the water, because countercurrents are immediately set up at some considerable depth below the surface, and these countercurrents compensate for the transport within the surface layers. As the swells approach the shallow water near the coast line the motion of the swells toward the shore may extend almost to the bottom of the water, and this fact plus the frictional effect along the bottom greatly retards the speed of the countercurrent below the surface and as a result water is piled up on the beaches. The forerunner alone may produce tides three or four feet above normal, the exact amount depending upon the strength of the wind that produced the swells, the length and duration of the fetch, the angle between the storm path and the shore line, and the shapes of both the continental shelf and the coast.

The forerunner may cause rises in the water level along several hundred miles of coast, whereas the more rapid and much greater rise associated with the hurricane surge is fortunately restricted to a relatively small section of the coast line. This normally occurs just to the right of the cyclone center and at about the same time. However, [78] there are occasions when the surge generated on the coast moves into a long channel, such as Long Island Sound, and the rise in the sea at the end of the channel may reach its peak many hours after the fury of the hurricane winds has passed. Hoover [34] investigated the surge profiles of a number of hurricanes and found that the peak occurred on the average about ten to twenty miles to the right of the storm track, Figure 82. However, in at least one case, hurricane Carol (1954), the peak surge was about forty miles to the right of the hurricane track. Occasionally the greatest rise in the water is observed to the left of the track. This usually occurs at such locations as the Hampton Roads–Norfolk, Virginia, area, where the northerly winds on the left side of the hurricane funnel the water into the partially landlocked harbor.

The hurricane surge is superimposed upon the rise in the water level created by the forerunner and also includes the inverted-barometer wave, which may be amplified as it approaches the coast in the manner described above. Some of the other factors which affect the height of the surge are:

1. The angle the hurricane track makes with the coast line. As a rule in order for the maximum hurricane surge to be produced, the center of the storm must approach the coast so that the angle between the coast and the right side of the track is 90° or less. If the storm approaches the coast at an angle of considerably less than 90° and if the coast line is such that the shortest distance between the coast and the hurricane is growing rapidly less, such as occurred in the Galveston hurricane of 1900, extreme surge heights may be reached. The optimum angle of approach cannot be definitely established, however, since the shape of the coast line is also an important factor in determining the maximum surge heights. If a storm approaches a coast such as the Pensacola-Apalachicola area of Florida from the southwest so that the angle to the right of the track is greater than 90°, the tide may rise as much as four to six feet as far south as Tampa, but the extreme surge normally will not be observed at any point along the coast.

2. Convergence of wind-driven currents at sea. It was mentioned in Chapter 5 in connection with the discussion of the spiral rain bands in a hurricane that low-level convergence is concentrated along narrow bands. A somewhat analogous situation exists concerning the drift currents produced by the hurricane winds, which must produce currents of different speeds and directions. When two of these currents converge the surface of the water will be elevated along the line of convergence. In deep water (as in the case of the transport of surface water by the hurricane swells) deep-water countercurrents compensate for the surface-water convergence and the net effect on the water level is small. As the hurricane moves over

shallow water, the compensating effect of the countercurrent is retarded, just as it is when swells approach the coast, and the rise in the water level may be quite rapid. This rise may, too, be amplified just as are the swells and the inverted-barometer wave.

3. The shape of the coast line. Obviously if a great quantity of water is driven upon a coast line the height to which the water level can rise will depend upon the area over which the total water mass can be spread. The greatest amplification is created by funneling the water into bays and estuaries. The magnitude of this effect naturally depends upon the size and shape of the enclosure. No general rules can be given, since local variations are so large and each section must be studied individually.

4. The shape and slope of the continental shelf. Amplification of the rise in the sea produced by the several means listed previously is partly dependent upon the depth of the water near the coast, which in turn is determined by the slope of the continental shelf, with the greatest amplification occurring with a gently sloping shelf which results in relatively shallow water some distance offshore. However, if the water becomes too shallow, the amplification may be reduced. A protective barrier, such as a reef, offers some protection from hurricane surges.

5. The stage of the astronomical tide. This is important, since the absolute tide heights will of course be greater if the surge occurs at high tide rather than at low tide. In evaluating the effect of the storm tide the normal astronomical tide is usually subtracted from the total tide height.

6. Short-period waves, breakers, and swells. These are superimposed upon the maximum tide heights. They are important in the total destructive effect of the hurricane but are usually eliminated from hurricane-tide measurements.

To the left of the center of the advancing hurricane strong offshore winds may result in abnormally low tides. A storm entering the West Florida coast south of Tampa and moving toward the east or northeast will be attended in the Tampa Bay area by northeast winds which will push the water out of the bay to such an extent as to impede navigation at times. The hurricane of September 20, 1926, resulted in tides 10.9 feet below normal at Mobile, Alabama, which was in the left front quadrant of the storm, while at Pensacola, Florida, which was in the right front quadrant tides were 7.0 feet above normal. This resulted in a considerable slope to the water surface. When the winds of the hurricane relaxed, the water surface was permitted to readjust itself to normal sea level. This resulted in a periodic oscillation of the water level, such as that occurring when a pan of water is tilted and then permitted to return to a level position, although in the case of a hurricane this "resurgence," as it is called, takes place over a considerable distance. Resurgencies were also observed along the New England coast [78] in connection with hurricane Carol (1954).

A storm of hurricane intensity moving toward or crossing a coast line will always be accompanied by tides above normal, particularly near and to the right of the center. The surge may be as little as three or four feet or less if only a few of the factors are making their maximum possible contribution, and fifteen to twenty feet or more if all factors are making the maximum possible contribution to the total elevation of the sea surface. Due probably in part to the concavity of the coast line, hurricanes in the Gulf of Mexico are usually attended by abnormally high storm tides and occasionally devastating surges. High tides will occur at considerable distance ahead and to the right of the advancing hurricane.

In Florida there is an old record of a tide of fifteen feet in Tampa Bay in connection with the severe hurricane of September 25, 1848, which destroyed old Fort Brooke before present-day Tampa was named. The next highest in that area was 10.5 feet during the hurricane of October 25, 1921. The Miami hurricane of September 18, 1926, was accompanied by a tide of 11.7 feet at the gauge at the mouth of the Miami River, and 10.7 feet on Miami Beach. In the Keys hurricane of September 2, 1935, it was reported that the tracks of the Florida East Coast Railway were washed from the Long Key Viaduct at an elevation of thirty feet above mean low water, but a survey by the United States Engineers some time after the storm indicated that the tide level never reached the rails there. Wave action superimposed on the tide probably smashed the roadway with tremendous fury and was responsible for carrying the tracks away. The wind was also thought to have played some part.

There is one additional and very important (though rare) sea effect which may occasionally be superimposed upon the usual hurricane tide — usually with disastrous results. This is the hurricane wave, sometimes erroneously called a "tidal wave," although it has nothing to do with tides. It is nearly always described as a "wall of water" advancing with great rapidity upon the coast line. Authenticated cases of a true hurricane wave are relatively rare and some authorities in this field doubt its existence. Others believe that it is some form of resonance wave but there is no general agreement as to its cause. However, some of the world's greatest natural disasters have occurred as a result of the hurricane wave, which may be nothing more than an unusually rapidly rising and abnormally high hurricane surge.

In India in 1876 the so-called Backergunge tropical cyclone moved inland over the province of Bengal between Calcutta and Chittagong near the mouth of the Megna. It was accompanied by a hurricane wave superimposed upon the storm tide which engulfed the islands and the coastal area, drowning more than one hundred thousand people. It is noteworthy that in three of the most disastrous hurricanes in the history of the United States, from the standpoint of loss of life, a hurricane wave is clearly and definitely mentioned.

On August 27, 1893, a hurricane moved inland between Savannah and Charleston, South Carolina, accompanied in the Charleston area by a tremendous wave which submerged all of the coastal islands. Between 1,000 and 2,000 lives were lost. Later that same year, on October 1, a hurricane moved between New Orleans and Port Eads on a northeast-ward course, and damage on the Louisiana and Mississippi coasts was reported as phenomenal. Reports tell of a tidal wave which engulfed everything, killing 1,800 persons. In savagery it appears to bear some resemblance to the Labor Day storm on the Florida Keys in 1935.

The disastrous Galveston hurricane of September 8, 1900, which drowned about six thousand persons, is discussed in Chapter XIV.

On September 16, 1928, the wind-driven waters of Lake Okeechobee were largely responsible for the death of more than 1,500 people. In this case it was not directly a hurricane wave but a wall of water moving out over the flat mucklands as the dike gave way.

The French have a word for it: *Raz de marée,* or rise of the sea. Piddington [77] translates the official French report describing the Martinique hurricane of October 10, 1780: "An awful 'raz de marée' completed the misfortune under which we were suffering. It destroyed in an instant upwards of 150 houses on the seashore, of which 30 or 40 were newly built; those behind them had mostly their fronts driven in, and the goods contained in them were almost totally lost. It was with much difficulty that the inhabitants escaped with their lives."

In his first memoir published in 1830, William C. Redfield, describing a cyclone the center of which passed close to New York, said "the gale was from northeast to east and then changed to west. More damage was sustained in two hours, than was ever before witnessed in the city, the wind increasing during the afternoon, and at sunset was a hurricane. At the time of [normal] low water, the wharfs were over-flowed, the water having risen 13 feet in one hour." This was quite possibly a resurgent-type wave, and occurred in the Atlantic hurricane of August 17, 1830.

On September 2, 1935, the most intense hurricane of which we have historical record in the Western Hemisphere passed over the Florida Keys. This hurricane and its associated hurricane wave is vividly described in a report prepared by J. E. Duane, co-operative observer for the Weather Bureau and in charge of a fishing lodge on Long Key, over which the center passed [15].

> September 2 — 2:00 p.m. Barometer falling, heavy sea swells and a high tide, heavy rain squalls continued. Wind from N or NNE, force 6.
>
> 3:00 p.m. Barometer still falling slowly, rain the same, but ocean swells had changed — large waves now rolling in from SE, against winds which were still in N or NE.
>
> 4:00 p.m. Wind still N, increasing to force 9. Barometer dropping .01 every five minutes. Temperature 79, rain continued.
>
> 5:00 p.m. — Barometer still falling, wind N, hurricane force, ocean swells from SE.
>
> 6:00 p.m. — This observation could not be reported as all communication was gone. Barometer 28.04,[1] still falling. Heavy rains, wind still N, hurricane force and increasing in velocity. Seas now very, very rough, as water was rising on north side of island.
>
> 6:45 p.m. — Wind backing to NW. Barometer 27.90[1]; wind increasing. A beam 6 inches by 8 inches about 18 feet long was blown from north side of camp — about 300 yards — through observer's house, wrecking same, nearly striking 3 persons, wind has increased in velocity and there were plenty of flying timbers (and heavy timber too!) — seemed it made no difference as to weight or size as all seemed to be urged along with these high winds that seemed to be increasing with every puff. Water was 3 feet from top of railroad grade, or about 16 feet.
>
> 7:00 p.m. — We are now located in main Lodge building of camp — barometer kept falling — flying timbers had begun to wreck this lodge and it was shaking with every blast. Water had now reached the level of the railway on north side of camp. These puffs would hold their strength a full 10 or 11 minutes before letting up, as timed by my own watch.

---

[1]These barometer readings are obviously incorrect, since they could not have been this low two to three hours before the center arrived.

9:00 p.m. — No signs of storm letting up. Barometer still falling very fast.

9:20 p.m. — Barometer now reads 27.22 inches, wind has abated. We now hear other noises than the wind and know the center of the storm is over us. We head for the last and only cottage that I think can stand the blow due to arrive shortly. A section hand reports that a man, his wife and four children, are in an unsafe place a half mile down the track. Aid is given them and now all hands, 20 in number, are in this cottage waiting patiently for what is to come. During this lull the sky is clear to northward — stars shining brightly; and a very light breeze continued throughout lull — no flat calm. About middle of lull (which lasted a timed 55 minutes) the sea began to lift up, it seemed, and rise very fast, this from ocean side of camp. I put my flashlight out on sea and could see walls of water which seemed many feet high. I had to race fast to regain entrance to cottage, but water caught me waist deep. An idea as to rapidity with which we were inundated may be gained from the fact that the writer was about 60 feet from the doorway of the cottage. All people inside house now; water is lifting cottage from foundations. Cottage now floating.

10:10 p.m. — Barometer now 27.02 inches, wind beginning to blow from SSW.

10:15 p.m. — This was our first blast from SSW, which came full force. Seemed blast took one section of house away. House now breaking up — wind seemed stronger now than any time during storm. I glanced at barometer which read 26.98 inches, dropped it in water and was blown outside into sea — got hung up in fronds of coconut tree and hung on for dear life. Could see cottage now going to sea as parties inside were flashing a light. I was then struck by some object and knocked unconscious.

September 3 — 2:25 a.m. — I became conscious in tree and found I was lodged about 20 feet above ground. All water had disappeared from island. The cottage had been blown back on the island from whence the sea receded and left it. I dropped from the tree and regained the cottage after great difficulty, where I found all people safe. A barometer found in cottage was showing signs of going up, but very, very slowly. Hurricane winds continued until 5 a.m. and during this period terrific lightning flashes were seen. After 5 a.m. strong gales continued throughout day with very heavy rain. No lives were lost, but whole camp was demolished; damages will amount to hundreds of thousands of dollars. The F.E.C. railroad crossing, Long Key, was considerably damaged.

The railroad has never been rebuilt. Many persons were literally sandblasted to death and found with no skin and no clothes except for belt and shoes. During the height of the storm, electro-statical discharges were emitted from wind-driven sand, appearing like millions and millions of fireflies.

The greatest hurricane catastrophes in history from the standpoint of loss of life have always occurred in connection with a storm wave, and for the most part, naturally, in densely populated areas, notably India. The tremendous catastrophes of earlier years in India do not seem to have recurred in this century; whether due to protective measures of some sort or for some other reason is not known. Some noteworthy hurricane waves follow:

1737 — Mouth of the Hooghly River, near Calcutta — forty-foot storm wave killed 300,000.

1864 — Mouth of the Hooghly River, near Calcutta — 50,000 drowned.

1875 — September 15 — Indianaola, Texas — 176 killed.

1876 — Backergunge, India — Storm tide and wave killed 100,000, while 100,000 more died later of disease following the storm.

1881 — Haifung, China — 30,000 killed by drowning or subsequent starvation.

1886 — August 19-20 — Indianaola, Texas — Town destroyed by wave and never rebuilt.

1893 — August 27 — Charleston, South Carolina — Tremendous wave drowned between 1,000 and 2,000 persons.

1893 — October 1 — Louisiana and Mississippi coasts — Tidal wave killed 1,800.

1900 — September 8 — Galveston, Texas — 6,000 killed, mostly by drowning.

1919 — September 14 — Corpus Christi, Texas — Tide sixteen feet above normal, 284 killed.

1926 — September 18 — Miami, Florida — Storm tide but probably no hurricane wave, 100 plus killed.

1928 — September 16-17 — Palm Beach — Lake Okeechobee — about 2,000 killed mostly from drownings around lake.

1932 — November 9 — Santa Cruz Del Sur, Cuba — 2,500 killed in storm wave.

1935 — September 2 — Florida Keys — 400 killed, majority by drowning.

1935 — September 28-29 — Bimini, Bahamas — fifteen-foot wave but island sparsely populated and deaths few.

1938 — September 21 — New England — 600 killed.

1954 — August 31 (Carol) — Long Island and New England — 60 killed.

1954 — October 15 (Hazel) — South Carolina to Canada — 149 killed, many by drowning around Toronto, Canada.

1955 — August 18-19 (Diane) — Northeastern states — 200 killed, mostly by drowning in flash floods.

1957 — June 26 (Audrey) — Louisiana — Nearly 500 dead or missing resulting mostly from hurricane surge.

Following the 1954 hurricane disasters, the Weather Bureau began to formulate plans for an intensive research program designed to develop means of forecasting the heights of hurricanes tides and surges. Official Weather Bureau advisories had long contained warnings to coastal residents to expect "abnormally high tides" or "dangerously high tides" in connection with the approach or landfall of the hurricane center. These warnings were not specific enough, and the tide-research program hoped to develop means which would enable the hurricane forecaster to foretell the actual tide heights in feet.

Tide specialists were assigned to all the major hurricane forecast centers and to a few of the more vulnerable stations along the Gulf and Atlantic coasts. The research program was well under way by the hurricane season of 1955, and during the past three years some progress has been made, although many more years of intensive research are needed.

One of the most widely accepted and useful tide-forecast techniques has been developed by Conner and Kraft [11] for Gulf hurricanes. Realizing that there is a lack of knowledge as to the numerical effect many of the parameters listed earlier in this section have on tide heights and that the time the hurricane forecaster has to devote to the preparation of the tide forecast is very limited (due to the press of other duties during a hurricane emergency), they were content to relate the expected tide heights to the lowest barometric pressure at the center of the storm.

Table 16 contains some of the tide heights and central pressures used in the preparation of the graph of Figure 83, which is the basic part of their forecast method. Experience has shown that this graph gives reasonably good forecast tide heights.

Two factors are perhaps responsible for the success of the Conner and Kraft system. First, the height of the inverted barometer wave is directly proportional to the lowering (relative to the surroundings) of

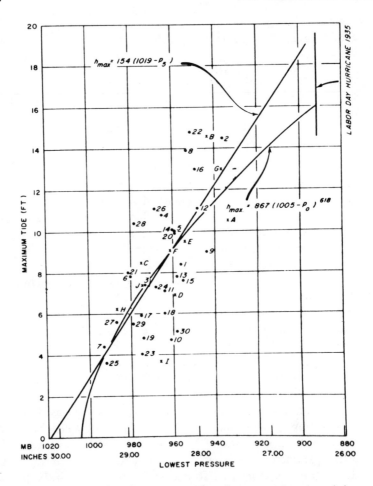

Fig. 83. Maximum Surge Heights on the Open Coast as a function of the central
pressure. (After Conner, Kraft, and Harris)

the pressure at the center of the hurricane. Second, the maximum winds
vary with the square root of the pressure difference existing between
the surrounding area and the hurricane center. Both the wind speed
and the inverted-barometer wave have an important bearing upon the
tide heights observed along the coast. The graph of Figure 83, by
making use of the minimum pressure at the center of the hurricane,
takes into account these two factors. That the correlation is not perfect

TABLE 16

Lowest Central Pressures and Highest Tides
of Gulf of Mexico Hurricanes
(After Connor, Kraft, and Harris)

	Date			Location of Highest Tide on Open Coast	Lowest Pressure (mb)	Maximum Tide Height (feet)
1	Oct.	2,	1893	Mobile, Ala.	956	8.4 m.s.l.
2	Sept.	8,	1900	Galveston, Tex.	936	14.5 m.s.l.
3	Aug.	14,	1901	Mobile, Ala.	973	7.4 m.s.l.
4	Sept.	27,	1906	Fort Barrancas, Fla.	965	10.8 m.s.l.
5	July	21,	1909	Galveston, Tex.	959	10.0 m.s.l.
6	Sept.	20,	1909	Mobile, Ala.	980	7.8 m.s.l.
7	Sept.	13,	1912	Mobile, Ala.	*993	4.4 m.s.l.
8	Aug.	16,	1915	High Island, Tex.	953	13.9 m.s.l.
9	Sept.	29,	1915	Grande Isle, La.	944	9.0 m.s.l.
10	July	5,	1916	Fort Morgan, Ala.	961	4.7 m.s.l.
11	Sept.	28,	1917	Fort Barrancas, Fla.	964	7.1 m.s.l.
12	Sept.	14,	1919	Port Aransas, Tex.	948	11.1 m.s.l.
13	Oct.	25,	1921	St. Petersburg, Fla.	958	7.8 m.s.l.
14	Aug.	25,	1926	Timbalier Bay, La.	959	10.0 m.s.l.
15	Sept.	20,	1926	Pensacola, Fla.	955	7.6 Ab. Nor.
16	Sept.	5,	1933	Brownsville, Tex.	949	13.0 m.s.l.
17	July	25,	1934	Galveston, Tex.	†975	5.9 m.s.l.
18	July	31,	1936	Panama City, Fla.	964	6.0 m.s.l.
19	Aug.	7,	1940	Calcasieu Pass, La.	974	4.8 m.s.l.
20	Sept.	23,	1941	Sargent, Tex.	959	9.9 m.s.l.
21	Oct.	7,	1941	St. Marks, Fla.	981	8.0 m.s.l.
22	Aug.	30,	1942	Matagorda, Tex.	951	14.8 m.s.l.
23	July	27,	1943	Galveston, Tex.	975	4.0 m.s.l.
24	Aug.	27,	1945	Matagorda, Tex.	968	7.3 Ab. Nor.
25	Aug.	24,	1947	Sabine Pass, La.	*992	3.6 m.s.l.
26	Sept.	19,	1947	Biloxi, Miss.	968	11.1 m.s.l.
27	Sept.	4,	1948	Biloxi, Miss.	*987	5.6 m.s.l.
28	Oct.	4,	1949	Freeport, Tex.	978	10.4 Ab. Nor.
29	Aug.	30,	1950	Pensacola, Fla.	979	5.5 m.s.l.
30	Sept.	5,	1950	Cedar Key, Fla.	*958	5.1 Ab. Nor.

*Pressure data from *Monthly Weather Review*.

†An observed pressure of 986 mb is reported in *Monthly Weather Review*. Data on file in the New Orleans Weather Bureau Office indicate that the central pressure was at least as low as 975 mb.

is evident from Figure 83 and this reflects the influence of the other parameters on the observed tide heights — influences which at the present cannot be numerically evaluated.

Hoover [34] at Washington National Airport and McGehee at Miami have worked out similar graphical techniques for forecasting tide heights for other geographical areas. They also make use of the minimum pressure at the center of the storm as a basis for their forecasts of tide heights.

The tide-forecast problem is further complicated by the fact that in order to predict the exact points along the coast where tide heights will present a hazard great enough to necessitate mass evacuation of the population, it is necessary to know well in advance (twelve to twenty-four hours) the exact spot where the hurricane center will move inland. At present techniques used to forecast the motion of a hurricane (Chapter 10) are not sufficiently accurate to make such forecasts possible. Also, a knowledge of the exact intensity of the hurricane while it is still at sea as well as expected changes in intensity before going inland are needed. Constant aircraft surveillance is now giving the forecaster rather detailed information on the current intensity of most hurricanes, but the changes in intensity during the next twelve to twenty-four hours are a forecast problem that has not been completely solved. In a recent paper, Harris [31] summarized the tide-forecast problem in these words:

> The average error in a 12-hour forecast is approximately 60 nautical miles, and if warnings are to be effective, an area several times as large as that actually affected must be alerted.
>
> Disasters such as that which occurred with Hurricane Audrey, can be eliminated by evacuation of the coastal plain in the threatened region to an elevation of 10 to 20 feet above the normal high water level. In marshland, where high ground may be as much as 40 to 100 miles away by highway, many mass evacuations may be required to avoid one catastrophe. With improved instrumentation and forecasting techniques, the number of evacuations, later proved to be unnecessary, will be reduced, but no technique now in sight will permit the prediction of hurricane motion with timetable accuracy.

Waves

The hurricane tide alone may result in extensive damage, but well-constructed and well-anchored buildings are usually able to withstand the rise in the water level, the main damage being done to furnishings, plaster, etc., unless the tide is unusually high and heavy wind-driven waves are superimposed upon the crest of the tide. A cubic yard of water weighs about three fourths of a ton, and the breaking wave which may be moving shoreward at speeds up to 50-60 mph is one of the most destructive elements connected with the hurricane. This is especially true when debris such as tree trunks, heavy beams, etc., are picked up by the waves and used with pile-driving effect, which will wreck houses and even thick concrete installations in short order. Highways, buildings, and sand dunes, upon which some coastal structures are built, are undermined very quickly.

The erosive power of hurricane-driven waves is almost beyond the imagination. They can scour out thirty to fifty feet of beach within a few hours. A severe hurricane of five or six hours duration may completely wash away miles and miles of sand dunes 10 to 20 feet high and 100 feet through at the base. In a great hurricane of half a day's duration, when all factors coincide to produce the maximum possible effect, the retreat of the coastline may be such that the results of a century or more of ordinary wave action can be canceled. This effect is more pronounced when deep water is present a short distance offshore. On the other hand, reefs and shallow water tend to break up wave action and to protect shore-line construction to a considerable extent.

Wind and wave actions were particularly severe along the North Carolina coast during hurricane Hazel (1954). Many beach communities were literally wiped out. At Long Beach, only 5 out of 357 buildings were left intact.

Floods

Following sea action, the next major cause of deaths, injuries, and destruction due to hurricanes, is floods. This was brought forcibly to everyone's attention by hurricane Diane in 1955. This hurricane was the greatest natural catastrophe, from the standpoint of damage, in the history of the United States and earned the unenviable distinction of being called the "first billion-dollar hurricane." The deaths, about two hundred in number, and most of the damage resulted from floods produced by the torrential rains long after the winds had subsided. That the damage was almost complete can be seen from Figure 84.

Hurricane-produced floods are not a rarity by any means. In Haiti,

Fig. 84. Destruction Beyond Description. A section near Waterbury, Conn.,
following the floods of Diane. (Courtesy American Brass Co.)

Jamaica, and many of the Central American countries, floods caused by
hurricane rains have killed thousands. Even in the United States since
1886, at least sixty-three floods due to the rains of hurricanes or other
tropical cyclones have been listed by the Hydrometeorological Section,
Hydrologic Services Division of the United States Weather Bureau.
Nearly every coastal state from Texas to Maine has been affected, and
some of the interior states, including Oklahoma, Missouri, Ohio, and
West Virginia, have been affected by hurricane floods at one time or

another. Even Arizona and California have been visited by floods caused by tropical cyclones.

The heavy rains associated with the dying Texas storm of September, 1921, caused severe flooding over portions of Central Texas. At San Antonio water reached depths of five to nine feet in hotels, stores, and theaters. Fifty-one lives were lost and damage was estimated at five million dollars. The New England hurricane of September, 1938, caused record-breaking floods. Heavy rains had been falling for several days before the hurricane, and the streams were already running bankfull. Up to seventeen inches of rain occurred with the passage of the storm, the greatest amounts being recorded in Massachusetts and Connecticut. At Hartford the crest was 35.42 feet, just 2.10 feet short of the all-time high, which occurred in 1936. In connection with the hurricane of August, 1928, for which rainfall totals are shown in Figure 57, flooding occurred from Florida to Maryland. The Savannah River reached a crest of 40.4 feet at Augusta, Georgia, where the flood stage is 32.0 feet, at 9:00 p.m. on the seventeenth. Hurricane Alice of June, 1954, resulted in rains of up to twenty-seven inches over Southwest Texas, where orographic lifting contributed greatly to the total accumulation. Severe flooding resulted on the Pecos and Rio Grande rivers. The all-time flood crest was exceeded at Laredo, Texas, where a stage of 60.5 was reached, which is more than 30 feet above flood stage. The International Bridge connecting Mexico with the United States was washed away. Another severe flood occurred in Georgia and South Carolina, following the hurricane of September, 1929. Prehurricane rains, however, contributed greatly to the flooding, which set the crest record of 46.3 feet on the Savannah River at Augusta. Records show that on the average, flooding from rains associated with tropical cyclones have occurred in almost half the years since 1886. Many of the floods, however, were produced by dying or decadent storms, insofar as their wind circulations were concerned.

Hurricane rainfall has already been discussed in Chapter 5. The resulting floods are dependent upon the physical characteristics of the drainage basin (e.g., area, topography, type of soil, degree of saturation of the ground, vegetation, etc., which control runoff), the rate and total accumulation of precipitation, and the river stages at the time the rains begin. When heavy rains fall over flat terrain the countryside may be underwater for a month or so, with some damage to buildings, furnishings, and underground communication lines, and considerable inconvenience and discomfort to the populace, but few or no fatalities usually occur. In mountainous or hilly country, disastrous floods develop very rapidly and may be attended by great loss of life.

The setting of the stage for the catastrophic floods of Diane began on August 12-13, 1955, when hurricane Connie moved inland over North Carolina, thence northward and northwestward through the Middle Atlantic States, accompanied by excessive rains from North Carolina to New England, Figure 60. At LaGuardia Field, New York, a total of 12.20 inches fell in a thirty-eight-hour period. Amounts in excess of nine inches fell in eastern Pennsylvania and central New York. In western New England the totals exceeded six inches. Due to previous dry weather, only bankfull streams, some local flooding, and an almost complete saturation of the soil resulted, but Diane was to come along a few days later.

Diane was never much of a hurricane from the standpoint of wind and sea action. Highest winds were estimated at about 125 mph while Diane was still at sea and the lowest pressure was about 28.61 inches. The hurricane lost force as it approached the coast, and the highest winds reported from any station in North Carolina were 50 mph at Hatteras and 74 mph at Wilmington, although it is practically certain that winds of greater velocities occurred at some points between. The center passed near the Raleigh-Durham Airport during the middle of the afternoon of the seventeenth and on into Virginia near Lynchburg before midnight. From this point it moved on a north to northeast course during the night and then turned gradually to an almost easterly course on August 18, passing very near Philadelphia, Pennsylvania; Atlantic City, New Jersey; and Nantucket, Massachusetts, on the eighteenth and nineteenth. Winds had decreased to 30 to 35 mph, with occasional gusts to 40, by the time the storm reached Lynchburg, and no strong winds were reported after the storm left Virginia. Damage from wind, tidal action, and flooding in the Carolinas and Virginia was comparatively light (about $42,000,000).

Forecasters tended to relax after Diane's winds subsided, and advisories were discontinued. But long after Diane had become a minor disturbance from the standpoint of wind, record-breaking rainfall developed. By the morning of the seventeenth, as Diane crossed the coast line, rains of one to three inches had spread across eastern North Carolina into southeastern Virginia. As the center of the storm moved across North Carolina into central Virginia in a north-to-northwest direction, rains spread rapidly to the north and northeast to a distance about 250 miles ahead of the storm center. Rains became heavy in central Virginia on the evening of the seventeenth and amounts up to ten inches or more fell in a twenty-four-hour period along the southern and eastern slopes of the Blue Ridge Mountains.

The storm continued moving in a northerly direction until it reached Mason and Dixon's line during the afternoon of the eighteenth, where it turned sharply in an easterly direction. This brought the heavy-rain area directly in focus over eastern Pennsylvania, New York, New Jersey, and the southern New England area. Rainfall rates were intensified by orographic effects, as the moist-air currents were forced upward over higher terrain.

The rains in southern New England were prolonged, as the storm center, which was moving eastward along the fortieth parallel for about twelve hours, curved to an east-northeast direction paralleling the southern New England coast. At Bradley Field, Windsor Locks, Connecticut, the hourly precipitation averaged nearly 0.6 inch per hour for fifteen hours. The greatest twenty-four-hour amount from this record was 12.05 inches for the period beginning at 10:00 A.M. on the eighteenth. This fall broke the old twenty-four-hour rainfall record for Hartford, a record which extended back ninety years.

Rains began in Pennsylvania during the night of the seventeenth, and by next morning many of the streams were in flood. The rains spread quickly to New York and New England, and just as quickly were followed by floods.

Table 17 shows the flood crests at selected stations compared to the maximum stage of record. Smaller rivers in some areas rose to heights more than ten feet higher than floods previously known. The Lehigh River exceeded the record May, 1942, flood at Allentown and Bethlehem, Pennsylvania. The upper Schuylkill was in record flood, and approached record stages downstream from Reading to Pottstown. The Lackawanna River exceeded the old record at Old Forge, Pennsylvania, by nearly five feet. Most of the tributary and coastal streams in western Connecticut exceeded all previous floods of record.

The extreme heights of the river stages, the quickness of the rise, and the swiftness of the currents added to the destruction. In some areas where no stream channels existed, the torrential rains gouged out new ones, undermining roads and buildings. This, too, is a region of heavy

TABLE 17
Flood Crests for Selected Stations (August, 1955)

River and Station	Flood stage	Crest August, 1955		Maximum flood crest prior to August, 1955	
		Stage	Date	Stage	Date
ATLANTIC SLOPE	*Feet*	*Feet*		*Feet*	
Blackstone: Woonsocket, R.I.		*21.8	19	14.43	July 24, 1938
Quinebaug, Putnam, Conn.		*26.5	19	19.45	Sept. 21, 1938
Westfield: Westfield, Mass. (near).		*34.2	19	*29.4	Sept. 21 and 22, 1938
Farmington: Rainbow, Conn.		*23.5	19	13.83	Jan. 1, 1949
Connecticut:					
Springfield, Mass.	20	21.1	19	28.6	March 20, 1936
Hartford, Conn.	16	30.6	20	37.56	March 21, 1936
Naugatuck: Naugatuck, Conn. (near).		*25.7	19	12.40	Dec. 31, 1948
Housatonic: Stevenson, Conn.		23.42	19	*23.5	March 12, 1936
Rondout Creek: Rosendale, N.Y.		23.93	19	21.9	Aug. 27, 1928
South Branch Raritan: Stanton, N.J.		15.22	19	12.2	March 15, 1940, July 19, 1945
Lackawaxen: Hawley, Pa.	9	*20.6	19	*20.1	May 23, 1942
Neversink: Oakland Valley, N.Y.		12.74	19	12.62	Nov. 26, 1950
Brodhead Creek: Minisink Hills, Pa.		*29.9	19	14.43	Dec. 11, 1952
Lehigh:					
Lehighton, Pa.	9	20.3	19	20.7	May 23, 1942
Allentown, Pa.	14	23.4	19	*22.0	Feb. 28, 1902
Bethlehem, Pa.	16	25.9	19	25.6	May 23, 1942
Neshaminy Creek: Langhorne, Pa.		*22.84	19	*17.3	Aug. 23, 1933
Perkiomen Creek: Graterford, Pa.	8	14.5	13	18.26	July 9, 1935
		14.1	19		
Schuylkill:					
Reading, Pa.	13	18.06	19	*26.2	Sept. 2, 1850
Pottstown, Pa.	14	18.08	19	*21.0	Feb. 28, 1902
Fairmount Dam, Philadelphia, Pa.	11.5	14.3	19	14.8	March 1, 1902
Delaware:					
Hale Eddy, N.Y.	11	12.7	19	*20.3	Oct. 10, 1903

*Stage derived from high water mark.
†Not referred to present gage site and datum.
‡Highest stage observed.

TABLE 17 (Continued)
Flood Crests for Selected Stations (August, 1955)

River and Station	Flood stage	Crest August, 1955		Maximum flood crest prior to August, 1955	
		Stage	Date	Stage	Date
ATLANTIC SLOPE (continued)	*Feet*	*Feet*		*Feet*	
Delaware (*Continued*):					
Fishs Eddy, N.Y.	10.5	15.6	19	*23.6	Oct. 9, 1903
Port Jervis, N.Y.	18	23.91	19	*25.5	March 8, 1904
Milford, Pa.		35.2	19		
Portland, Pa.		32.65	19	26.50	October 1903
Belvidere, N.J.	20	28.4	19	*28.6	Oct. 10, 1903
Easton, Pa.	22	*43.7	19	*38.3	Oct. 10, 1903
Riegelsville, N.J.		36.6	19	35.9	Oct. 10, 1903
Point Pleasant, Pa.		31.3	20		
Lambertville, N.J.		24.3	20		
Yardley, Pa.		25.5	20		
Trenton, N.J.	12	20.5	20	*22.8	March 8, 1904
Lackawanna: Old Forge, Pa.	11	20.05	19	*17.0	July 28, 1934
North Branch Potomac:					
Cumberland, Md.	17	22.64	18	*29.2	June 1, 1889
South Branch Potomac:					
Springfield, W. Va.	15	22.30	18	†34.2	March 18, 1936
North Fork Shenandoah:					
Cootes Store, Va.	15	16.64	18	25.3	Oct. 15, 1942
Shenandoah: Riverton, Va.	22	‡29.0	19	46.05	Oct. 16, 1942
Monocacy: Frederick, Md.	15	16.0	13	†28.1	Aug. 24, 1933
Potomac:					
Paw Paw, W. Va.		35.4	19	54.0	March 18, 1936
Hancock, Md.	30	32.30	19	47.6	March 18, 1936
Williamsport, Md.	23	27.9	20	48.6	March 18, 1936
Harpers Ferry, W. Va.	18	23.9	20	36.5	March 19, 1936
Washington (near) D.C.	10	17.62	20	28.1	March 19, 1936
Washington, D.C.	7	7.1	18	17.72	Oct. 17, 1942
		8.48	20		
		8.77	20		
Rapidan: Rapidan, Va.	14	22.50	18	27.6	Oct.—,1942
Rappahannock:					
Remington, Va.	15	23.48	18	17.4	Nov. 22, 1952
Fredericksburg, Va.	18	26.8	19	42.5	Oct. 16, 1942

*Stage derived from high water mark.
†Not referred to present gage site and datum.
‡Highest stage observed.

TABLE 17 (Continued)

Flood Crests for Selected Stations (August, 1955)

River and Station	Flood stage	Crest August, 1955		Maximum flood crest prior to August, 1955	
		Stage	Date	Stage	Date
ATLANTIC SLOPE (continued)	*Feet*	*Feet*		*Feet*	
James:					
Bremo Bluff, Va.	19	26.7	18	*38.52	Sept, 30, 1870
Columbia, Va.	18	30.4	19	37.4	Sept. 19-20, 1944
Richmond, Va.	8	16.9	20	26.5	March 20, 1936
Dan: Danville, Va.	11	11.0	18	21.2	Aug. 15, 1940
Roanoke:					
Altavista, Va.	18	24.35	18	40.08	Aug. 15, 1940
Randolph, Va.	21	‡26.3	19	*36.0	Nov. —, 1877
Weldon, N.C.	31	‡34.0	21	58.0	Aug. 18, 1940
		‡34.0	23		
Scotland Neck, N.C.	28	‡30.4	25	41.98	Aug. 19, 1940
Williamston, N.C.	10	11.7	29	20.5	Aug. 22, 1940
Tar:					
Rocky Mount, N.C.	9	10.0	19	*19.0	Aug. —, 1908
		11.1	22		
Tarboro, N.C.	19	‡23.6	25	34.0	July 27, 1919
Greenville, N.C.	13	‡16.1	26	24.5	July 28, 1919
Neuse:					
Neuse, N.C.	14	‡19.0	21	26.0	Sept. 20, 1945
Smithfield, N.C.	13	‡21.0	20	26.5	Oct. 3, 1929
Goldsboro, N.C.	14	‡23.9	24	26.72	Sept. 23, 1945
Kingston, N.C.	14	‡19.6	28	25.0	July, — 1919
Cape Fear:					
Moncure, N.C.	20	‡21.0	18	35.6	Sept. 18, 1945
Fayetteville, N.C.	35	41.18	19	68.9	Sept. 21, 1945
Elizabethtown, N.C. (Lock No. 2)	20	‡29.5	20	43.2	Sept. 23, 1945
OHIO BASIN					
Cheat: Parsons, W. Va.	11	11.3	13	†20.5	July 10, 1888
		12.1	18		

*Stage derived from high water mark.

†Not referred to present gage site and datum.

‡Highest stage observed.

concentration of population and industry, and in the case of the mountain areas the floods occurred at about the peak of the summer-camp and tourist season. In a few cases small reservoir dams broke and added to the natural flood of water. Large amounts of debris became jammed against bridges and other obstructions, damming the water. When these dams broke, the destruction downstream was magnified. The wild torrents, coursing directly through many cities, ripped many buildings apart or moved them off their foundations and tore up street pavements, exposing underground utility lines. Many industrial plants were wrecked and closed down. Summer camps were hard hit; one camp in the Poconos was almost completely wiped out. In the Brodhead Creek–Stroudsburg area of Pennsylvania the death toll was listed at seventy-five persons.

Damage has been estimated at $754,706,000, of which $600,000,000 occurred in New England. In other states the damage was $21,000,000 in New Jersey, $15,000,000 in New York, $76,740,000 in Pennsylvania, with lesser amounts occurring in Maryland, Virginia, and North Carolina. These figures are admittedly incomplete, and the actual damage will never really be known. However, direct and indirect damage would indicate that Diane earned her title of "Billion-Dollar Hurricane." Estimates of the death toll vary from 180 to 200 persons.

A combination of factors produced the gigantic disaster: Unusually heavy rains, which followed closely on the heels of the almost equally heavy rains of Connie, came at a time when streams were already full and the soil almost saturated. They fell over relatively small drainage basins, mostly located in hilly or mountainous regions, so that runoff was very rapid and unusually high, averaging as high as 63 to 72 per cent of the total rainfall in some sections.

In order to have provided fully adequate flood warnings, river forecasters would have had to know in advance the expected rainfall over the areas that were actually flooded. There is no known generally accepted technique which will yield forecasts of rainfall amounts with sufficient accuracy to be used in flood forecasting. There are a few meteorologists who believe quantitative precipitation forecasts can be made without first forecasting the wind and pressure patterns, but so far they have not developed a successful technique for doing so. Certainly the first requirements are accurate surface and upper-level prognostic charts, and these the river forecasters did not have in connection with Diane, at least not twenty-four hours in advance of the flood-producing rains. Even if the prognostic charts available had been perfect, it is very doubtful that the magnitude of the rainfall would have been anticipated. At any rate most river forecasters are reluctant to base flood forecasts on anything less than actual measurements of rainfall amounts. Even in mountainous regions, valuable short-range flood forecasts can be issued if the forecasters know the total areal distribution of the rainfall within a short time after it falls. The time-honored method of using a dense network of rain gauges over the basin and preparing isohyetal analyses over the drainage area at six-hour intervals works well, but it is time consuming and in extreme emergencies may be too slow. Some recent studies made at the University of Miami have indicated that it may be possible to measure rainfall amounts over a large area simultaneously by the use of radar. This is a difficult and complicated problem, but it does offer one means of getting the desired rainfall information into the hands of the flood forecaster within a short time. Additional research is needed before the measurement of rainfall by radar becomes commonplace, but it is hoped that it may one day lessen somewhat the threat some future Diane may offer.

Winds

In the destructive and death-dealing features of the hurricane, wind ranks third behind sea action and floods. The area of destructive winds in a hurricane varies considerably. While in a small storm the width of the destructive area may be as small as 15 miles, in some of the Great Atlantic hurricanes the width of damaging winds may be 300 miles or more, and in some of the large Pacific typhoons may exceed 500 miles. Perhaps, on the average, it is 50 to 100 miles.

The length of time hurricane winds will prevail at any given point is also important, since damage is progressive and continues during the entire life of the storm. The duration will depend upon the size and rate of movement of each individual storm and the position of the locality relative to the storm's track. Occasionally hurricanes have loitered in the same area for several days, but fortunately this has usually occurred while the storm was at sea. In the few cases where this has happened on the coast line the hurricane has usually tended to decrease in intensity.

Wind is air in motion, and the wind velocity increases with the pressure gradient or the pressure difference between two places. In

hurricanes, winds frequently reach velocities (averaged over one minute) of 100 to 135 mph. In the more severe storms velocities reach
135 to 160 mph and in a few of the most violent hurricanes such as the
Labor Day storm on the Florida Keys in 1935 and Janet at Chetumal,
Mexico, in 1955, reach or exceed 200 mph. Good maximum-wind data
in hurricanes have been difficult to obtain. Not long after the wind
rises above 100 mph, more often than not, the anemometer cups will
break off or the wind tower will collapse. Indeed most of the extreme
winds in hurricanes are never measured. During the past fifty years at
one time or another wind data have been recorded in five-minute averages, one-minute averages, fastest mile, extreme gusts, with three-cup and
four-cup anemometers, and with all types of wind-instrument exposures.
Thus, for comparative purposes, any recorded value means nothing
unless all the circumstances are known, which is often not the case. In
newspaper accounts of a hurricane in any particular locality, one often
does not know whether momentary gusts or one-minute velocities have
been used or whether the recording instrument was 30 feet or 400 feet
above ground level.

Most of the anemometers are of the rotating-cup type, consisting of
metal cups rotating in a horizontal plane and geared to record the
passage of each mile, or portion of a mile, of wind. These necessarily
have a certain amount of inertia and lag, so the majority of records to
date do not show accurately the gusty character of the higher velocities.
Gust recorders have now been installed in the hurricane-susceptible
areas of the United States. A number of tests have been made to determine the ratio of peak velocities measured by anemometers to gusts,
with varying results. Perhaps the average of these tests indicate the
"extreme" velocity may be 25 per cent more than the one-minute
velocities and the momentary gusts 50 per cent higher than the sustained
wind.

In a storm with a sustained 100-mile wind, there may be brief gusts
of 150 mph, and in the not-too-unusual case of a sustained 150-mile
wind, there may be gusts of 225 mph or more. Since it is the gustiness
of the wind that results in the uneven intermittent pressures and the
wrenching effects, the speed of the peak gusts should be considered in
designing structures to withstand the onslaught of hurricanes. Another
important consideration in relation to construction and hurricane damage is the rapid rise in the actual force of the wind at higher speeds.
The force exerted does not increase proportionately with the velocity,

but with the square of the velocity, so that doubling the velocity results in approximately four times the force. The pressure in pounds per square feet may be computed from the formula $P = KV^2$, where P is the force exerted by the wind on an exposed surface, V the wind velocity, and K a value used by some as a constant and by others as a value varying from .003 to .006 increasing with the velocity. A 60-mph wind will result in only 15 pounds per square foot while a 125-mph wind gives the terrific force of 78 pounds per square foot.

Some representative wind pressures derived by Gentry [28] are given in Table 18:

TABLE 18

Representative Wind Pressures Derived by Gentry

Wind Speed (mph)	K	Pressure per Square Foot (pounds)
60	.004	15
80	.004	26
100	.0045	45
125	.005	78
150	.005	112

Other wind speed–pressure ratios vary somewhat depending upon the value assigned K.

In any habitable area construction will vary all the way from the most flimsy to the most solid. Some significant damage will begin when the wind pressure reaches approximately fifteen to twenty pounds per square foot. Where construction is generally poor, entire cities may be destroyed, as was the case with the old city of Santo Domingo (now Ciudad Trujillo) on September 3, 1930, and Corazal, British Honduras, and Chetumal, Mexico, on the night of September 27 and 28, 1955, by hurricane Janet. In Chetumal, a town of about 2,500 people, only four badly battered buildings were left standing. In addition to wind damage to buildings, trees may be uprooted or broken off and crops laid waste.

A committee of the Structural Division, American Society of Engineers, sought to arrive at some sort of an estimation of wind pressure exerted by the Miami hurricane of 1926 [3]. On top of the Mayer-Kiser Building there was a small observation room, about eighteen by twenty-one feet, with four small columns in the corners supporting the roof.

The walls were blown out and the columns bent. The committee estimated that a pressure of about sixty-five pounds per square foot would have been required to produce the distortion which occurred (a wind pressure of seventeen pounds[2] per square foot represents a velocity of 75 mph for air of average density) but this figure cannot be taken too seriously because area of exposure at time of failure is unknown. There is evidence, however, that for areas of moderate size, the storm probably exerted a pressure of more than fifty pounds per square foot; but there is no indication this was the case over the entire area of the building. In fact buildings which were properly designed and constructed to withstand a wind load of twenty pounds per square foot suffered no serious damage.

But the problem is even more complicated. Hurricane winds passing over and around a building will develop both positive and negative forces. Positive forces are those pushing in and negative forces are those pulling out (suction) on the outside of the building. The United States Bureau of Standards has shown that for tall buildings the total force acting may be one and one-half or more times the direct pressure against the windward side of the building, due to the negative or suction pressure on the lee side of the structure. This effect is familiar to students of aerodynamics as the type of negative pressure that exists in the wind current over the top surface of an airplane wing and contributes most of the lift. The College of Engineering, University of Florida, shows that for certain angles of incidence of the wind, the negative pressure may be considerably larger than the frontal force. Thus there may be, under certain conditions with the typical sloping roof, or even a flat roof, a greater force tending to lift the roof and to pull some of the walls outward than there is to push in the wall on the side directly exposed to the wind.

The damage to small buildings by hurricane winds varies considerably, depending upon the type of structure and the degree of exposure. A common type of damage which occurs to buildings of one-story frame construction with peaked roofs is the removal of the entire roof or a portion of the roof. With improper construction, roof damage may occur with any type of structure. The primary cause of loss of roofs by homes and industrial and other buildings is the lack of anchoring. But even where the roofing structure proper stays on, severe roofing damage

---

[2]Based on a different K value from that used by Gentry.

may result. Improperly bonded or poorly maintained roof covering or flashing will result in damage. "Built-up" roofs of only three- or four-ply thickness, merely nailed, may give trouble as the wind tears the felt from around the nails. On the other hand, almost all types of roofs, such as composition, shingle, and clay tile laid in cement suffer little when properly constructed. Reinforced concrete chimneys, when properly built, stand up very well. Tile roofs will come through hurricanes in good shape if the individual tiles are properly cemented. Poor or weak construction will inevitably lead to roofing damage as the positive and negative force of the wind exploits every weak point. Almost all types of damage will permit water to enter the building, resulting in additional water damage.

Damage due to the collapse of large wall areas is commonly observed when walls have been constructed without proper supports and ties. Beerbower [4] examined the damage done to the Professional Building in Hollywood, Florida, in the Miami hurricane of 1926 and reported:

> With respect to wall construction, one of the worst examples was presented in the Professional Building. This structure was about 120 feet long, 3 stories high and fitted with a high parapet. The structure is a reinforced skeleton with concrete block curtain walls. Columns and lintels, as well as curtain walls, were only 8 inches thick, from the foundation up, and the entire west side, which fell, showed no legitimate wall anchor . . . In general it may be said that in no case where a wall was wrecked could any wall anchors be discovered.

Walls not properly designed to resist both positive and negative pressures are likely to be severely damaged. The Methodist Church in Hollywood, Florida, had walls of reinforced-concrete skeleton construction with interlocking terra cotta–tile curtain walls. The columns were fourteen inches thick and about thirty feet high. The side walls fell out, but undoubtedly they could have been saved by adequate buttresses. The roof trusses of this church were spanned from column to column but were not held down by anchors. The entire roof, framing and all, was carried away.

Great damage was done by this same storm in Miami. This was the first hurricane since Miami was a small village and followed a period of frenzied boom-time construction. The violence of the storm far exceeded that for which adequate provision was made at that time in design, and Miami's buildings had been planned on the same basis as in more northern latitudes, in spite of its being in the hurricane belt.

13

PREPARATION FOR THE HURRICANE

IN 1954 ALL PREVIOUS RECORDS OF HURRICANE DAMAGE IN the United States were broken, and in the following year even that record high was surpassed. Economic losses from these storms are truly appalling, and at first it would seem that hurricane damage is not being greatly reduced over the years although the number of fatalities definitely has been. The record-breaking damage totals of 1954-55 were largely due to the fact that the densely populated and highly industrialized northeastern quarter of the United States was hit repeatedly. Hurricane building codes were not in effect in this section and the public was not well educated in precautionary measures. In fact, in the sections most susceptible to hurricanes, the ratio of damage to the total value of the property in the stricken areas has actually decreased.

The casualty list, once so inevitable and terrible in nearly all great hurricanes, has been markedly reduced in the past thirty years. The Palm Beach–Lake Okeechobee hurricane of September, 1928, caused the death of nearly 2,000 persons. Due to protective measures adopted by state and local governments and by private agencies such as the Red Cross, a better-informed public, and an improved warning service, the average death total is now only about 3 per cent of what it was twenty-five years ago. In fact, all recent cases of heavy fatalities have been in the Northeast until the Louisiana disaster of 1957. For the first time in Florida history, the hurricane of October 5, 1948, did not cause a single death.

Building Construction: Long- and Short-Range Planning

One does not begin to prepare for a hurricane the day before it strikes, or a week, a month, or even a year. Complete preparations require careful planning years in advance. All seaside resorts should have proper zoning laws which will not permit structures to be built too close to the edge of the ocean, or on sand dunes unless piling goes down to rock. All areas where hurricanes are likely should have a hurricane building code. Structures of all types *can* be built to withstand wind damage from ordinary hurricanes. In areas subject to inundation from the hurricane tide or the hurricane wave, protective devices such as high and strong bulkheads will be necessary; sea walls and jetties may have to be built. In many places more massive and solid foundations may have to be sunk deep into the ground before shore structures are built. There are many sections subject to hurricanes which should immediately decide whether certain areas should be protected at all, how much protection is warranted, and what type is desirable for particular areas. Many exposed areas require protection which would cost more than the value of the property, and no attempts should be made to protect such places.

Since the late twenties communities along the southeast Florida coast have adopted strict hurricane building codes for all types of buildings. According to Grady Norton, the Weather Bureau's chief hurricane forecaster until his death in 1954, these codes have incorporated many of the suggestions made by Gray [73], who made surveys of the damage wrought by the 1926 and 1928 Miami and West Palm Beach hurricanes, plus those of other persons based on experience through subsequent years. Buildings erected in conformity with these codes are withstanding the hurricane winds without serious damage. Norton goes on to say, however, that there are still some people who have not provided storm shutters for windows, etc., and there are still some old flimsy buildings and many old roofs that have not been replaced with proper materials. Such structures continue to suffer damage. There is no question that modern building codes are paying off in greatly reducing property damage whenever they are properly enforced.

The extremely violent Florida Keys hurricane of September, 1935, and Janet of 1955 have shown that we must accept the foregoing conclusions with reservations for such superhurricanes. Fortunately hurricanes of such violence are rare, and building codes to protect against them are probably not justified from an economic standpoint. An examination of the damage in these storms indicates that substantial damage would have resulted to many buildings constructed in accordance with current building codes.

One of the primary goals of each community's building code should be that each structure be a safe shelter in time of emergency. For further information concerning recommendations for hurricane-proof construction the reader is referred to the City of Miami Building Code and Bulletin Number 28, College of Engineering, University of Florida at Gainesville.

The damage to buildings resulting from a storm is quite varied depending on the degree of exposure of the site and on the type of construction employed in the structure. Roof losses are quite common due to the upward pressures created by the wind in passing over the building.

These recommendations for sound wind-resistant construction of frame and concrete-block buildings are believed to be economical measures relatively easy to incorporate in plans for a new building. Unfortunately, it is not usually possible to incorporate these strengthening recommendations in buildings already constructed. However, in some cases roof rafters may be accessible for anchoring, and in many cases porch columns are sufficiently exposed to allow tie-down anchors to be installed. Each case needs to be individually examined for its possibilities.

Sound construction should include consideration of the following:

1. Size and reinforcement of foundation and piers.

2. Adequate connections between foundation and sills.

3. Anchoring of roof and ceiling framing to side walls.

4. Secure attachment of roof coverings and sidings.

5. Concrete- and masonry-block strength.

6. Provisions for vertical columns and tie beams for hollow-wall structures.

7. Provisions for plate-attachment bolts or roof and ceiling-joist anchors in the pouring of tie beams in exterior masonry walls.

8. Installation of shutters to cover glass windows.

Broad roof overhangs which permit the wind to get under and to lift them up may lead to trouble. A hipped roof with about a 30° pitch is about ideal. Flat roofs are undesirable. Roof surfaces should be inspected once a year just before the hurricane season and repaired when necessary.

Precautions as the Hurricane Approaches

Get and use only official information. When the Weather Bureau advisories request that you keep on watch or on the alert for all future advices since the hurricane is now a threat to your area, keep your radio or television on and listen for the latest official storm information. If power fails, use a battery radio. Even after the hurricane arrives, keep the radio or television on, if possible, for you may receive information which will be of value to you. After hurricane warnings are ordered up, the area of display becomes one big rumor factory. Pay no attention to these rumors. Even your best friend may not have heard or may not remember the warning correctly. When hurricane warnings are first ordered up, decide what you are going to do and where you are going to ride out the storm. If your house is out of danger from high tides and is well built, then it is probably the best place to weather the storm. All owners and operators of ships, but especially small craft such as dredges, tugboats, fishing boats, pleasure craft, etc., should keep constantly in touch with the hurricane advisories once a hurricane has been located. Small craft should keep in mind seas become rough many miles in advance of the storm area.

Avoid low-lying coastal areas. Residents should get away from low-lying beaches or other locations which may be swept by high tides or storm waves. If passage to high ground is over a road likely to be underwater, leave early. Do not run the risk of being marooned. Tides are always higher than normal near and to the right of the center and on occasion, which forecasters are not always able to predict, much higher. And then in addition there may be the even more unpredictable hurricane wave which sweeps all before it. Never bet your life against the ocean by remaining in a low, exposed position when the center of a hurricane may come close. To be on the safe side, persons should evacuate all areas which could be covered by ten feet of water above mean low tide. And in the hurricanes of great intensity, evacuate if twenty feet of water can reach you. Get away from any possible action by the ocean and your chance of injury or death is reduced by 85 to 90 per cent in hurricanes. Remain in a good shelter away from water and you will be almost 100 per cent safe.

Persons living in houses built in conformity with modern building codes should remain at home during hurricanes. If yours is a modern home, built to withstand storm winds and kept in good condition, you should be perfectly safe and you will feel more at ease about your property. However, whether you stay at home, go to a hotel, or some other place you consider safe, there are certain things to be done at home first. And wherever you are, continue to keep in touch with official hurricane advisories.

Board up windows or put storm shutters in place. When you board up, use good lumber and fasten securely. Makeshift boarding may do more damage than none at all. Brace outside doors and be sure door locks work. Remove or lash awnings.

Get in extra food, especially things which can be eaten without cooking or with very little preparation. Remember that electric power may be shut off as a safety measure or may fail because of damage and you may be without refrigeration. If emergency cooking facilities are necessary, be sure they are in working order. A camp stove is a good investment. Have a supply of canned goods and milk sufficient for two days, but do not have too many perishables on hand. Refrigeration should be conserved. Turn your refrigerator and freezer to the coldest setting. Open only when absolutely necessary and close quickly. Both will stay cold much longer if these precautions are taken. Well-constructed and properly insulated home freezers, if well filled with food, will maintain food-preserving temperatures up to forty-eight hours after which dry ice may be used.

Your water supply may fail. Sterilize the bathtub and fill it with water. Also sterilize and fill all jugs, bottles, cooking utensils, and other containers. Even for some time after service has been restored it may be wise to boil drinking water unless you are sure the supply received from the city's water mains is safe.

Have flashlights or other emergency lights in working condition and keep them handy. Lanterns or candles may be usable and, if so, matches will be needed. But if a window should shatter, a candle overturned by the wind could cause a dangerous fire. Remember, fire apparatus may have difficulty reaching your home because of fallen trees and other debris. Have a good supply of batteries and bulbs for your flashlight.

Check on everything that might blow away or be torn loose. Garbage cans, garden tools, signs, porch furniture, awnings, and other objects become weapons of destruction in hurricane winds. Store them all inside if possible. Loose objects on the roofs of buildings are especially dangerous. Lash down or take inside dollhouses and doghouses, and secure any outside gas tanks.

Be sure that a window or door can be partially opened on the lee side of the house. This will keep pressures on the outside and inside equalized. Without such equalization, higher indoor pressures may become strong enough to force doors and windows open.

Most gasoline tanks at filling stations are now operated by electricity. It may take several days after the storm before electricity is again available; therefore, have the gasoline tank of your automobile full.

There are almost always large numbers of small craft in resort areas along the coast. As soon as a hurricane warning is issued, remove your boat to anchorage in sheltered water, preferably a mile or more from the ocean or any other large body of water. A safe distance should be maintained from other boats. Boatowners keeping their craft on trailers at home should tie them securely or get them inside a building if possible. Where it is impossible to remove a boat to a secure place, anchor it and sink it. After the hurricane has arrived, leave your boat alone. Many lives in recent years have been lost when boatowners have foolishly attempted to remove their boats to safety during hurricane conditions.

Riding It Out

Be calm and be cautious. Panic spreads rapidly, and your re-action to the hurricane will affect the reactions of other people. As the storm progresses, continue to listen to your radio or television for the latest advisories from the Weather Bureau, the Red Cross, and other official local agencies. If the electricity is off, use your automobile radio or portable radio, if you have one. Keep inside. Do not venture out to see how things look, because lethal objects will be flying through the air from time to time. Watch the wind direction in order to close any open window on the windward side. Keep a window open on the leeward side.

If the center, or eye, of the storm passes directly over you, there will be a lull in the wind lasting from a few minutes to half an hour or more. Stay in a safe place. Make emergency repairs during the lull if necessary, but remember the wind will return suddenly from the opposite direction, frequently with even greater violence. Every hurri-cane is different. Just because you may have seen one that did not live up to a hurricane's reputation for destructiveness, do not be lulled into a false sense of security. For those who live within a few blocks of the ocean, the passing of the eye is the most treacherous and dangerous portion of the hurricane.

Keep a close check on continuous gas flames, such as pilot lights on stoves. If a flame goes out, shut off the valve controlling it; if all flames go out, shut off the main gas-supply valve and leave it off. Commerce and industry should keep strongly in mind anything which may be a fire hazard. Washed-out or flooded highways, streets blocked by fallen trees, poles, and wires, may prevent fire apparatus reaching your plant. During the storm, continue to check electrically-operated alarms and other safety devices. Under certain conditions it may be desirable to shut off electrical power, furnaces, and boilers. Have tarpaulins and other coverings available to protect equipment and stock if roof or walls are damaged and water enters the plant.

After the Hurricane Has Passed

Obtain prompt medical care at Red Cross disaster stations or hospitals for persons injured during the storm.

Be cautious of every move. Do not touch loose, dangling, or low-hanging wires of any kind under any circumstances. Report such damage to the light-and-power-company or to the nearest police officer.

If damage is widespread, do not jam the telephone system to report interruptions in individual electric, gas, water, and telephone service. Utility companies have plans for complete service restoration. Report individual trouble to utility companies *only* after services are back on in your neighborhood. Use your phone for emergencies only. Jammed switchboards may prevent emergency calls for police, firemen, doctors, and Red Cross disaster units. *Do* report immediately to police or utility companies any hazardous conditions such as live electric wires, broken gas and water mains, and overturned bottled-gas tanks.

Use extreme caution with emergency lighting or cooking flames to avoid fire hazards. Protect your health by boiling water before drinking. Do not empty water stored in bathtub or other receptacles until you are sure that a safe water supply has been restored. Guard against spoiled food in mechanical refrigerators if power has been off any length of time.

Unless you are qualified to render valuable emergency assistance, stay away from disaster areas where you may hamper first-aid or rescue work. Many electrocutions and shocks from fallen live wires occur following hurricanes. If necessary to attempt to free someone from a live wire, use a poor electrical conductor, such as a dry stick, to push the wire away. Attempt this with extreme caution.

Walk and drive cautiously. Be on the alert for trees or branches that may be weakened and ready to fall, for buildings that may be near collapse, and for bridges or roads that may be damaged or ready to give way under the added weight of passing cars. Debris-filled streets are dangerous, so keep your eyes on the road. Along the coast and near streams, the soil may be washed from beneath the pavement, which may collapse under the weight of vehicles.

Prevent fires. Lowered water pressure makes fire fighting difficult.

If you need help after the storm, watch for police or Red Cross disaster workers.

Salt water or spray may cause severe damage near the ocean. This can be ameliorated by hosing down the shubbery and lawn thoroughly with fresh water after the storm passes. Broken branches should be sawed off. Many trees, such as palms which are uprooted, can be reset. In the more severe storms, trees are often defoliated. Foliage will return within a comparatively short time. It is recommended that pruning of shrubbery be deferred for a week or two after the storm, when the extent of the damage is more apparent.

Keep an accurate record of the amount and cost of any hurricane damage. If it is not covered by insurance, you may take it as a tax deduction. But you must get property appraisals immediately after the storm to back up your claims. In commerce and industry, premises and buildings should be checked immediately and thoroughly. Temporary or permanent repairs should be made for any structural damage. See that your motors, furnaces, and boiler room are dry. If not, take steps to correct the situation. Check the fire-protection equipment in the plant. Test the water and fire pumps. If your fire-protection equipment is impaired, notify your local fire department, then take immediate action to correct the impairment. Examine any processing machinery. If wet, wipe it dry and oil it to prevent rusting. Check the stock and contents in the building for water damage and start any necessary salvage operations or drying out that can be done. Keep in mind that some materials, when damp, will heat and spontaneous combustion may result. For example, damp bales of wool, sisal, rags, leather, packing materials, etc. not only will heat up by themselves but also can swell up and push out the walls of a building.

Precautions for Flooded Buildings

Disconnect the main electrical switch to prevent short circuits when current is restored. Shut off the gas valve until an examination has been completed. Make sure gas piping is secure and has not broken before reopening the valve. Use flashlights for the examination and avoid bringing lanterns or open flames into buildings. Remove all chemicals that might start a fire, such as carbide, lime, phosphorus, etc. Keep watchmen patrolling all unoccupied areas at all times for several days and nights. Trouble may develop slowly, and can develop quickly.

14

THE HURRICANE HAZARD BY REGIONS

1. South Atlantic States

(NORTH CAROLINA, SOUTH CAROLINA, AND GEORGIA)

The monthly frequency of tropical cyclones affecting North Carolina, South Carolina, and Georgia is listed in Table 19. August, September, and October are the main hurricane months, with only six out of fifty-nine tropical cyclones since 1885 occurring in other months. Of the significant cyclones since 1885, there were forty-three of hurricane intensity and sixteen that were not. All major hurricanes move in directly from the Atlantic. Most of the weaker storms arrive in this area after moving overland from Florida or the Gulf States.

Hurricanes of extreme intensity are known to have struck the area in 1804, 1813, 1879, 1885, 1898, 1954(Hazel), and 1958(Helene). It is evident that there was a very high frequency of exceptionally severe hurricanes in the late 1800's and that the twentieth century has been comparatively free of major hurricanes.

TABLE 19

Frequency of Tropical Cyclones (by Months) along the Carolinas and Georgia Coasts, (1885-1958)

	June	July	Aug.	Sept.	Oct.	Nov.	Dec.	Total
Hurricane Intensity	0	4	18	13	7	0	1	43
Less than Hurricane Intensity	1	0	1	5	9	0	0	16
Total	1	4	19	18	16	0	1	59
Percentage of Total	2	7	32	30	27	0	2	100

Like those storms affecting New England and the North Atlantic States, most appear north of the Antilles, one of the principal exceptions being that of Hazel (1954), which moved out of the Caribbean. A list of all known tropical storms affecting this section can be found in the Appendix.

One of the most recent severe hurricanes to strike this area was Hazel.

Hurricane Hazel (1954)

On October 3, 1954, forecasters in San Juan and Miami noted the presence of an easterly wave to the east of the Lesser Antilles. It appeared to be of average intensity, but on the following day pressure fell 2 to 3 mb in the Windward Islands. By the fifth Barbados reported a wind of Beaufort force 8, and a Navy reconnaissance aircraft was dispatched to search the area. At 3:27 p.m. a poorly defined eye and winds of 95 mph were located about fifty miles east of the island of Grenada. This was the beginning of mighty hurricane Hazel, which was destined to live another ten days, spreading death and destruction through the Carribbean, the Carolinas, the Middle Atlantic States, and Canada.

On the fifth the diameter of hurricane winds was very small and the storm was in a very immature stage. The center passed between the islands of Grenada and Carriacou, but all the Grenadine Islands except Carriacou escaped with minor damage and no loss of life. At Carriacou, 140 homes were demolished and 240 more damaged. Total damage was estimated at $42,500. Highest winds on Carriacou were estimated at 100 mph, but on Grenada, only twenty-five to thirty miles to the south no strong winds occurred. Hazel was definitely less severe than Janet in this area (1955).

On October 6, Hazel continued on a west to west-north-westward course at about 15 mph. The lowest pressure measured by aircraft was 29.44 inches, and the highest winds were 110 mph in squalls. The SS *Atlantic Importer* passed through a squall at 12.8° N and 65.3° W at 11:30 a.m. The barometer was 29.77 and the wind was from the south, hurricane velocity, or Beaufort force 12. Two and one-half hours later the ship's winds had subsided to 20 to 25 mph. Next day Navy aircraft detected winds of 125 mph in squalls, and the lowest pressure was 29.35 inches. There was one particularly severe squall line, or spiral band, radiating outward from the center. Only four hours after the reconnaissance plane had found winds of 125 mph in the northeast quadrant, the SS *Ventura,* only thirty to forty miles south of the eye, reported southwest winds of 20 to 25 mph, barometer 29.71 inches, rough, southwesterly sea and heavy swells, occasional rain, but otherwise none of the severe weather normally expected so close to the center of a hurricane. Hurricane Hazel was still poorly organized and the eye was too diffuse to permit accurate tracking by means of radar.

October 7. At 7:00 a.m. the reconnaissance plane found some additional deepening with a central pressure of 29.12 inches and winds up to 125 mph. The aircraft encountered severe turbulence; one crewman was badly injured, requiring hospitalization, and another sustained minor injuries. Low-level penetrations were discontinued, and as a result no eye-pressure readings were obtained until after the hurricane had turned northward and passed over Haiti. By the eighth, however, the storm was becoming better organized, winds of 125 mph were found to extend outward about twenty miles in the southwest quadrant, and the wall cloud around the eye began to give a good return on radar for the first time. The extreme turbulence on this date is rather difficult to explain on the basis of minimum pressure and maximum winds.

October 9. No information on intensity was received on this date. Three center fixes were obtained, and these indicated a slowing in forward speed and a more northwesterly course. Previous movement of Hazel had been somewhat erratic, and forecasters were reluctant to accept these new fixes with complete confidence. Ralph Higgs, Meteorologist in Charge of the Hurricane Forecast Center at San Juan, described Hazel's course up to this point: "After passing the Grenadine Islands, hurricane Hazel followed a zigzag course across the southern Caribbean, moving westward at night and west-northwestward during the day." Of the two most definite oscillations, the period of one was nineteen hours and that of the other thirty-four hours. The amplitude of one was about thirty miles, while that of the other was about forty-five miles. Yeh [116] has described an internal mechanism which affects the movement of a hurricane, brought about by the fact that the superposition of a steering current on a vortex results in a nonlinear path, but recent computations at the National Hurricane Research Project indicate that Yeh's formula cannot fully account for Hazel's oscillations.

On the tenth, Hazel showed a definite turn to the northwest and later to the north-northeast, and on the eleventh continued on a slow but steady course toward the western tip of Haiti; maximum winds on both days remained above 100 mph. However, no measurements of the central pressure were obtained.

October 12. The hurricane crossed the tip of Grande Pointe, Haiti, between 2:00 and 5:00 a.m. The mountain peaks, some of which are almost eight thousand feet, weakened the central core of the storm, although winds of 90 mph occurred as Hazel moved over the Golfe de Gonaires. The much lower mountains of Cape du Mole, however, were able to further disrupt it to the point where the eye was lost on radar, and the storm's intensity may have decreased briefly to below hurricane force.

Dame Marie, Anse d'Hainault, Mole St. Nicholas, and Jean Rabel were almost totally demolished. The larger cities of Jérémie, Les Gayes, and Port de Paix were severely damaged by winds and high tides from Les Cayes westward. Rains were torrential over most of Haiti. A landslide buried the mountain village of Berley, a short distance southwest of Port au Prince, and only 2 of Berley's 260 inhabitants escaped unhurt. Estimates of deaths ranged from 400 to 1,000 or more, including the 200 or more buried by the landslide. Extreme winds of 125 mph or more were reported at several places in the western portions of the southern peninsula by the Corps d'Aviation. Winds were estimated by aircraft reconnaissance from 95 to 135 mph.

Even Puerto Rico, far away from the high winds of Hazel, did not escape fully the fury of the storm. A second easterly wave followed closely on the heels of the one that spawned Hazel. This wave passed over Puerto Rico on the tenth, and partly due to the influence of Hazel, the winds aloft over Puerto Rico remained fresh and out of the southwest for several days. The combination of saturated air up to about twenty thousand feet, strong convergence, and the orographic effect of the southern slopes of Puerto Rico produced torrential rainfall of extraordinary duration and intensity [33]. The maximum fall was 26.07 inches at Toro Negro Dam during the period October 12-15. The resulting floods were the greatest since the San Ciriaco hurricane of 1899 and may have been equal to those associated with that severe hurricane.

October 13. Hazel now passed from the Caribbean through the Windward Passage and into the Atlantic. The eye quickly reformed after leaving Haiti and was picked up again by the reconnaissance aircraft before midnight of the thirteenth.

Up to this time the path of Hazel (particularly the recurvature) had been very difficult to forecast, and even in retrospect its movement can be only partially explained. Now at 500 mb, the anticyclone which had been oscillating from Texas to the Southeastern States began to move eastward, and on the morning of the twelfth, was located between Hatteras and Bermuda, some 1,100 miles due north of Hazel. The trough which had apparently brought about the recurvature collapsed, and the Riehl-Haggard computations indicated a turn to the north-northwest. The upper-air pattern became steadily more clear-cut with time, and the flow at both the 500- and 200-mb levels agreed closely with the storm's movement. The general wind flow around the storm became southeast to south and increased in velocity. Imbedded in this flow, Hazel turned north-northwestward, and its forward speed increased gradually.

The hurricane passed over Great Inagua about 9:00 a.m. with a minimum pressure of 29.34 inches and highest winds of 40 mph. The exposure of the wind instruments is excellent. Yet some four hours later, the reconnaissance plane reported the central pressure as 28.70, a drop of 00.64 inches, and maximum winds of 85 knots (98 mph), an increase of more than 50 mph. Three hours later winds had increased to 100 knots (115 mph), truly a remarkable intensification.

October 14. At 1:00 p.m. EST the Air Force reconnaissance plane found further increase in intensity, winds up to 150 mph, pressure down to 28.29 inches, turbulence severe, and seas phenomenal. The center position was about one hundred miles east of Great Bahama Island. While damage in the Bahamas was small, six persons were killed when a sailboat capsized while seeking shelter in Inagua. During the fourteenth, Hazel accelerated in forward speed to 20 mph or more.

Captain William E. Harrell, meteorologist of the Air Force hurricane-hunter plane, stated that at this time the eye of Hazel was so small — about eight miles in diameter — that it was difficult to keep the plane in it. The pilot flew in a tight circle to avoid penetrating the wall cloud, but at one time a wing hit the wall and received a "terrific jolt." The crew reported the winds were whipping the ocean into a solid sheet of white, and Captain Harrell called it a "terrific sight." He went on to say that usually the sea under a hurricane has some color to it, but the sea below Hazel showed only shades of white.

Along almost the entire length of the Carolina coast there is a chain of long, low, narrow sand bars and islands. During the present century and particularly in recent decades, many beach resorts and expensive summer cottages and homes have been constructed in this area. Through the many inlets between the islands pass hundreds of pleasure and fishing craft. Most all of the hurricanes that move up the Atlantic coast pass well to the east of Cape Fear, North Carolina, but a few move inland between Savannah, Georgia, and Georgetown, South Carolina. But from Georgetown to Wilmington a feeling had grown among the inhabitants that for some obscure reason — perhaps the contour of the coast or the Gulf Stream — destructive hurricanes would be steered away from this section. However, old records and reports indicate that perhaps as many as eight destructive hurricanes had struck this section since 1740.

Hurricane Hazel was watched with interest by coastal residents during the week it meandered across the Caribbean. No one believed it posed any threat to the Cape Fear section. It was generally felt the hurricane would pass to the east, perhaps near Cape Hatteras, which juts out into the Atlantic, and this seemed confirmed when hurricane warnings were ordered at 11:00 a.m. EST on the fourteenth, on the North Carolina Capes. Storm warnings were hoisted from Wilmington southward to Charleston.

The weather worsened somewhat during the forenoon. There were scattered cumulus and stratocumulus clouds moving from the east and altostratus moving rapidly from the south. Additional weather-bureau personnel were dispatched by plane to the Wilmington office. Intermittent rain squalls began at 5:00 p.m. and hurricane warnings were ordered for the Wilmington District.

The rain squalls increased in frequency. At 10:30 p.m. the meteorologist in charge at Wilmington, Reuben L. Frost, visited Wrightsville Beach to check on sea conditions there and to discuss the situation with the mayor and the police. The heavy storm swell was breaking on the beach at fifteen- to twenty-second intervals and the tide was already higher than Frost had ever observed it in his five years in the area. A representative of radio station WGNI was present, and a special emergency broadcast was arranged on the spot. The people were told that the hurricane was only a few hours away and that all possible measures must be taken immediately for the protection of their lives and property. Broadcasts were repeated at intervals of one hour or oftener throughout the night. State and village police, Civil Defense, Red Cross, Weather Bureau displaymen and co-operative observers, and many other volunteers spread warnings to every beach resort and inland hamlet up and down the coast, knocking on doors of homes when necessary.

At 2:00 a.m. on the fifteenth, when the reconnaissance plane noted on radar an apparent swing of the hurricane center to the west, hurricane warnings were ordered as far south as Charleston. However, the change in direction, if any, was temporary and hurricane Hazel moved inexorably on toward the Carolina coast.

October 15. Hurricane Hazel, the most severe tropical storm in over one hundred years in the Cape Fear area and one of the most severe combined tropical and extratropical storms ever to visit the northeastern United States and southeastern Canada, reached the North Carolina coast line during the middle of the forenoon on this date, having accelerated to 27 mph, and was followed by three more hurricanes in the same general area during the next eleven months. The really extreme winds preceded the arrival of the eye by only an hour or two, indicating that Hazel was surrounded by a rather large envelope with an intense, concentrated inner core around the eye. There is some question whether there was a lull at Myrtle Beach, South Carolina, which is an official weather station. Their lowest pressure was 28.47 inches at 9:25 a.m. with the highest wind 106 mph. If a lull did occur, Myrtle Beach was located on the extreme western edge of the eye and on the weaker side of the storm.

The shrimp boat *Nina Fay,* operated by Captain Julian Fulford, was able to ride out the storm in the vicinity of Holden Beach Bridge. The eye of the hurricane passed a little before 11:00 a.m. when the barometer read 27.90 inches. Captain Fulford reported that the wind velocity greatly exceeded anything he had ever experienced in many years at sea and was probably around 150 mph. His boat was the only one in the vicinity to remain afloat.

The fishing boat *Judy Ninda,* with Captain LeRoy Kinlaw, rode out the hurricane at Tilgham Point, where the inland waterway crosses Little River. At 10:30 a.m. the boat was in the eye of the hurricane, and at that time the barometer read 27.70 inches. The estimated time of the relative calm was thirty minutes, which was the longest reported anywhere, and it is thought the geometric center of the hurricane passed over this point. The barometer was checked by the Wilmington Weather Bureau office and found to be accurate. According to Captain Kinlaw, the highest wind and water came just after the eye passed, and the highest tide was estimated at 14.5 feet.

Reuben L. Frost interviewed many people in the area and states there was general agreement that in the eye the rain ended, the clouds thinned, but there was no sunshine. He further describes the local reaction to the central calm of the hurricane: "Local people on the North Carolina coast use the Old English pronunciation of 'kam' for calm. People at Calabash stated the sudden 'kamming' of the wind and low pressure affected their ears, and there was a spooky, eerie feeling or sensation. One local lady said the 'kam' spell gave her the 'creeps.' After a few minutes she saw a very black and ugly bank of clouds approaching from the southwest. There was an awful roaring noise that scared her worse than ever. In just a matter of seconds the 'kam' was over and the awful wind began blowing from the southwest."

Along the Carolina coast where wind and wave action combined, the devastation was almost unbelievable. Serious damage began at George-town, South Carolina, and every fishing pier from Myrtle Beach to Cedar Island, North Carolina, a distance of about 170 miles, was destroyed. Damage to property in South Carolina, mostly along the beaches, was $27,000,000. At Garden City, south of Myrtle Beach, a two-story concrete-block store was mute evidence of the terrific fury of this hurricane. The store was comparatively large for this section, about eighty by forty feet. The lower floor simply disintegrated and the upper story, almost intact, was hurled some three hundred feet west into the inlet. The business section of Garden City became a pile of rubble and only 3 of the 275 residences remained habitable. Northward along the coast full communities were completely demolished. Grass-covered dunes from ten to twenty feet high, along and behind which beach homes had been built in a continuous line, in some areas for as long as five miles, simply disappeared, dunes, houses, concrete-slab floors and all.

In North Carolina going north or northeastward along the coast the first settlement is Calabash. Here the estimates of the length of the calm period ranged from six to fifteen minutes. Highest water and wind came after the eye passed, and the highest tide was estimated at eighteen feet above mean low water. At the next village, Ocean Isle, fortunately all persons were evacuated. Here the calm lasted about ten minutes, the area was washed clean by the storm tide, and all buildings disappeared.

The next populated area, Holden Beach, lost all of its two hundred buildings. The tide was 17.6 feet above mean low water. It was in this section that most of the loss of life occurred. Many, if not most, of the homes were without telephones, and perhaps some of the occupants may have been without knowledge of the hurricane warnings.

On Long Beach, west of Southport, there were many new homes, but everything on the island was destroyed. Where three hundred homes existed at daybreak, all had disappeared by noon — far worse than the destruction of a tornado. Well-built concrete-block buildings with concrete floors and paved driveways were carried away. No litter or debris remained — it had been swept clean. The homes had been built in a space of some 75 to 100 yards between the beach and the highway, but after the hurricane the beach reached the highway and beyond.

At Oak Island the lowest pressure reported by the Coast Guard Station was 28.60 inches, with highest wind estimated at 140 mph. Highest velocity came after the wind shifted to southwest as did the highest water, which was ten feet above mean low water. At nearby Southport the hurricane tide reached thirteen feet.

The largest shore community was Carolina Beach. Here 475 buildings were destroyed, another 1,365 damaged — half of the wealth disappeared in a few hours. In this town engineers removed 100,000 cubic yards of sand from the streets. Two weeks after the hurricane much private property was still buried under tons of sand. Ridges of sand six feet or more high lined the highways and in some places resembled the northern snowbanks along the sides of the cleared highways.

At Wrightsville Beach near Wilmington, the wind reached 125 mph and the island was submerged by five feet of water. Eighty-nine houses were destroyed, 530 damaged, which resulted in losses of about $3,000,000.

At the Wilmington airport seven miles inland, the barometer fell to 28.68 inches, and here the strongest wind occurred before the wind shift. The temperature fell 11° F. with the shift, indicating that cold air was sweeping around the storm and that it had become, or was becoming, extratropical. All communications into Wilmington were destroyed and the city was isolated from 10:15 a.m. to 12:03 p.m. Half of the telephones (10,500) were knocked out. The city was without electricity, which was not fully restored for three days. Water in the Cape Fear River reached the highest stage on record and buildings and warehouses along its banks were flooded.

A summary of meteorological data on the Carolina coast during the passage of Hazel appears in Table 20. The total damage along the North Carolina–South Carolina beaches was estimated at $61,000,000. In spite of the severity of the hurricane the total casualties in this area

TABLE 20

Meteorological Data on the Carolina Coast During Passage of Hazel, 1954

Station	Highest Water above MLW	Highest Wind	Lowest Barometer
Myrtle Beach, S.C.	....	106 mph	28.47
Little River, N.C.	14.5 ft.	150 mph	27.70
Calabash	18.0	150 mph	....
Holden Beach Bridge	17.6 & 18.0	150 mph	27.90
Lockwoods Folly Inlet	....	140 mph	....
Oak Island	10.0	140 mph	28.60
Frying Pan Shoal Lightship	....	60? mph	28.30
Southport	13.0	....	....
Masonnonboro Sound (Wrightsville Sound Drawbridge)	14.6	125 mph	....
Cape Fear River at Wilmington	8.2	....	....
Wilmington WBO	....	98 Gust	28.68
Swansboro	8.0	....	....
Hurst Beach Bridge	7.9	....	....
Beaufort–Morehead City	8.8	100 mph	....
Atlantic	5.0	85 mph	....

were only nineteen — a tribute to the excellent warnings, the devotion to duty of meteorologist Frost, and public-spirited citizens such as Mrs. Jessie Taylor at Southport, F. C. Simmons at Shallote, and Waldo Jones at Myrtle Beach, who by telephone and in person spent long hours, at considerable personal risk, in warning the populace.

Hazel's record of destruction along the Carolina coasts attests to the destructive power of the combined winds and waves of a hurricane. However, by June, 1956, most of the badly battered beach communities had been substantially rebuilt.

Inland, out of reach of rising waters, an estimated one third of all buildings in the eastern two thirds of North Carolina received some damage. Effects of the hurricane as it passed inland were remarkable. Forests of pine and other trees appeared to be scorched as if by fire. Plants along the coast presented a burned appearance, probably due to salt-water spray carried inland by the wind or from sand blasting caused by hurricane-blown sand and dirt.

The entry of hurricane Hazel into the continental United States coincided with a major convulsion in the broad-scale circulation pattern which, since early in the fall, had existed over the Northern Hemisphere from the Pacific across North America and the Atlantic and which required about one week to consummate. As Krueger [49] has described it: "During the first half of October the westerlies were stronger than normal with a ridge present over the East, a weak trough in the Northern Plains states and another off the Pacific coast. The circulation after the passage of Hazel represented a ridge-trough phase shift of about 180°, with troughs replacing ridges in the eastern half of the United States, and the Pacific, while a ridge developed in the western United States."

The beginning of the violent shift in the hemisphere circulation was first seen on the 500-mb chart at 10:00 p.m. on the twelfth, as marked deepening occurred in a closed low in the western Gulf of Alaska, while at the same time pressures began to rise to the eastward and a trough with very cold air over extreme western Canada began to move southeastward.

By 10:00 p.m. on the thirteenth, twenty-four hours later, the amplitude of the ridge over the extreme eastern Pacific and the trough over the eastern Rockies and western Great Plains had increased markedly and the pool of cold air with temperatures −30° C. to −35° C. had moved to eastern Iowa. The amplitude of the Atlantic ridge had now increased greatly, with one station in the Canadian Maritime Provinces reporting a 500-mb height rise of 700 feet. With this increasing gradient the southerly flow intensified and Hazel accelerated northward until its forward progress reached 60 mph at one time as it raced northward through the Atlantic states. The center crossed the North Carolina coast line at 9:25 a.m. on the fifteenth and some fourteen hours later was passing over Toronto, Canada.

Normally hurricanes dissipate or at least lose considerable intensity when they move inland. Hurricane Hazel did neither. In this case, as in all such cases, the new source of energy in the form of the very cold air aloft which we have previously noted and the strong cyclonic vorticity ahead of the deepening major trough compensated for those factors which normally lead to the dissipation of hurricanes. This situation has been quite frequent during the past six or eight years (to 1957) and is now easily recognized by experienced forecasters. Indeed, it was not hurricane Hazel but a new extratropical storm which moved through the North Atlantic States into Canada.

At what point did Hazel become an extratropical storm? That we cannot say. It was strongly under the influence of the intensifying trough to the west when it crossed the coast line. It possessed extreme asymmetry for a tropical cyclone, although it still had a warm core. The western edge of the eye passed east of Myrtle Beach at 9:25 a.m.; the exact time the cold front passed is unknown since the station was abandoned, but it did pass sometime within two hours after the eye, since by 11:28 a.m. the temperature had dropped from 75° F. to 64° F. The center of the hurricane passed just about over Raleigh, North Carolina. A strong cold front and wind shift occurred with the passage of the center and the highest winds followed the cold-front passage. Since the cold air had now reached the center of the hurricane, it is doubtful whether it should any longer be called a tropical storm. By 10:00 p.m. on the fifteenth at 500 mb, the tropical storm had been completely absorbed in the circulation around the deep cold low then over extreme southeastern Illinois.

At least ten stations in North Carolina reported the highest twenty-four-hour rainfall of record in connection with Hazel, with amounts up to more than eleven inches, which is especially amazing in view of the rapid movement of the storm. As Hazel became extratropical in North Carolina, the band of heavy rain shifted to the west of the storm center with comparatively little rain to the east. New twenty-four-hour rainfall records were established in eastern West Virginia, mostly in the Charleston-Martinsville areas, and considerable flooding resulted. Flash floods in the tributary streams of western Maryland were the highest in the memory of the older people. Flooding also occurred in the Pittsburgh, Pennsylvania, section.

This storm which still bore the name Hazel, whether tropical or extratropical, continued its devastating course from Virginia to Lake Ontario, with some $88,630,000 damage and seventy-five more fatalities. Washington, D.C., experienced the highest wind ever recorded there, as Hazel passed a few miles west of the nation's capital, 78 mph for one minute and 98-mph gusts. Half of the individual power and telephone installations in Virginia were out of service for varying periods of time. The one-minute maximum wind of 58 mph and gusts of 98 mph broke all previous records at Wilmington, Delaware. Peak gusts of 94 mph at Philadelphia, 86 mph at Reading, and 80 mph in Harrisburg were recorded in Pennsylvania. The New York Weather Bureau Office reported an all-time local record of 113 mph, although it should be kept in mind that the anemometer is some 450 feet above the street level.

Control towers at the Newark, New Jersey, and LaGuardia airports were abandoned. By the time Hazel moved out over Lake Ontario, she had killed ninety-five persons in the United States and wrought $251,630,000 damage.

Hazel passed over western Lake Ontario at about 11:00 p.m. on the fifteenth, still a very severe storm, and the Toronto disaster was yet to come. Aloft, a marked temperature contrast existed between the deep, cold closed low and the warm maritime tropical air, which by late on the fourteenth covered southeastern Ontario and the northeastern United States seaboard at all levels. A cold front that had been moving across southern Ontario finally came to a halt not far east of the city of Toronto at 7:30 a.m. The front decelerated from 25 mph to no movement at all within six hours.

Hazel, now a deep extratropical storm, passed over the city of Toronto at 11:00 p.m., moving northward at 50 mph. According to Knox [48], the passage of the center over Toronto was attended by a marked variation in temperature and wind between the center of the city and Malton Airport, twelve miles to the west. Malton remained in the cold air west of the center; the temperature rose no higher than 52° F. and the wind backed from northwest 42 mph at 10:30 p.m. to west-southwest 36 mph at 11:30. On the other hand, the city came into the warm sector. The wind at Toronto Island, although of comparable speed, veered from north through east during the passage of the low, and at the Bloor Street meteorological office, which is more or less in the center of the city, the temperature rose to 63° F. Residents of some west-Toronto suburbs about this time reported a distinct lull in the storm, and one suburban observer reported the wind nearly calm, temperature 64° F. and stars occasionally visible. Even extratropical Hazel had an eye!

Knox states the Toronto floods occurring with Hazel resulted from two main factors. Heavy rains had already occurred in the Toronto area from thunderstorms in advance of the very steep cold front. Then the front became stationary, the precipitation pattern shifted from east to west of the front, and, since the frontal surface was very steep, the steady warm-front type of rain was exceptionally heavy and did not stop until the storm passed on the following day. Perhaps in part due to hurricane Hazel, a tremendous supply of moisture was contained in the strong southerly flow over the stationary front, and the combined effect of convergence due to the extratropical development and lift over the steep frontal surface resulted in a record-breaking rainfall in the Toronto area. About eight inches fell immediately west of the city and even larger falls to the north and west. This excessive precipitation fell on a watershed already saturated.

According to Boughner [5] the greatest devastation occurred in the Humber and Credit River valleys and the Etobicoke Creek valley in the densely populated western suburban area of Toronto. There are no flood-control dams on the Humber and the catchment area is generally denuded of trees; thus the natural conditions in the Humber and other similar catchments in the Toronto area were conducive to rapid runoff. There had been considerable construction near the natural watercourse during the past few years, and during the early morning hours of the sixteenth the flood waters rose rapidly, sweeping automobiles off bridges and highways and damaging, destroying, and sweeping away homes and other buildings.

In spite of most excellent warnings, seventy-eight persons died and damage of $100,000,000 was done in this last wild fling of Hazel several thousand miles from the hot, humid region deep in the tropics where she was born. Hazel continued on as a harmless storm after leaving the province of Ontario, passed into the North Atlantic, and was last heard of north of Scandinavia.

Boughner's investigations indicate that out of some 358 Atlantic tropical cyclones during the fifty years from 1900 to 1949, only 25 had any noticeable effect on the weather of southern Ontario and only eight of these caused high winds and/or excessive rain in the province.

Altogether, from the Grenadines in the extreme southeastern Caribbean, across Haiti, and up the east coast of the United States to Canada, Hazel killed between 600 and 1,200 people and damaged property to the extent of $350,400,000. Warnings throughout the storm were unusually good, and the number of fatalities could easily have been many, many times more.

2. Middle Gulf Coast

(LOUISIANA, MISSISSIPPI, AND ALABAMA)

With two exceptions the major hurricanes affecting the middle Gulf coast in the last sixty-three years have all passed through or formed in the Caribbean Sea, moved through the Yucatán Channel or over the extreme northeastern corner of the Yucatán Peninsula, and pursued a broad recurve toward the mouth of the Mississippi River.

During the period 1885 to 1958 there were sixty-two tropical cyclones, twenty-six (42 per cent) of hurricane intensity and thirty-six (58 per cent) not of hurricane intensity, according to the best available information. Thus the middle Gulf coastal section has the highest proportion of comparatively weak tropical cyclones of all the several regions of the hurricane belt. Many of these would develop into hurricanes if they did not reach land so quickly.

The distribution of tropical cyclones in this section by months is shown in Table 21. September is the outstanding hurricane month, having almost twice as many storms as any other month.

TABLE 21
Frequency of Tropical Cyclones (by Months) along the Middle Gulf Coast
(Based on a 74-Year Record Ending in 1958)

	June	July	Aug.	Sept.	Oct.	Nov.	Total
Hurricane Intensity	2	1	5	13	5	0	26
Less than Hurricane Intensity	4	3	10	15	3	1	36
Total	6	4	15	28	8	1	62
Percentage of Total	10	6	24	45	13	2	100

A list of all tropical cyclones occurring in this section can be found in the Appendix. Typical of the rather rare occurrence of extremely severe hurricanes was Audrey (1957).

Hurricane Audrey (1957)

June hurricanes are more likely to reach the Gulf of Mexico coast, particularly Texas, than any other section of the hurricane belt. As a rule these early-season storms are small and not too violent, but once every ten or fifteen years or so, a small but intense hurricane will hit somewhere along the west Gulf coast. On the morning of June 27, 1957, hurricane Audrey, one of the most destructive June hurricanes ever recorded in the United States, struck savagely the coast near the Louisiana–Texas border and particularly in the Cameron–Creole section of Louisiana. Figure 85 indicates the major path of destruction (see page 260).

Hurricane Audrey was reminiscent of an equally fatal storm which, on the night of August 10, 1856, just about a hundred years earlier, completely devastated the fashionable hotel and pleasure resort on Last Island, or Île Dernière as the French call the narrow island lying off the Louisiana coast, 150 miles east of Cameron. During this earlier hurricane, a storm tide swept an estimated four hundred persons to their death. Last Island is now only a haven for pelicans and other sea birds, mute testimony to the fury of the storm which struck a century ago.

Other notable hurricane disasters on the middle Gulf coast are:

1. October 1, 1893, New Orleans, Louisiana; the hurricane was accompanied by a tidal wave and caused the loss of approximately 2,000 lives.

2. September 29, 1915, Mississippi Delta; highest tides of record (to that time) observed on the delta; extreme wind speed was 140 mph, 99 out of 100 buildings destroyed in Leeville; 275 deaths reported.

The existence of a tropical depression in the southwestern Gulf of Mexico was first suspected when upper-air winds showed evidence of a weak circulation over the Bay of Campeche on June 24, 1957. Later in the day additional confirmation was received when the shrimp dock at Brownsville reported that one of their boats in the Gulf of Campeche was experiencing rough weather with a steady wind of 35 to 40 knots, gusts to 55 knots in squalls. At 10:30 p.m. the Hurricane Warning Center at New Orleans issued its first bulletin and arrangements were made for a Navy hurricane hunter to reconnoiter the area the next morning. During the night the circulation intensified steadily, and the next forenoon aircraft reconnaissance found that the storm, while remaining almost stationary in location, had become a full hurricane.

Hurricane Audrey now began a steady northward movement, increasing in size and intensity. During the forenoon of June 26, a Navy reconnaissance plane penetrated the eye of the storm and found a minimum pressure of 973 mb and maximum winds of 90 knots (104 mph), i.e., a hurricane of average intensity. Unfortunately, no additional penetration was made until after the center had moved inland. A radar-tracking flight during the night of the twenty-sixth reported the precipitation as considerably more intense than observed previously. The tanker *Tillamook* found herself in the eye of the hurricane from 4:00 to 5:25 a.m. EST June 27, with a minimum pressure of 973 mb, the same pressure as reported by reconnaissance the previous day. Thus, the

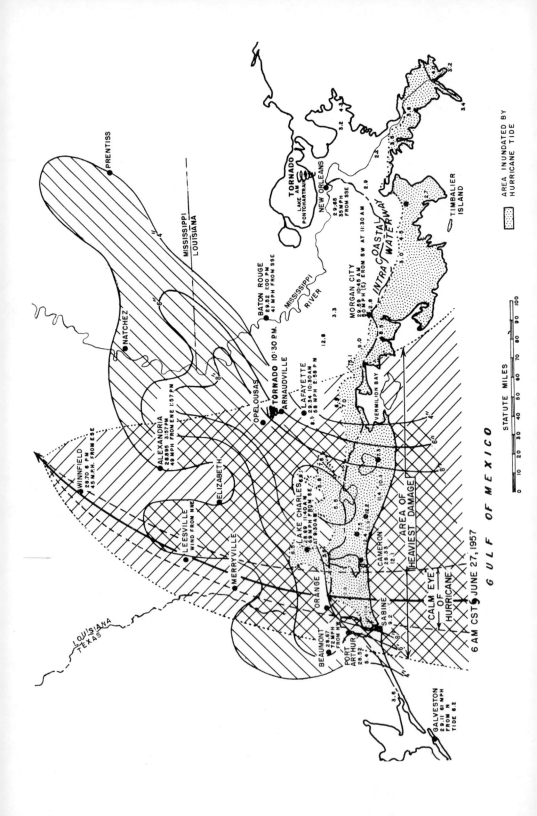

forecaster received conflicting evidence in regard to intensification during the last several hours before the intense inner core of the hurricane
struck the coastal areas with maximum fury.

The exact minimum pressure as the center crossed the coast has not
been determined. The Calcasieu Coast Guard station, twenty miles
east of the storm center, observed 960 mb (28.35 inches) and a slightly
lower reading was observed at Hackberry, slightly closer to the eye.
An analysis of data collected after the storm indicates that between
about 5:00 a.m., when the *Tillamook* was in the eye, and 10:00 a.m.,
when the storm crossed the coast line, pressure in the eye may have
fallen nearly 40 mb. Computations, based on the barometer reading at
Calcasieu, indicate a possible pressure in the eye between 930 mb and
936 mb (27.64 inches).

The highest official wind report was 105 mph at Sulphur, Louisiana,
before the anemometer blew away. However, an unofficial report from
an oil rig gave winds of 180 mph and a pressure of 925 mb. Several
tornadoes were reported in connection with the hurricane, and it is
possible these values may have been associated with a localized disturbance. Four tenders of the Continental Oil Company broke loose from
their moorings and drifted to the coast line during the storm. Personnel on the tenders reported winds up to 150 mph. It is believed they
had some kind of wind-recording devices on board and that these
velocities may be regarded as reasonably accurate. These winds and the
observed tides support a minimum-pressure value under 28.0 inches.

Tides rose along the east-Texas and entire Louisiana coast line,
reaching six feet or more from Sabine Lake to Cocodrie, Louisiana.
The highest tides were approximately 12.0 feet at Calcasieu Pass, 10.6
feet above mean sea level measured from a water mark inside a building
at Cameron, and 9.5 feet above mean sea level at Pecan Island. Tidal
salt water covered all of Cameron and most of Vermilion Parishes and
penetrated far inland in Terrebonne, Lafourche, and Jefferson Parishes.

The New Orleans Weather Bureau issued a hurricane watch for the
Texas and Louisiana coasts at noon on Tuesday, June 25. At 10:00
a.m., Wednesday, the twenty-sixth, hurricane warnings were ordered up

Fig. 85. Destructive Path of Hurricane Audrey, 1957. Wind speeds given are
the fastest mile or the highest one-minute speed. (E) = estimated.
Pressure (inches) is the lowest observed at the point plotted. Tide
heights are in feet above mean sea level, and were measured by the Corps
of Engineers.

along the Louisiana coast. The warning included the following information: *"The hurricane gales will start along the Louisiana coast tonight. Tides are rising and will reach 5 to 8 feet along the Louisiana coast and over Mississippi Sound by late Thursday. All persons in low exposed places should move to higher ground."* This warning was repeated at intervals during the day and following night. At 10:00 p.m. information that the tide might reach nine feet was included in the advisory. During the night it became apparent the storm was accelerating and the time of arrival of the center was speeded up.

The hurricane warnings in connection with this storm were almost perfect except for the acceleration during the twelve hours preceding landfall which was not forecast in the earlier warnings. Hurricanes are notoriously subject to variations in direction and rate of movement, and in this case the accuracy of the warnings were well above the average. Yet, as the hurricane tide surged over the swamplands of coastal Louisiana on that fateful forenoon of Thursday, June 27, some 500 persons were drowned. Why?

Numerous investigations of this disaster have been made by state and federal agencies, newspapers, free-lance writers, and the like. While they have differed from one another to some extent in the assessment of blame, at the same time there has been considerable unanimity in their conclusions. Many felt there was a definite failure of the hurricane forecaster to get his message through to the people he was trying to warn and that the warnings failed to contain a compelling sense of urgency or emergency. The advisories said: "All persons in low and exposed places should move to higher ground." Many people in Cameron lived on property seven to eight feet above sea level several miles from the Gulf, and they did not consider themselves as living in "low and exposed places." They failed to realize how a nine-foot tide could burst upon them with additional waves and swells superimposed upon that tide. The advisories said: "The center will arrive . . . ." There was a general feeling among the people that they did not need to worry or to evacuate until the forecast time of arrival of the center, even though the advisories also said the winds and tides would begin to rise long before. They did not seem to realize the hurricane is half over by the time the center arrives.

There is no question but that a feeling of complacency existed. Like many other towns in the hurricane belt, Cameron had grown very rapidly since the war, but it is interesting that almost all the new residents evacuated and it was the older residents who stayed — and died. During the previous twenty years Cameron had been affected by some nine tropical cyclones, but only one of these was of full hurricane intensity, and that just barely so. The last major hurricane in that area was forty years before. Another in 1886 was remarkably similar to Audrey in its effects. During the recent two decades, many persons in coastal Louisiana lost consciousness of the individuality of hurricanes, their widely varying intensities, and the tremendous differences in winds and tides near the center and on the fringes. That this was a major hurricane with stronger winds and higher tides failed to sink in.

Hurricane Audrey is a lesson for every person and every community in the hurricane area from Brownsville to Boston. A major hurricane can strike anywhere in this area. Read every advisory, every word in the warning, if it applies to your area. Is it a *major* hurricane? Will the forecast tides reach the doorstep of your home? If so, evacuate to a place of safety well above and beyond the area forecast to be reached by the tide. Use some margin of safety — no type of weather forecasting is completely accurate and tides and winds may be even a little worse than forecast. Keep in mind that what happened in the last hurricane is no indication of what may happen in the next one.

Even many months after the hurricane the facts of the inundation in hurricane Audrey are not too clear. Looking at a map of Louisiana, one can consider the coast as the line of low tide. The northern limit of the marsh area may be regarded as the southern continuous limit of the high-tide line. Even though the tide range is only about 2.0 feet in this area, the distance between the low-water elevation and the high-water elevation varies from ten to twenty miles. Most of the land between Lake Charles and the coast is marsh. In the area south of Cameron there are several narrow ridges with elevations about five or six feet. The coast line itself consists of a three- or four-foot ridge.

At a Coast Guard station, located at the southern tip of the island created by Calcasieu Pass and Calcasieu River, the water began to rise at a significant rate by 4:00 a.m. on Thursday morning and rose at the rate of 1.5 feet per hour for several hours. (There was no rapid rise or wave at this point.) Although there is some uncertainty, a value of 11.7 feet has been accepted as the maximum water level at this point. Northward from the shore line there are a series of more or less parallel old sand dunes several miles or more long, a few hundred yards apart, varying in height from three to eight feet and open at the end near the river. A small amount of water entered the troughs between these dunes at their open end from the river, but there was no significant rise of water north of any dune until the water level at the coast reached the top of the dune. However, as soon as this occurred the space between the shoreward dune and the next dune was rapidly filled. Thus, it becomes easy to understand why Cameron, which is situated on a ridge between four and eight feet above sea level and which is protected by several dunes with elevations of five to six feet, would experience a rapid rise after the dune immediately to the south had been topped and why the water in Cameron rose much more rapidly than it did along the open coast. It resembled the situation when a dam gives way, and many residents in the area described it as a wave.

There are several east-west streets in Cameron, and by far the greatest damage was to buildings along the street closest to the Gulf. According to the residents the initial wave moved all the frame houses and buildings from their foundations. As the water built up in depth, the wind-generated waves began to bounce the houses around, and against brick and concrete block structures, damaging them. The wind carried the frame buildings along like sailboats until they disintegrated by battering against other buildings, became water- or mud-logged and sank, or came to rest against some other objects or buildings. The initial wave rushed some ten and one-half miles north of Cameron before feathering out completely.

The town of Creole was virtually destroyed. Only one building, a concrete structure, remained on its foundations, and only four others came to rest within the city limits. East of Creole there was a little community in which only one home was fit to be restored.

The owners, Oliver Boudreau and his wife, escaped death by climbing onto a portion of the roof of their barn. They hung on until its slatted remnants became entangled in the telephone or power lines in front of their home. There they rode out the flood for some twenty-four to thirty hours. The wires were about fifteen to eighteen feet above ground, and at the height of the wave action, one moment the Boudreau's were at the level of or above the telephone wires and the next their feet would touch the ground.

At Grand Chenier, where by and large the houses were considerably better constructed, only about 10 per cent of the homes were completely destroyed.

Some four and one-half miles east of Creole a well-constructed home drifted off its foundations and floated intact for some nine miles. So much mud accumulated in the house that it eventually sank in the marshland to a depth of some five feet. When the water subsided it was impossible to float the house back, and it is now a sumptuous home for rodents and cottonmouth moccasins. Other houses floated as much as twenty and thirty miles from their original location. In this area all graves are at or just below ground level and all caskets are encased in sealed solid-concrete tombs. Many of these concrete tombs floated fifteen to twenty miles.

The exact number of dead will never be known, but five hundred fatalities appears to be a conservative estimate. The total damage has been estimated at $150,000,000, of which $120,000,000 was in Louisiana. Hurricane Audrey became a severe extratropical storm as it moved northeastward through the Ohio Valley and New York State, with additional deaths and damage. Four persons were reported killed, even after it reached Canada.

3. Florida

Florida, jutting like a thumb into the sea between the subtropical Atlantic and the Gulf of Mexico, is the most exposed of all states, since hurricanes approach from the Atlantic to the east, the Carribean to the south, and the Gulf of Mexico to the west. Since it also extends farther southward than any other state, Florida experiences hurricanes which on the average are more intense. Because of their frequency and severity they are a most important factor in the Florida economy.

Two well-defined tracks appear, one composed of storms developing east of the Antilles in August and September, which are usually known as Cape Verde hurricanes because it was earlier thought many formed in that area, and another which includes the late September and October hurricanes, which form in the Caribbean. The first group approaches Florida from the east and, fortuitously perhaps, in this century have affected mostly southern Florida. The second group approaches the state from the south and affects mostly the southern and western portions of the state.

The points of entry and the direction of travel of all Florida hurricanes from 1885 through 1958 are shown in Figure 86. Hurricanes are most frequent in the extreme southern portion of the peninsula and

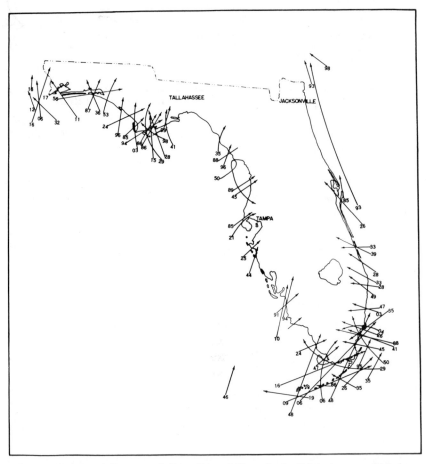

Fig. 86. Points of Entry and Direction of Travel of all hurricanes which have affected Florida from 1885 through 1958. Numerals indicate the years.

in the panhandle section. The low frequency on the northeast coast is probably due to the fact that the direction of the coast line is parallel to the mean storm track and if the storm recurves sufficiently to miss the southeast coast it will also miss the northeast coast. The apparent low frequency on the Gulf coast between Cedar Key and St. Marks is not believed real. This area is very sparsely settled and the exact point where many of the storm centers reached the coast line is not known, so there has been a natural tendency to place the track too close to the· nearest observing point.

During the seventy-four years from 1885 to 1958, inclusive, 119 tropical cyclones of all intensities have entered or affected Florida significantly. Some 71 (60 per cent) are known to have been of full hurricane intensity, and only 48 (40 per cent) were of less than hurricane force or doubtful. Table 22 shows the distribution of these storms throughout the seventy-four years. The average for the period is 1.6 storms per year, but individual years range from none to as many as five. The state has never gone longer than two years without a tropical cyclone. The longest period since 1880 without a *major* hurricane is nine years which began in 1951 and is still continuing at the time this book is written (1959). The table indicates a greater frequency of storms beginning about 1924 and continuing through 1953. In this thirty-year period there were 52 storms, or an average of 1.7 per year; or taking the six-year period 1932 to 1937, when 15 storms occurred, the average was 2.5 per year. During the fifteen-year period 1885 to 1899 the average was also 2.5 per year. Between 1900 and 1923 the average was only 1.0 per year. Increases or decreases of hurricane frequency of the order of 100 per cent or more over periods in excess of a decade would indicate the existence of some sort of cycle.

The average frequency for different sections of the state of Florida varies greatly. Mitchell [64] has shown that the frequency per 100 miles of coast line for storms of hurricane force is 1 in 20.0 years on the east coast of Florida and 1 in 13.9 years on the west coast.[1] The greater frequency found on the west coast by Mitchell was due to the relatively large number of storms that occurred between Cedar Keys and Mobile during the period of his study, which has since been altered to some extent by later statistics. Only seven or eight storms of hurricane force have passed inland on the west coast from south of Cedar Keys to Fort Myers in seventy-four years. Tampa and St. Petersburg, located in this coastal area, have been more nearly exempt from hurricanes than any of the other cities on the west coast of Florida. On the extreme northeast coast from St. Augustine to Jacksonville, no tropical cyclone of full hurricane force has been experienced during our period of record. The city of Jacksonville is unique in that it is the only large city in Florida and indeed the only large city on the Atlantic coast from Boston southward which has never had sustained winds of hurricane force in a tropical cyclone in modern times. This is probably fortuitous,

---

[1] Higher hurricane incidence in the 1930's and 1940's has increased these ratios somewhat.

TABLE 22
Frequency of Tropical Cyclones in Florida
(by Years), 1885-1958

Year	Of Known Hurricane Intensity	Not or of Doubtful Hurricane Intensity	Total	Year	Of Known Hurricane Intensity	Not or of Doubtful Hurricane Intensity	Total
1885	3	0	3	1923	0	1	1
1886	3	1	4	1924	2	1	3
1887	1	1	2				
1888	2	1	3	1925	1	0	1
1889	1	1	2	1926	3	0	3
				1927	0	0	0
1890	0	0	0	1928	3	0	3
1891	1	1	2	1929	1	0	1
1892	0	2	2				
1893	3	2	5	1930	0	1	1
1894	2	0	2	1931	0	0	0
				1932	1	1	2
1895	1	3	4	1933	2	2	4
1896	3	0	3	1934	0	0	0
1897	0	1	1				
1898	2	0	2	1935	3	0	3
1899	1	2	3	1936	1	2	3
				1937	0	3	3
1900	0	1	1	1938	0	1	1
1901	0	2	2	1939	1	1	2
1902	0	1	1				
1903	1	0	1	1940	0	0	0
1904	1	0	1	1941	1	1	2
				1942	0	0	0
1905	0	0	0	1943	0	0	0
1906	3	1	4	1944	1	0	1
1907	0	1	1				
1908	0	0	0	1945	2	1	3
1909	1	0	1	1946	1	1	2
				1947	2	1	3
1910	1	0	1	1948	2	0	2
1911	1	0	1	1949	1	0	1
1912	1	0	1				
1913	0	0	0	1950	2	1	3
1914	0	0	0	1951	0	1	1
				1952	0	1	1
1915	1	0	1	1953	1	2	3
1916	3	0	3	1954	0	0	0
1917	1	0	1				
1918	0	0	0	1955	0	0	0
1919	1	0	1	1956	1	0	1
				1957	0	3	3
1920	0	1	1	1958	0	1	1
1921	1	0	1				
1922	0	0	0	Total	71	48	119

since the weighted averages indicate the probability of a hurricane force wind there once in about every fifty years.

From Key West to Miami, because of the exposed location in and near the Florida Straits, and in the Pensacola area, because of the tendency of many Gulf hurricanes to recurve in that direction, hurricanes have been experienced with greater frequency than in any other section of the state. Table 23, prepared by Norton [73], indicates approximately the chances in any given year for a hurricane to occur in, and adjacent to, several of the principal coastal cities of Florida. The table is based on a record of some seventy-five years, which, however, is too short a time to indicate expectancy with any high degree of accuracy for so variable a phenomenon.

TABLE 23
Chances of Hurricane-Force Winds in Florida in Any Given Year*

Cities	Chances	Cities	Chances
Jacksonville	1 in 50	Key West	1 in 7
Daytona Beach	1 in 40	Fort Myers	1 in 12
Melbourne–Vero Beach	1 in 20	Tampa–St. Petersburg	1 in 20
Palm Beach	1 in 10	Apalachicola–St. Marks	1 in 15
Miami	1 in 7	Pensacola	1 in 10

*Weighted averages based on all available records.

As shown by Table 24, approximately the same number of hurricanes has occurred in Florida in September and October from 1885 to 1958. No October storm has moved inland on the east coast with two exceptions: the Yankee hurricane of 1935 which approached from the northeast and the severe hurricane of 1950 which moved in over Miami from the south-southeast. All others have either struck the western or extreme southern coasts. There is a decided tendency for hurricanes to form over the western Caribbean Sea or southeastern Gulf of Mexico near the end of the hurricane season, and most October and November storms that have affected Florida had their origin in that area. And looking at it another way, October hurricanes appearing in the western Caribbean and southeastern Gulf are more likely to strike Florida than hurricanes in any other area and in any other month.

A list of all known tropical cyclones affecting Florida can be found in the Appendix.

The Miami hurricane of September 18, 1926, was typical of the

TABLE 24
Frequency of Tropical Cyclones in Florida (by Months)
(Based on 74-Year Record Ending in 1958)

	Feb.	June	July	Aug.	Sept.	Oct.	Nov.	Total
Hurricane Intensity	0	6	6	13	21	22	3	71
Doubtful, or Not Hurricane Intensity	1	7	2	7	17	13	1	48
Total	1	13	8	20	38	35	4	119
Percentage of Total	1	10	7	17	32	30	3	100

occasional very severe storms that can strike almost any portion of the Florida coast line.

On the afternoon of September 14, telegraphic reports indicated the existence of a tropical cyclone about two hundred miles northeast of St. Kitts in the Antilles. The storm moved rapidly west-northwestward and passed near Turks Island on the afternoon of the sixteenth with winds of at least 150 mph. Observations in the Cape Verdes in the days prior to the first appearance of this hurricane failed to indicate any unusual conditions. On the other hand, this storm had all the characteristics of the typical Cape Verde hurricane, and no doubt it reached hurricane intensity somewhere between longitudes 30° and 60°.

During the twenty-four hours prior to the arrival of the hurricane at Miami, it moved at the rate of 19 mph, which is considerably above normal for the latitude. The forecaster labored under a considerable handicap, since the 1:00 p.m. special observation from Nassau on the seventeenth was the last and only report of any kind received east of the Florida coast on that date. R. W. Gray, Meteorologist in Charge at Miami at that time, describes the hurricane as coming "with great suddenness." The fall in barometer during the day on the seventeenth was quite moderate. There were no unusual meteorological conditions to herald the approach of the storm and the heavy rain that frequently precedes a hurricane did not set in until after midnight, when the wind began blowing a fresh gale. At 10:00 p.m. of the seventeenth the barometer began to fall rapidly, and from midnight to 6:45 a.m. on the eighteenth it fell at the rate of 00.28 inch per hour. From 5:30 to 6:10 a.m. it dropped 00.40 inch to a sea-level pressure of 27.61 inches. After passage of the eye, the barometer rose even more rapidly than it had fallen, and by noon it had reached 29.30 inches.

The center of the storm passed over the central and southern portions of Miami. Over the extreme northern part of Miami Beach there was no pronounced lull. At the Weather Bureau Office in downtown Miami, the wind dropped to 10 mph at 6:30 a.m. At the same time, the velocity at Allison Hospital (now St. Francis) about halfway up Miami Beach and five and one-half miles away, was 80 mph. The lull lasted thirty-five minutes, during which time the streets became crowded with people. Many lives were lost when the other and stronger side of the hurricane suddenly struck. The distribution of wreckage indicated greater damage was done during the second half than during the first half. The anemometer on Allison Hospital blew away at 8:12 a.m., when it was recording 120 mph. A maximum wind of at least 135 mph is estimated.

The storm tide on the Miami side of Biscayne Bay was about eight feet, while at Miami Beach it was between eight and nine feet. The water front at Miami was flooded for two to three blocks back from the bay, and low parts of the city near Miami River were also inundated. After the storm, the entire bay-front section was strewn with boats ranging in size from small pleasure craft to large schooners and barges. Water rose in hotels and residences near the bay to a depth of three to five feet. The storm tide occurred with the shift of the wind from east to southeast, following the arrival of the center of the storm. In the Miami River, the tide came in the form of a bore, and it left a mass of wreckage from boats that had sought safe anchorage.

According to Gray the intensity of the storm and the wreckage it left cannot adequately be described. The continuous roar of the wind, the crash of falling buildings, flying debris, breaking plate glass, the shriek of fire apparatus and ambulances that rendered assistance until the streets became impassable, the terrifically driven rain that came in sheets as dense as fog, and the electric flashes from live wires have left the memory of a fearful night in the minds of many thousands that were in the storm area.

The number of fatalities in Florida was in excess of two hundred and total damage amounted to $111,775,000.

4. New England

New England is outside the main hurricane belt, yet the most destructive, although not the most intense, hurricanes of record have occurred here. Since the pilgrims landed at Plymouth Rock in 1620, some eight hurricanes of extreme intensity (most of these storms have been placed in this classification on the basis of tides and not wind) have struck New England, four of these since 1938. The dates are 1635, 1638, 1815, 1938, 1944, 1954 (two), and 1955. The 1955 storm is classified as "extreme" only because of the accompanying floods, since winds and tides were of little consequence. The hurricane of 1869 appears to almost merit inclusion in the "extreme" classification. There are four other hurricanes, in addition to the one in 1869, which can be described as major: 1723, 1761, 1821, and 1866. The remaining New England hurricanes were either minimal or minor, comprising those that brush Cape Cod as the centers move northeastward some distance offshore and others affecting the area as they move northeastward some distance inland after becoming extratropical. Damage from these storms is usually small, although many of the coastal storms are quite severe out to sea.

The first in a series of recent hurricanes of extreme intensity struck New England on September 21, 1938, and was called by some "The Long Island Express" because of its unusually rapid movement as it approached Long Island and the Connecticut coast. No really extreme hurricane had hit New England since 1815. Until 1954, the 1938 New England hurricane held the all-time record for storm property damage in the United States, and probably the world as well, of approximately one third of a billion dollars. If the current dollar value were used, the damage was exceeded only by that of Diane — the billion-dollar hurricane of 1955.

This 1938 hurricane was first encountered late on September 16 in latitude 21° 12″N and longitude 53° 46″W by the Brazilian SS *Alegrete,* which reported a barometer reading of 28.31 inches and hurricane winds. Thus, it was already a severe hurricane when first reported and it probably reached hurricane intensity some 15° west of the Cape Verdes; however, the easterly wave when it passed through the Cape Verdes was only slightly more unstable than usual. During the period of the eighteenth to the twenty-first the SS *Corales* reported a barometer reading of 27.90 inches and the SS *Carinthia,* 27.85. The Bellport Coast Guard Station on Long Island reported 27.94 inches; therefore it would appear the central pressure remained about the same — slightly below 28.00 inches — from the time the hurricane was first discovered east-northeast of the Leeward Islands until it made landfall on the New England coast.

The hurricane moved on a normal west-northwestward course north of the Antilles, averaging slightly more than 20 mph. For a short time it threatened Florida, but on the nineteenth and twentieth it slowed to about 15 mph and recurved to the northward around the western side of the Azores-Bermuda HIGH. On the evening of the twentieth it began to accelerate until its forward progress was in excess of 50 mph for awhile on the twenty-first. Off the New Jersey coast it seems momentarily to have speeded up to 70 mph.

At about 7:00 a.m. on the twenty-first the center was some 100 miles east of Cape Hatteras, where a barometer reading of 29.30 inches and a wind of 50 mph from the northwest was observed. At 1:00 p.m. the center was some 100 miles east-southeast of Atlantic City, where the barometer read 28.99 inches and the wind was west at 61 mph. Brentwood on Long Island experienced the relatively calm eye between 1:50 p.m. and 2:50 p.m. At New Haven, Connecticut, the lowest pressure was 28.11 at 3:50 p.m. and at Hartford 28.04 inches at 4:30 p.m. The hurricane continued rapidly northward through Vermont, with Burlington reporting 28.68 inches pressure at 8:00 p.m.

During its passage over New England the eye became distorted along a north-south axis and was in excess of fifty miles long. The isobars had spread out considerably, reducing the pressure gradient, and destructive winds extended only a short distance west of the eye. However, for a distance of 100 miles on the east side of the storm its rapid motion, or a portion of it, added to the gradient wind, produced some very high winds. Block Island reported SE 82 mph; Boston, S 73; Nantucket, SE 52; New Haven, NE 38; Providence, SW 87; Mt. Washington, 136 mph; and Blue Hill Observatory at Milton, Massachusetts, 121 mph with 183 mph in gusts. Most of these maximum velocities were averaged over a period of five minutes. Momentary gusts would be 50 per cent or more higher.

Damage to property and shipping was very heavy in southern New England and to a lesser extent in the northern portion of this area. In some of the bays, particularly Providence Bay, the water level rose some fifteen to twenty-five feet above mean low tide, and a large proportion of the business section of Providence was inundated as it has been in similar situations since the city was first built. About 600 persons were killed and 2,000 injured. Approximately 100,000 persons faced some economic loss. The breakdown by states of damage and fatalities is as follows:

State	Deaths	Damage
Maine	0	$ 135,000
New Hampshire	14	22,000,000
Vermont	7	15,000,000
Massachusetts	99	100,000,000
Rhode Island	380	125,000,000
Connecticut	85	125,000,000

Brooks [7] in discussing the hurricane hazard in New York and New England says:

The conditions under which a West Indian hurricane will strike our North Atlantic coast with full vigor are that 1) the general pressure gradient from east to west must be great throughout the troposphere; 2) the terrain in front of the storm must be well bathed in moist tropical air; and 3) the storm remains over the open sea all the way from the West Indies to its northern landfall. Without the rapid progressive movement the storm would have a chance to lose much of its whirling velocity over the cooler waters north of the Gulf Stream. The presence of moist tropical air over the region helps to prevent a too rapid reduction in energy. Friction with the land is a quick reducer of the velocity of the wind at the surface, causing a decrease in both the deflective effect of the earth's rotation and the centrifugal force of the whirling wind. This results in a considerable flow of air across the isobars into the low pressure center and, consequently, in a marked reduction of the pressure gradient, which is immediately felt on all sides of the storm. In order to have one of these hurricanes strike the North Atlantic coast from the open sea it is, of course, first necessary that the general winds in the middle levels of the troposphere shall be directed essentially northward or perhaps northwestward, so as to give the storm a movement from the south or southeast.

Winston [115] in discussing the movement of Carol stated: "This acceleration and more northerly course of the storm were related to the development and intensification of a long wave trough of large amplitude farther west over the eastern U.S. than it had been in the preceding weeks. Inspection of the charts with the concepts of vorticity advection in mind leads one to conclude qualitatively that a region of strong cyclonic relative vorticity (made up of both strong cyclonic shear and cyclonic curvature) near Lake Superior was advected southeastward to form the low over the Lower Lakes on the 31st."

If only the hurricane-wind- and surge-producing storms are considered, the general tropospheric situation described by Winston in the foregoing paragraph must be present if a major hurricane is to strike New England. Associated with this, a pool of unusually cold air will almost always, if not invariably, be present to intensify and retrograde the long wave trough, and although the necessary upper-air data prior to 1954 are not available to the authors, it is believed that the conditions just described have been present in every major New England hurricane. Otherwise it would not be possible for the necessary acceleration described by Brooks to occur. Thus, unless favorable conditions for the acceleration of the movement of the hurricane to 35 mph and preferably to 40 to 45 mph or more north of Cape Hatteras are present, no *major* hurricane will strike New England.

The majority of the most severe New England hurricanes followed very similar tracks, moving into the field of observation northeast of the Antilles, gradually recurving to the vicinity of Cape Hatteras, and then accelerating very rapidly toward New England. Although the September 3, 1821, hurricane caused the tide to rise thirteen feet in one hour along the water front of New York City, apparently it was small and not extremely severe in New England. However, several writers list this storm in the extreme classification. Its track is also suspect, since the rate of movement on September 1 and 2 exceeds anything ever observed since in that area.

Two storms of tropical origin, since the beginning of record, have affected New England in July, ten in August, fifteen in September, and nine in October. No tropical storms are known to have affected this area in any other month. All the known tropical storms significantly affecting New England are listed in the Appendix.

5. Middle Atlantic States

(FROM VIRGINIA TO NEW YORK)

The Middle Atlantic States, with the possible exception of the Virginia Capes, are normally considered outside the hurricane belt, and no hurricanes of extreme intensity and very few major tropical cyclones have occurred in this area. Almost no hurricanes have moved inland from the ocean on a track normal to the coast. Therefore most of the tropical cyclones affecting this area either move northward with their centers off the coast or are moving north or northeastward inside the coast after having made landfall some distance to the south. The most severe hurricanes reaching this area are those moving inland over eastern North Carolina. Hurricane Hazel (1954) is typical of the major hurricanes affecting this area and is described in the "South Atlantic States" section.

All the known tropical cyclones affecting the Middle Atlantic States are listed in the Appendix. Many became extratropical during their passage through this section and some may have become so before reaching here. The seasonal distribution is the same as in New England.

6. Texas

From 1885 to 1958 most of the tropical cyclones influencing Texas, it is believed, have been listed. During this seventy-four-year period there have been thirty-four (56 per cent) storms classified as hurricanes and twenty-seven (44 per cent) as not of hurricane force. In any one year there is a 70 per cent chance that Texas will be affected by a tropical cyclone and a 40 percent chance that it will have a full hurricane.

An analysis by the Army Corps of Engineers [105] on the basis of known storms indicates that the incidence of Texas hurricanes alternated from 1829 to 1955 between 1 every 9.0 years and 1 every 1.4 years. When hurricane incidence is analyzed by decades the peaks are separated by lows every thirty to forty years. Also, according to the same source, in the hundred years ending in 1949 hurricanes affected the Texas coast in every month from June to October. Two November hurricanes are known, one in 1839 and one in the sixteenth century, when a merchant fleet was destroyed on Galveston Island (other sources

TABLE 25

Frequency of Tropical Cyclones in Texas (by Months)
(Based on 74-Year Record Ending in 1958)

	June	July	Aug.	Sept.	Oct.	Total
Hurricane Intensity	6	4	11	10	3	34
Less than Hurricane Intensity	8	4	5	8	2	27
Total	14	8	16	18	5	61
Percentage	23	13	26	30	8	100

say the wreck occurred elsewhere). The Texas hurricane frequency by months is shown in Table 25. Storms are rare after October 1. A list of all known Texas tropical cyclones can be found in the Appendix.

On September 8, 1900, the most disastrous hurricane wave ever reported in the United States occurred at Galveston, Texas, killing 6,000 human beings. It is graphically described by the late Dr. I. M. Cline, who was in charge of the Weather Bureau there at the time [25].

I reached home and found the water around my residence waist deep. I at once went to work assisting people, who were not securely located, into my residence, until forty or fifty persons were housed therein. About 6:30 p.m. Mr. J. L. Cline [his brother] who had left Mr. Blagden at the office to look after the instruments, reached my residence, where he found the water neck deep. He informed me that the barometer had fallen below 29.00 inches; that no further messages could be gotten off on account of all wires being down, and that he had advised everyone he could see to go to the center of the city; also, that he thought we had better make an attempt in that direction. At this time, however, the roofs of houses and timbers were flying through the streets as though they were paper, and it appeared suicidal to attempt a journey through the flying timbers. Many people were killed by flying timbers about this time while endeavoring to escape to town.

The water rose at a steady rate from 3 p.m. until about 7:30 p.m. when there was a sudden rise of about four feet in as many seconds. I was standing at my front door, which was partly open, watching the water, which was flowing with great rapidity from east to west. The water at this time was about eight inches deep in my residence, and the sudden rise of 4 feet brought it above my waist before I could change my position. The water had now reached a stage 10 feet above the ground at Rosenberg Avenue [Twenty-fifth Street] and Q Street, where my residence stood. The ground was 5.2 feet elevation, which made the tide 15.2 feet. The tide rose the next hour, between 7:30 and 8:30 p.m., nearly five feet additional, making a total tide in that locality of about twenty feet. These observations were carefully taken and represent to within a few tenths of a foot the true conditions. Other personal observations in my vicinity confirm these estimates. The tide, however, on the bay or north side of the city did not obtain a height of more than 15 feet. It is possible that there was 5 feet of backwater on the Gulf side as a result of debris accumulating four to six blocks inland. Debris was piled eight to fifteen feet in height. By 8 p.m. a number of houses had drifted up and lodged to the east and southeast of my residence, and these with the force of the waves acted as a battering ram against which it was impossible for any building to stand for any length of time, and at 8:30 p.m., my residence went down with about fifty persons who had sought it for safety, and all but eighteen were hurled into eternity. Among the lost was my wife, who never rose above the water after the wreck of the building. I was nearly drowned and became unconscious, but recovered through being crushed by timbers and found myself clinging to my youngest child, who had gone down with myself and wife. My brother joined me five minutes later with my other two children, and with them and a woman and child we picked up from the raging waters, we drifted for three hours, landing 300 yards from where we started. There were two hours that we did not see a house nor any person, and from the swell we inferred that we were drifting to sea, which, in view of the northeast wind then blowing, was more than probable. During the last hour that we were drifting, which was with southeast and south winds, the wreckage on which we were floating knocked several residences to pieces. When we landed about 11:30 p.m., by climbing over floating debris to a residence on Twenty-eighth Street and Avenue P, the water had fallen 4 feet. It continued falling, and on the following morning the Gulf was nearly normal. While we were drifting we had to protect ourselves from the flying timbers by holding planks between us and the wind, and with this protection we were frequently knocked great distances. Many persons were killed on top of the drifting debris by flying timbers after they had escaped from their wrecked homes. In order to keep on top of the floating masses of wrecked buildings one had to be constantly on the lookout and continually climbing from drift to drift. Hundreds of people had similar experiences.

Sunday, September 9, 1900, revealed one of the most horrible sights that ever a civilized people looked upon. About three thousand homes, nearly half of the residence portion of Galveston, had been completely swept out of existence, and probably more than six thousand people had passed from life to death during that dreadful night. The correct number of those who perished will probably never be known, for many entire families are missing. Where 20,000 people lived on the 8th, not a house remained on the 9th, and who occupied the houses may, in many instances, never be known.

The Galveston hurricane of 1900 is the subject of a recent most interesting book by John Edward Weems [112].

15

RESEARCH — A LOOK TO THE FUTURE

THE READER WHO HAS REACHED THIS CHAPTER, UN-
doubtedly will have gained the impression that meteorologists still
have a great deal to learn about hurricanes.* Such an impression
would be a true one. There are many unanswered questions in meteorology, and in the field of tropical meteorology (which includes the
study of hurricanes) in particular. Although man has always been
vitally concerned with weather in virtually everything he does (many
of the ancient writers, notably Aristotle, speculated about it), meteorology as a science is scarcely a hundred years old. Progress has been
slow and tedious, and understandably so, since meteorology is the most
complex of the physical sciences. Modern meteorology may be said to
date back to World War I, when Scandinavian meteorologists under
the leadership of Vilhelm Bjerknes developed the air-mass theory. Up
to World War II all the major weather services were located in the
Temperate zones and almost all research was devoted to the problems
of the middle latitudes. Due to military requirements of World War II,
some remarkable progress was made in tropical meteorology under the
leadership of Drs. Herbert Riehl and Clarence Palmer.

Very few hurricanes in recent years have reached the United States
mainland without adequate warning. Among these few exceptions
have been those that have accelerated with extreme rapidity, and
perhaps New England has been the chief sufferer in this respect. More
often in other sections the public is overwarned and indeed, in the
present stage of the science of meteorology, the hurricane forecaster
must operate with a certain margin of safety if the public is always to
be adequately warned.

Techniques for forecasting the motion of hurricanes have been
developed by both dynamical and statistical means. These techniques

---

*References for this chapter are listed at the end of the chapter.

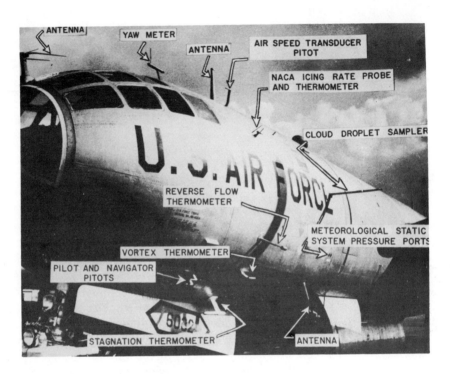

Fig. 87. B–50 Aircraft and Special Instruments used by National Hurricane Research Project, 1956–1958.

have resulted in some improvement in the accuracy of hurricane forecasts during the past few years, and the average errors for twenty-four hour forecasts are within acceptable limits in the tropical regions where there are enough data to permit the application of objective techniques. It is only in the areas where the cyclone movement is controlled by middle latitude systems or in areas of very little upper-air data that the average forecast errors become large. In a recent paper Dunn [10] showed that the accuracy of the official hurricane forecasts within a given area is highly dependent upon the density of the upper-air network for that area. This probably indicates that further improvement in hurricane forecasting may depend upon the establishment of additional upper-air sounding stations in oceanic regions.

The United States Weather Bureau since 1956 has pressed forward with an accelerated program of hurricane research on a broad scale. It embraces the following projects:

1. The National Hurricane Research Project, which is using specially instrumented aircraft (Figure 87) to investigate the internal mechanisms of the hurricane and its environmental problems.

2. The development of experimental prediction models for use with electronic computers in forecasting hurricane movement.

3. The use of coastal radar to analyze hurricane structure and hurricane micromovements and to improve short-term forecasts.

4. Investigations of the nature and cause of coastal inundations resulting from hurricanes and the development of storm-surge forecasting techniques.

5. Further studies of the role of planetary circulations in the development and recurvature of hurricanes.

6. Studies of the variation in the incidence of hurricanes along coastal areas and the relation of these variations to possible climatic changes.

7. Correlation of hurricane characteristics with excessive rainfall and development of improved quantitative rainfall forecasting.

8. Statistical studies of regional frequencies of hurricanes and of selected characteristics and correlation of these with the probabilities of occurrence in various regions.

In the early summer of 1956, the Weather Bureau in co-operation with the Air Force, the Navy, leading universities, and other research organizations inaugurated the National Hurricane Research Project. The nation's best technical talent has been enlisted to try to find out as much as possible about hurricane formation and development. The first director of the project was Dr. Robert H. Simpson, who stated that aircraft investigations have the following specific objectives:

1. To investigate the distribution of energy in the hurricane and to develop an accurate energy budget for the storm.

2. To determine the specific mechanism which causes the hurricane to move.

3. To determine the part which internal forces within the storm play in causing the hurricane to move.

4. To determine whether there are any practicable means by which man can successfully reorder the internal forces to materially affect the movement of hurricanes.

The Department of Defense provided two B-50's and one B-47 for use of the project. The B-50's were used for reconnaissance up to

25,000 feet and the B-47 up to 40,000 feet. All three aircraft were equipped with the latest and best available meteorological measuring and recording equipment. At the end of the 1958 season the Department of Defense reduced its support of the project. To fill the gap, the Weather Bureau leased two DC-6's, one B-26, and one B-57 aircraft, which are operated by civilian crews. These planes began operations in 1960. A new agency, the Research Flight Facility, was created, and it has assumed the responsibilities associated with the operation of the research aircraft. To supplement the data collected by aircraft a relatively dense network of radiosonde stations in the Caribbean has been maintained. The Dominican Republic, the Netherland Antilles, the French West Indies, Jamaica, Colombia, and Mexico have all cooperated in the project. It is expected another rawinsonde station in Barbados will begin operation in the near future.

Prior to the 1962 hurricane season, research aircraft concentrated upon the collection of the data needed to describe the structure of the hurricane vortex, its life cycle, and the energy transformations which take place during its life cycle. The achievement of these goals required the measurement of detailed data at several levels on a synoptic scale. By the end of the 1961 season it was apparent that considerable progress had been made in understanding the synoptic scale features of the hurricane's structure, dynamics, and kinematics, but that a complete understanding of the hurricane mechanism could not be achieved until the role of the convective scale phenomenon was better understood. Accordingly the 1962 season brought a slight change in emphasis insofar as data collection was concerned, and one of the primary objectives was the collection of data needed to describe and understand the dynamics and thermodynamics of the rainbands of the hurricane.

In the spring of 1959 the National Hurricane Research Project was combined with the Hurricane Forecast Center in Miami to form the National Hurricane Center. The joint facility is a center for research in tropical meteorology and the hurricane problem and for study and training at an advanced level. It provides space and limited facilities and personnel to support collaborative work by visiting scientists and by co-operating research institutions interested in tropical meteorology. Institutions such as Florida State University, Colorado State University, and the University of Chicago have utilized the center in connection with extension schools of tropical meteorology or as participants in the hurricane and allied research programs.

Recent Advances in Hurricane Research

Since the organization of the National Hurricane Research Project in 1956, there has been significant progress in several aspects of hurricane research. While much of this progress has been made at the project itself, many outstanding contributions have been made by other agencies, both in this country and abroad (principally in Japan), either independently or in co-operation with the project. It is evident, however, that a large portion of the progress may be attributed to the stimulus given to hurricane research by the project. This stimulus has been either in the form of data collection and processing, renewed emphasis on the hurricane problem, or of actual financial support in some cases. The progress has been of several forms, and while the entire field of research in tropical meteorology cannot be covered a brief discussion of the more important advances in recent years will follow.

A major accomplishment since 1956 has been the collection of a vast amount of research data by aircraft. Many of these measurements have been made at various levels within the high energy portion of the cyclone where, prior to 1956, very few detailed observations had been recorded. At the end of the 1962 hurricane season research missions had been flown into more than twenty-five tropical cyclones. Many of these were multiplane missions and data were collected at more than one level at the same time. These research flights represent several hundred hours flying time and many million bits of recorded data. The data include measurements of winds, temperatures, pressures, humidity, cloud and radar photographs, measurements of liquid water content, and other parameters of interest to the research meteorologist. Most of the data are recorded automatically on the aircraft. During the early years of the project, data were recorded on punch cards; now magnetic tape is used. The data are subsequently processed by high-speed electronic computers and made available for study by research workers both at Miami and elsewhere. A partial listing of available research flight data is contained in a recent inventory issued by the project [18].

With the aid of the data collected, a fairly complete description of the structure of the mature hurricane is now available. In some respects the new data confirmed or simply filled in the details of structural features previously suspected or partially known. In others, they forced revision of earlier ideas. Of the latter, perhaps the most important is the finding that the warm core of the hurricane is much smaller in diameter than had been thought previously. The region of very large positive temperature anomalies extends for only a few miles outside the wall cloud [8]. These anomalies have been shown to be slightly negative outside the cyclone center at 5,000 feet and below and increasingly positive with height, reaching a maximum near 40,000 feet in the core. In Daisy (1958), temperaturess at the 34,000-foot level were more than 12° C above the mean tropical atmosphere. It is now known that the wall cloud which surrounds the eye is almost vertical, in contrast to earlier ideas which had postulated an appreciable outward slope. The vertical variation of the wind below 20,000 feet has been found to be slight [19].

The structure of the rainbands can also now be described. Gentry [16] found that the thermal structure of the bands was quite variable and strong temperature gradients were found both normal to and along the bands. Wind variations along the normal to the bands were also found to be significant. Diffusion between the bands and the environmental air was found to be greater than had been previously suspected. It has been found that the liquid water content of clouds in hurricanes is surprisingly low [1]. In only a few cases was it over 3 or 4 grams per cubic meter. The bulk of the measurements (based on the 1957-58 data) were below 1 or 2 grams per cubic meter. Water content consistent with the undiluted adiabatic cloud model was seldom found, and almost all the measurements were less than 50 per cent of that expected from such a model.

The small scale variability of the various elements (wind, temperature, pressure, etc.) along a radius as indicated by Figure 50 has been found to be a typical characteristic of the mature hurricane. Asymmetries in the isotach pattern (Figure 51) is also a common feature; pressure fields, however, are more symmetrical as long as a mature hurricane is surrounded by air possessing near normal tropical properties [27]. The strongest pressure gradients occur within the eye wall. The aircraft data show individual variations in the depth of the inflow layer, but confirm the existence of the three layers identified by E. Jordan [21]. These are the lower-level inflow layers, the middle layer where as a rule no significant inflow or outflow occurs, and the upper outflow layer.

The additional experimental data have led to significant advances in understanding the energy cycle of the hurricane and to the development of physical models. The extreme importance of processes in the inflow layer and at the air-sea interface has received increased attention. Malkus and Riehl [28] have formulated a semi-theoretical model of the inflow layer. It demonstrated the importance of the oceanic heat source by showing that the vertical flux of latent and sensible heat from the ocean is sufficient to provide the energy required to maintain the hurrican circulation. They showed that kinetic energy is produced from the oceanic heat source at a maximum rate during isothermal and horizontal motion into the cyclone, and they also demonstrated that the maximum winds near the core of a hurricane are essentially a function of the air-sea temperature difference. Malkus and Riehl compared their model with aircraft data and the overall correspondence was very good.

Later, Rosenthal [38] extended the Malkus-Riehl model to include the vertical variations of radial wind speed and of the density of air. He also removed a radial discontinuity in the divergence pattern implied by the earlier model. His results showed that the air parcels within the inflow layer must be heated at a rate which exceeds that possible when the release of latent heat alone was the heating mechanism. The magnitude of this heating depended upon the vertical wind shear. The Rosenthal model was more realistic than the Malkus-Riehl model and it also emphasized the importance of a surface heat source.

The processes which contribute to the dissipation of a tropical cyclone have also been related to the exchange of energy between the hurricane and the lower boundary. It has been suggested by several people, notably Byers [6] and Riehl [37], that a hurricane weakens over land because the oceanic heat source is cut off. Another view holds that increased friction over land causes the cyclone to fill up. Miller [32] has recently investigated in some detail the energy transformations which took place over a three-day period before and after hurricane Donna moved inland over Florida in 1960. He was able to show that within a few hours after the center moved inland that the rate of frictional dissipation of kinetic energy at the ground was less than it had been over water just prior to landfall. Over water the vertical fluxes of latent and sensible heat were very large, comparable to the fluxes postulated by Malkus and Riehl in their model. Over land, however, the vertical fluxes of heat were very nearly zero, such that a horizontal trajectory at the ground followed very closely a moist adiabatic path. Thermodynamic considerations lead to the conclusion that the cut off of the oceanic heat source was the major cause of filling over land and that friction was of minor importance in the filling process. These results may be applicable to the problem of forecasting the dissipation of hurricanes over land or over cold water. Miller also demonstrated that the inflow layer (which extended from the surface to 700 mb in Donna) generated enough kinetic energy to maintain the circulation of the entire cyclone. Part of the energy produced by the inflow layer was used up in overcoming surface and internal friction and a portion was exported to the environment.

In another paper, Malkus and Riehl [29] used the Daisy (1958) flight data to perform certain calculations including a volume integration of the kinetic energy equation. They were able to show that on the day the hurricane reached maturity the production plus the inward transport of kinetic energy greatly exceeded that dissipated by friction at the surface. This implied that the internal friction within the free atmosphere near the core of the cyclone was very large; the calculations showed that internal friction inside the 20 nautical-mile radius was about three times the surface friction. This internal friction Malkus and Riehl attributed to vertical eddies. Gray [17] investigated the balance of forces inside a number of hurricanes, also using flight data to perform his calculations. He evaluated the various terms in the gradient wind equation and found that in most cases gradient balance did not exist. He also found that internal friction plays an important role in balancing the radial equation of motion. The average magnitude of the radial frictional acceleration was about 25 to 30 per cent of the pressure gradient force and 35 to 40 per cent of the Coriolis and centrifugal accelerations. Gray also attributed these frictional forces to vertical eddies.

The magnitude of the internal frictional dissipation indicated by the results in the foregoing paragraph are much larger than had been suspected previously. If subsequent calculations show them to be correct, internal friction may be an important constraint to hurricane development. A partial verification of the Malkus-Riehl calculations has been obtained by Miller [31], who used the Helene (1958) flight data to perform a similar set of calculations. These results showed that the internal friction in Helene was somewhat less than it was in Daisy, but that near the core internal friction was substantially greater than surface friction. Another interesting result of Miller's calculations was that the coefficient of turbulent exchange for heat and moisture at the air-sea interface was somewhat larger than the coefficient for the exchange of momentum. This result is tentative and needs to be verified.

During the past year or two, significant progress has been made toward the formulation of a physical-mathematical theory of hurricane formation. In a recent survey of the field, Spar [44] summarized the older attempts to formulate a theory of hurricane formation. He traced the history in this area from the earliest qualitative theories through the more recent quantitative, linear theories and finally through the unsuccessful attempts by Syono [45] and Kasahara [22] to obtain numerical hurricane solutions to the dynamical equations which govern the atmosphere's behavior. The principal difficulty in the formulation of such problems is the theoretical treatment of the release of latent heat (which is the primary source of energy for the hurricane). In particular, if a theoretical model allows latent heat to be released by pseudoadiabatic ascent, the solutions yielded are more representative of cumulus clouds than they are of hurricanes. Spar pointed out that successful theories of hurricane development would come only after methods of uncoupling the interaction between the convective scale and the hurricane scale had been devised so that release of latent heat could be included in theoretical models by parametric representation.

Recent numerical experiments include the work of Rosenthal [40] in which condensation heating was treated by large-scale pseudo-adiabatic ascent. He was able to control the overgrowth of small scale disturbances by strictly numerical techniques. Rosenthal's initial conditions consisted of a weak, warm-core tropical cyclone. The integration showed initial deepening as a result of condensation heating. The condensation heating produced a strong barclinic field and, eventually, a neutral lapse rate. In the final phase of the experiment, the cyclone continued to intensify as a result of baroclinic overturning. These results closely follow those of Yanai [46] and indicate that Yanai's hypothesis is dynamically plausible. The major difficulty with Rosenthal's work is that development took place too rapidly to be realistic.

Kasahara's [23] most recent numerical experiment on hurricane development contained numerical solutions for a model in which the convective release of latent heat was taken as a known function of the space coordinates and as a constant in time. His initial conditions contained no rotational motion and the numerical solution covered about ten days of real time. At the end of that time hurricane force winds had developed. Kasahara intends to continue his work by allowing the heating function to vary in time in response to the large-scale motion. He will treat the convective elements by probabilistic methods similar to those employed by statistical mechanics.

Ooyama [34] hypothesized that the rate of heat production in a vertical column is determined by the convergence of water vapor in the surface layer. The large scale circulation was represented by a quasi-balanced circular vortex in two layers of incompressible homogeneous fluids plus a separately treated surface-layer. The transverse circulation in the vortex was induced by internal and surface friction and by simulated heat sources in such a way that the quasi-balanced state was maintained for all time. Free convective clouds in the natural cyclone were considered to act collectively as the heat source for the large scale fields. Ooyama's indirect treatment of the moist convective process seems to avoid the difficulty in the growth rate of convective clouds encountered in earlier studies by Syono [45] and Kasahara [22], in which the latent heat release was evaluated directly from the large-scale vertical motion. Ooyama was able to develop hurricane force winds after eight days of real time.

Kuo [26] and Charney [7] have proposed methods by which Ooyama's approach could be extended to more realistic models of the tropical atmosphere. They were concerned with treating condensation through the establishment of a water budget for the cloud system, with emphasis on the convergence of water vapor in the boundary layer and subsequent upward flux of this vapor into the base of the cloud system. These investigations have not yet reached the point where actual integrations of their models have been carried out.

Other recent numerical studies indicate progress in the theoretical treatment of other problems in tropical meteorology. Aranson [4] has extended earlier theories of tropical disturbances to include the latitudinal variations of the Coriolis parameter and the baroclinicity of the tropical atmosphere. Growing disturbances have, therefore, baroclinicity as well as latent heat to feed on and this has been shown to favor the growth of the synoptic scale perturbations. Estoque [13] has demonstrated that the main features of the radial and vertical velocity fields in the mature hurricane can be deduced theoretically if the temperature and tangential velocity fields are known.

The objective analysis of constant pressure charts has now been extended to tropical regions. Bedient, Moore, and Vederman [5] have prepared objective wind analyses at several levels over the tropical

Pacific Ocean by means of an IBM 704 computer. The machine analyses were compared with hand analyses and the results seem to be somewhat encouraging. These objective analyses have been used as the input data for a barotropic forecast model [41] and the results are such that some optimism has been generated with regard to the possibility of extending machine techniques to include routine forecasts for tropical regions. Objective analyses, on an experimental basis are also being prepared at the National Hurricane Research Project for the Caribbean, Gulf of Mexico, and adjacent areas of the Atlantic Ocean. The analysis area may be extended whenever data become available from currently data-void regions.

The problem of forecasting the development of a tropical cyclone is still by and large an unsolved problem. While forecasters are now able to identify the situations which are favorable for cyclogenesis, they are not yet able to say definitely which of these situations will produce a hurricane — actually few of them do. On the other hand, all of the numerical experiments cited above, which started out with initial conditions favorable for development, resulted in the formation of a hurricane after varying lengths of time. This indicates that neither from a theoretical nor an empirical standpoint have the triggering mechanisms or constraints on hurricane development been rigorously formulated. Some progress, however, has been made since Chapter 11 of this book was written.

Colón and Nightingale [9] have investigated the circulation patterns at the 200-mb level in connection with development. They found that the location of the low level disturbance under a southerly or southeasterly flow at 200 mb (i.e., there was a 200-mb anticyclone to the east or northeast of the surface disturbance) was most favorable for intensification. They investigated forty developing cases and their work may be considered a statistical verification of the earlier conclusions of Miller (Chapter 11).

About fifteen years ago Sawyer [42] proposed that dynamic instability in the upper troposphere could act as a triggering mechanism for hurricane development. This hypothesis has been revived recently by Alaka [2], who has been able to show by the use of the aircraft data that regions of dynamic instability may be found in the upper troposphere over low-level disturbances both before and following development. This has lead Alaka to postulate that dynamic instability is the triggering mechanism for hurricane development. Other investigators

[39, 47] have questioned this conclusion on the ground that pure inertial instability is too small and acts too slowly to permit it to play an important role in the formation of hurricanes.

Following a recent study of typhoon formation, Yanai [46] has suggested that the process of development may be divided into three stages. The first stage is the easterly wave, the "pre-existing disturbance" that is always listed as a prerequisite for development. These disturbances are usually cold core. The second stage is the formation of the warm core. The third stage is the period of rapid intensification. Prior to Yanai's work the warm core had generally been considered as a result of the development and not as a cause, although from time to time various people have suggested that the baroclinic field associated with a warm core should be favorable for development, notably Margules [30], and Sawyer [42], and Kleinschmidt [24].

Yanai's discovery that the major development comes after the formation of the warm core (further warming must obviously proceed along with the additional deepening) has led others to seek evidence of upper-level warming as an indication that cyclogenesis is about to take place. At the National Hurricane Research Project, the 500- to 200-mb thickness chart was prepared during the hurricane season on a routine basis during the past three years. Zipser [48] recently examined charts for evidence of upper-level warming prior to the development of a tropical cyclone. He found that, with one exception, all the developing cases he examined were preceded by above normal thickness in the 500- to 200-mb layer at least twenty-four hours before the most significant development. A control group of nondeveloping cases, however, showed that above normal thickness within the 500- to 200-mb layer was not always accompanied by development and that Yanai's criterion for development must be listed as necessary but not sufficient. Portig [35] has also found that upper-level warming usually preceded the development of tropical cyclones.

A final useful indication of development is the low inflow into the incipent disturbance. A more or less linear relationship between the low-level inflow and the central pressures of mature hurricanes, discovered by Krueger [25], has led to the use of the low-level inflow as a possible predictor of formation. Riehl et al. [36] have found that hurricane formation in the Gulf of Mexico is usually preceded by a low-level inflow (when averaged around the Gulf) of at least 1.7 knots. The main difficulty in using the low-level inflow as a predictor is in measuring it. Over the Atlantic one must resort to the use of ship reports composited about the disturbance for a period of about twenty-four hours in order to obtain a reliable estimate of the mass flow. In spite of these difficulties, however, work is now under way on attempts to predict development on a statistical basis by making use of the upper-level thermal field and the low-level inflow.

While it is expected that eventually all hurricane forecasts will be made by numerical techniques based on dynamical models, at present numerical forecasts made by currently operational models do not verify quite as well as those made by subjective or statistical means. Whether this is due to lack of data over the oceans or to the use of unrealistic predictive models is uncertain. Research on the improvement of numerical prediction models continues, and at the same time attempts to improve hurricane forecasts by statistical means are being made. A new set of prediction equations for forecasting the motion of a hurricane for periods up to forty-eight hours by twelve-hour steps has been developed, and these are now being tested operationally. These equations are based on data at the surface and 500-mb levels. Plans are now being formulated to use data from other levels plus some thermal parameters in an effort to improve these prediction equations. The results obtained by the use of these equations will be compared with the forecasts made by improved numerical models and, whenever a clear trend in favor of numerical prediction has been established, statistical prediction will be abandoned.

Satellite Meteorology

Easily the most spectacular development in meteorology during recent years has been the use of artificial earth satellites for photographing cloud systems and measuring the outgoing long-wave radiation from the earth's surface, or from the tops of thick cloud cover. Since the launching of Tiros I in April, 1960 (see pages 172-73) and the detection of the first tropical cyclone east of Australia, additional and more sophisticated weather satellites have been launched, with Tiros VI having been sent aloft in the summer of 1963. The more advanced Nimbus is scheduled for launching in 1954. A typical satellite photograph of a tropical cyclone is shown in Figure 88.

Over much of the tropical oceans, conventional weather observations

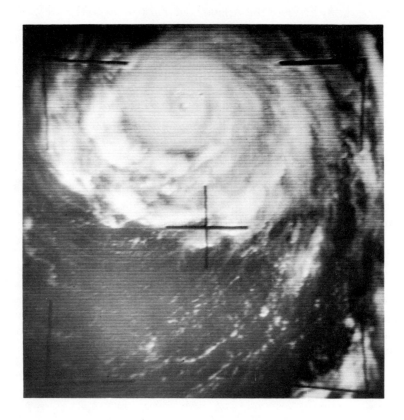

Fig. 88. Tiros V photograph of Typhoon Ruth, taken August 18, 1962, when the hurricane was about 300 miles south-southeast of Tokyo. The eye of the typhoon is visible in the lower left of the picture. (Courtesy U.S. Weather Bureau)

are usually insufficient or missing; hence the use of weather satellites is a particularly valuable aid in the detection and tracking of weather disturbances. The satellite pictures offer unusual opportunities for the study of the broad scale features of the circulations associated with these disturbances. In the Atlantic the first hurricane to be discovered by a weather satellite was Anna which formed during July, 1961. Later in the year hurricanes Betsy, Carla, Debbie, and Esther were photographed by Tiros III. In 1962, which was an inactive hurricane year, the contributions of Tiros V were less spectacular. It appears [11], however, that the disturbances from which Alma, Celia, and Daisy eventually developed were first observed by satellites. Becky, an eastern Atlantic tropical cyclone which did not reach hurricane intensity, was discovered by the satellite.

Detailed analyses of some of the photographs of hurricanes and other weather disturbances have shown that some more important features of the cyclone's structure and circulation can be detected by satellites [14]. Many of these features are not new, but the fact that they can be recognized on satellite photographs may lead to the development of models of these weather systems which can be incorporated into numerical schemes for objective analysis in the tropics. Among the more important features recognized by satellites are:

1. Marked clear channels (indicative of strong subsidence) between the rim of the high-cloud shield and the convective bands.

2. A pre-hurricane squall line (previously detected by conventional radar) exterior to the high-cloud shield.

3. Extensive areas of convective, cirrus generating cloudiness, extending hundreds of miles equatorward from the cyclone area.

4. Secondary vortices, sometimes linked to the hurricane.

The intertropical convergence zone (ITC) has also been identified and studied by means of satellite photographs [20]. These data show that the convective activity along the ITC is quite variable. At times it is weak and the ITC does not appear as a continuously identifiable line by any means. At other times the intense convective clouds and small vortices along the ITC are quite easily recognizable. The overall structure and activity of the ITC as seen by satellites seem to confirm the descriptions given on pages 28-30.

The current Tiros satellites have the capability of determining the temperatures of the underlying radiating surfaces. The principal radiation from regions covered by heavy clouds goes out from the cloud tops, whereas in regions of relatively clear skies much of the outgoing radiation originates at or near the surface of the earth. This fact permits the rough determination of the tops of the clouds as seen by Tiros. In the vicinity of developing tropical cyclones radiation temperatures of the order of -40° C have been detected; these indicate cloud tops up to 40,000 to 50,000 feet. Hence the use of radiation data in conjunction with the cloud photographs may permit the early detection of areas of potential cyclone development even before the characteristic spiral structure has formed.

To facilitate the use of satellite data in locating and tracking hurricanes in the Atlantic area, a direct read-out station for the reception of satellite photographs was installed at the National Hurricane Center in Miami in 1963, as well as at other centers in New Orleans, Washington, D.C., and San Juan. The main difficulty in using the satellite photographs for tracking hurricanes has been that over the oceans the photographs could be fixed with reference to the surface of the earth occasionally with an accuracy of only about 2 degrees of latitude. However, the more advanced models in the Tiros series have been modified, and it is expected that the probable error in the location of cyclone centers by satellite photographs will be greatly reduced during the 1964 hurricane season.

Hurricane Control

It has been suggested that hurricanes be seeded with dry ice or silver iodide for the purpose of either diverting or dissipating them. The first attempt to do this was apparently made in the hurricane of October 9-15, 1947. This hurricane passed over western Cuba, and thence across extreme southern Florida, where it was attended by an unusual electrical display and torrential rains. After it passed out to sea and was moving northeastward off the coast of Georgia, the cyclone was seeded. Within twenty-four hours the hurricane had apparently made a sharp turn to the west, and it eventually crossed the coast line near Savannah. Later, however, a study by Mook et al. [33], including a considerable amount of new data, showed conclusively that the hurricane had already turned sharply toward the west before the seeding took place, and therefore the seeding could not possibly have been responsible for the turn.

It is possible that if a certain portion of a hurricane were seeded, a concentration of energy could develop in one quadrant which might alter the course of the cyclone. The National Hurricane Research Project made four hurricane-seeding attempts in 1958. The seeding of hurricane Daisy on August 25 with silver iodide was successful; the other attempts were failures due to malfunctioning of equipment. There were no immediately obvious consequences.

In September, 1961, the Weather Bureau, U.S. Navy, and the National Science Foundation organized Project Stormfury, under the direction of Dr. Robert H. Simpson. Stormfury was designed to carry out a series of experiments which would test the hypotheses involving the release of small energy sources which might trigger changes in the structure and mechanism of a hurricane in such a way that would modify and reduce its destructive character. Two cloud seeding experiments were conducted in hurricane Esther on two consecutive days. Pyrotechnic generators, dropped from aircraft in the tops of clouds, released vertical plumes of silver iodide which were then distributed downstream by the hurricane circulation. Results were monitored by research aircraft which maintained continuous radar coverage of the test area and measured change in the kinetic energy before and after the seeding. The results of the seeding operations have been summarized by Simpson et al. [43]:

> A marked reduction in the reflectivity of 10 cm radar energy was observed in the test area after the silver iodide was released. Also the kinetic energy diminished. The initial experiments have provided interesting but by no means conclusive results. The change in the reflectivity of 10 cm radar energy is difficult to explain unless it was due to the rapid transformation of supercooled liquid water to ice. However, a portion of the radar energy was reflected from the clouds below the freezing level where such a transformation could not have occurred.
>
> On the 16th there was evidence that kinetic energy may have been diffused outward after the seeding, and maximum winds reduced by about 10 percent for a two hour period. These changes could have occurred from natural fluctuations in structure and intensity of the hurricane. However, after several additional experiments it should be possible to determine whether the results from the experiment of September 16 are repeatable and the tentative conclusions justified. If so, it should be feasible to extend the scope of the experiment to determine whether destructive winds in the hurricane can be reduced progressively by successive injections of silver iodide.

The results of the Esther experiments (as well as the earlier seeding attempts) should not be viewed with undue optimism. No definite answers to the questions about the possibility of altering the destructive forces of the hurricane have been found. But the ultimate prospects for eventual hurricane control should not be discounted. A beginning has been made; many more experiments and more basic research are needed to obtain the final answers to these questions.

The energy released by a hurricane is almost beyond belief, and once our knowledge of the structure, energy budget, mechanics of formation, dissipation, and movement are complete, it may develop that the energy of a hurricane can be used to start a chain reaction which will cause the storm to destroy itself. In fact, it may be that the only method of control may lie within the hurricane itself, simply because no other source of energy is great enough to make much impression on a well-developed tropical cyclone. Eventually some such method of hurricane control may be found, but even so its application may not be wise. First, hurricanes bring many benefits as well as destruction, mainly in the form of rains which may eventually result in more than the overall economic loss wrought by the floods, winds, and sea action. Second, the hurricane may be a rather essential cog in the general circulation of the atmosphere, for it serves as one very important way in which the heat balance between the tropics and the polar regions is maintained.

The tropics and subtropics receive more heat from the sun than they lose by radiation, whereas other regions of the earth lose more than they receive. Thus, heat must be transported poleward from the lower latitudes to prevent gradual cooling of the poles and gradual warming of the equatorial regions. Hurricanes provide one means of maintaining this balance, although they are not the only means nor in fact the most important. Perhaps, when other methods of maintaining the heat balance begin to fail and heat accumulates in the tropics, hurricanes occur. If hurricane control were successful and none were allowed to go through their full life cycle, nature would undoubtedly find some other method of maintaining the heat balance, and who can say that this new method might not be even more disastrous than the hurricane?

Some Unsolved Problems in Tropical Meteorology

Although the preceding pages of this chapter are intended only to be a brief summary of the hurricane research that has been done recently, it is obvious that significant progress has been made during the past few years. However, as there is still much to be learned about tropical meteorology, this chapter will conclude by calling attention to a few of the unsolved problems. It is hoped that these may receive the concentrated attention of research meteorologists.

One of the most urgent of the unsolved problems is that of hurricane development. In this field considerable progress has been made, but meteorologists are not yet able to specify both the necessary and sufficient conditions for cyclogenesis. The exact nature of the triggering mechanism or mechanisms cannot be stated explicitly. The precise manner in which cold-core disturbances are changed to the warm-core hurricane is not completely understood. This is undoubtedly due in part to the fact that most hurricanes form in regions where data are very scarce. Hence, the establishment of observational networks to collect data which would be required to describe the processes which contribute to hurricane formation must also be listed as an unsolved problem. The complicated interaction between processes of different scales (from convective to synoptic scale) is not very well understood. Both scales appear to be important, but not much is known about the mutual interaction and feed-back processes which result in hurricane formation. Numerical models of hurricane development are also incomplete and need to be improved. A completely successful numerical model, for example, would be extremely useful to Project Stormfury's hurricane modification experiments.

The source of energy for the hurricane is mainly the release of latent heat. This energy enters the hurricane circulation by means of evaporation from the oceans. Sensible heat is also added to the atmosphere by direct contact with the water. At the same time surface friction slows down the winds. The exact values for the various exchange coefficients for moisture, heat, and momentum are now well known, but the manner in which they vary with the wind speed (over water) and the stability of the atmosphere is not clearly defined. The vertical variation of the wind speed through the lowest few hundred feet above the surface (both over the water and over the ground) is not known for winds of hurricane force. This knowledge is of fundamental interest in understanding the vertical exchange process and of practical importance to engineers who design buildings. The solution of the problems may well require new data as well as the revision of theories of turbulence. The exact magnitude and importance of internal friction in hurricanes needs further attention.

The general circulation of the tropical atmosphere has not been completely described. The simple meridional cell is an over-simplification which is valid only in the mean; it is not applicable over all the tropics. Models (physical and numerical) of this circulation should be developed. The exact nature of the interaction between the disturbances of the lower troposphere with those of the upper troposphere is not completely understood. In some cases they seem to act independently of each other.

Many of the easterly waves do not conform to Riehl's classical model, for example, and a better understanding of how the surface wave is connected (or if it is connected) with the 200-mb circulation patterns is needed.

Weather in the tropics is substantially a reflection of disturbances of synoptic scale. Little is known about the frequency of the various types of disturbances over a major portion of the tropical regions. Even less is known about their structure, modes of development, life cycles, and typical weather patterns associated with them. In these areas, satellite photographs should be much help. Of particular importance are the disturbances along the intertropical convergence zone. These may be important in interhemispheric exchanges. The magnitude of these exchanges is not known, but they may well be significant.

With the advent of satellite measurements, the importance of the outgoing long-wave radiation has received considerable attention. Some unexpected variations in the magnitude of this radiation in the tropics have been detected. The role of differential radiation in the development and maintenance of tropical weather systems (including hurricanes) should be explored. The use of radiation data in locating potential cyclogenetic areas in the tropics should be extended.

It is not expected that the answers to all these problems (the list could be greatly extended) will be found soon. It is hoped that the accumulation of data heretofore unavailable will greatly accelerate progress both in our understanding of the physical processes of the hurricane and in forecasting hurricane growth, movement, and decay. Beyond question some of the problems that confront the hurricane forecaster will be solved, and given the necessary manpower and financial backing, the complete solutions could eventually be found, although it might well require several generations to fully realize that goal.

References

1. Ackerman, B., 1963: Liquid Water Content in Hurricanes. National Hurricane Research Project, Report No. 62, 41 pp.
2. Alaka, M., 1961: The Occurrence of Anomalous Winds and Their Significance. Mon. Wea. Rev., *89*, 482-494.
3. Alaka, M., 1963: On the Nature of the Triggering Mechanism in Hurricane Formation. Paper presented at the Third Conference on Hurricanes and Tropical Meteorology, Mexico City, D.F., June 6-12, 1963.
4. Aranson, G., 1963: The Growth of Incipient Disturbances of Synoptic Scale in the Tropics. Paper presented at the Third Conference on Hurricanes and Tropical Meteorology, Mexico City, D.F., June 6-12, 1963.
5. Bedient, H.A., Moore, P.R., and Vederman, J., 1963: Computer Analysis in the Tropics. Paper presented at the Third Conference on Hurricanes and Tropical Meteorology, Mexico City, D.F., June 6-12, 1963.
6. Byers, H.R., 1959: General Meteorology. McGraw Hill Book Co., New York and London, 540 pp.
7. Charney, J., 1963: The Dynamics of Hurricane Formation. Paper presented at the Third Conference on Hurricanes and Tropical Meteorology, Mexico City, D.F., June 6-12, 1963.
8. Colon, J.A., and Staff, 1961: On the Structure of Hurricane Daisy (1958). National Hurricane Research Project, Report No. 48, 102 pp.
9. Colon, J., and Nightingale, W.R., 1963: Development of Tropical Cyclones in Relation to Circulation Patterns at the 200 Millibar Level. Mon. Wea. Rev., *91*, 329-336.
10. Dunn, G.E., 1962: Hurricane Prediction. Paper presented at Amer. Met. Soc. Annual Meeting, New York, Jan. 22, 1962.
11. Dunn, G.E., and Staff, 1962: The Hurricane Season of 1961. Mon. Wea. Rev., *90*, 107-119.
12. Dunn, G.E., and Staff, 1963: The Hurricane Season of 1962. Mon. Wea. Rev., *91*, 199-207.
13. Estoque, M.A., 1963: Some Numerical Studies of Tropical Cyclones. Paper presented at the Third Conference on Hurricanes and Tropical Meteorology, Mexico City, D.F., June 6-12, 1963.
14. Fett, R.W., 1963: Details of Hurricane Structure Revealed by Satellite Photographs. Paper presented at the Third Conference on Hurricanes and Tropical Meteorology, Mexico City, D.F., June 6-12, 1963.
15. Fritz, S., 1962: Satellite Pictures and the Origin of Hurricane Anna. Mon. Wea. Rev., *90*, 507-513.
16. Gentry, R.C., 1963: The Role of the Rainbands in Hurricanes. Paper presented at the Third Conference on Hurricanes and Tropical Meteorology, Mexico City, D.F., June 6-12, 1963.
17. Gray, W., 1962: On the Balance of Forces and Radial Accelerations in Hurricanes. National Hurricane Research Project, Report No. 54, 72 pp.
18. Hawkins, H.F., Christensen, F.E., Pearce, S.C., and Staff, 1962: Inventory Use, and Availability of National Hurricane Research Project Data

Gathered by Aircraft. National Hurricane Research Project, Report No. 52, 358 pp.

19. Hawkins, H.F., 1962: Vertical Wind Profiles in Hurricanes. National Hurricane Research Project, Report No. 55, 16 pp.

20. Johnson, H.M., 1963: The Nature of the Intertropical Convergence as Revealed by Tiros Weather Satellites. Paper presented at the Third Conference on Hurricanes and Tropical Meteorology, Mexico City, D.F., June 6-12, 1963.

21. Jordan, E., 1952: An Observational Study of the Upper Wind Circulation Around Tropical Storms. J. Met., 9, 340-346.

22. Kasahara, A., 1961: A Numerical Experiment of the Development of Tropical Cyclones. J. Met., 19, 259-282.

23. Kasahara, A., 1963: Numerical Experiments on the Development of a Tropical Cyclone (II). Paper presented at the Third Conference on Hurricanes and Tropical Meteorology, Mexico City, D.F., June 6-12, 1963.

24. Kleinschmidt, E., 1951: Grundlagen einer Theorie der tropischen Zyklonen. Arch. Meteor. Goephys. Bioklim., A4, 53-72.

25. Krueger, D.W., 1959: A Relation Between the Mass Circulation Through Hurricanes and Their Intensity. Bull. Amer. Met. Soc., 40, 182-189.

26. Kuo, H.L., 1963: A Balanced and Unbalanced Dynamic Model for the Study of Hurricane Development. Paper presented at the Third Conference on Hurricanes and Tropical Meteorology, Mexico City, D.F., June 6-12, 1963.

27. La Seur, N., 1963: The Structure of Hurricanes—A Survey. Paper presented at the Third Conference on Hurricanes and Tropical Meteorology, Mexico City, D.F., June 6-12, 1963.

28. Malkus, J.S., and Riehl, H., 1959: On the Dynamics and Energy Transformations in Steady State Hurricanes. National Hurricane Research Project, Report No. 31, 31 pp.

29. Malkus, J.S., and Riehl, H., 1961: Some Aspects of Hurricane Daisy, 1958. National Hurricane Research Project, Report No. 46, 64 pp.

30. Margules, M., 1906: Zur Sturmtheorie, Met. Zeit, 23, 491-497.

31. Miller, B.I., 1962: On the Momentum and Energy Balance of Hurricane Helene (1958), National Research Hurricane Project, Report No. 53, 19 pp.

32. Miller, B.I., 1963: On the Filling of Tropical Cyclones Over Land. Paper presented at the Third Conference on Hurricanes and Tropical Meteorology, Mexico City, D.F., June 6-12, 1963.

33. Mook, C.P., Hoover, E.W., and Hoover, R.A., 1957: An Analysis of the Movement of the Hurricane off the East Coast of the U.S., October 12-14, 1947. Mon. Wea. Rev., 85, 243-248.

34. Ooyama, K., 1963: A Dynamical Model for the Study of Tropical Cyclone Development. Paper presented at the Third Conference on Hurricanes and Tropical Meteorology, Mexico City, D.F., June 6-12, 1963.

35. Portig, W.H., 1963: Atmospheric Conditions Immediately Prior to the Formation of Tropical Revolving Storms. Paper presented at the Third Con-

ference on Hurricanes and Tropical Meteorology, Mexico City, D.F., June 6-12, 1963.

36. Riehl, H., Baer, F., and Viegas, K., 1962: Prediction of Hurricane Formation in the Gulf of Mexico. Third Technical Report, prepared for the American Petroleum Institute, 27 pp.

37. Riehl, H., 1954: Tropical Meteorology. McGraw-Hill Book Co., New York and London, 392 pp.

38. Rosenthal, S.L., 1961: Concerning the Mechanics and Thermodynamics of the Inflow Layer of the Mature Hurricane. National Hurricane Research Project, Report No. 47, 31 pp.

39. Rosentahl, S.L., 1962: A Linear Analysis of the Combined Effects of Static and Dynamic Instability on the Initiation of Tropical Cyclones. National Hurricane Research Project, unpublished MS, 22 pp.

40. Rosentahl, S.L., 1963: Some Numerical Studies of Circularly Symmetric Motions with Applications to Tropical Cyclones. Paper presented at the Third Conference on Hurricanes and Tropical Meteorology, Mexico City, D. F., June 6-12, 1963.

41. Rosentahl, S.L., 1963: A Barotropic Model for Prediction in the Tropics. Paper presented at U.S.-Asian Military Symposium, John Hay Air Force Base, Phillipine Islands, Feb. 3-7, 1963.

42. Sawyer, J.S., 1947: Notes on the Theory of Tropical Cyclones. Quart. J. Roy. Met. Soc., 73, 101-126.

43. Simpson, R.H., Ahrens, M.R., and Decker, R.D., 1963: A Cloud Seeding Experiment in Hurricane Esther, 1961. National Hurricane Research Project, Report No. 60, 30 pp.

44. Spar, J., 1963: A Survey of Hurricane Development. Paper presented at the Third Conference on Hurricanes and Tropical Meteorology, Mexico City, D.F., June 6-12, 1963.

45. Syono, S., 1953: On the Formation of Tropical Cyclones. Tellus, 5, 179-195.

46. Yanai, M., 1961: A Detailed Analysis of Typhoon Formation. J. Met. Soc. Japan, 39, 187-214.

47. Yanai, M., 1961: Dynamical Aspects of Typhoon Formation. J. Met. Soc., Japan, 39, 282-309.

48. Zipser, E., 1964: On the Thermal Structure of Developing Tropical Cyclones. National Hurricane Research Project, Report No. 67, 23 pp.

APPENDIX A

A BRIEF GLOSSARY OF METEOROLOGICAL TERMS USED IN THIS BOOK

Air Mass — A large body of air with approximately horizontal homogeneity, i.e., its physical properties, level for level, are about the same over a wide area; sometimes an air mass may cover more than one million square miles.

Anemometer — An instrument for measuring the wind speed.

Anticyclogenesis — The formation of a new anticyclone or the increase in the strength of an existing anticyclone.

Anticyclone — An area of high pressure with the highest pressure at the center. The wind blows spirally outward in a clockwise fashion in the Northern Hemisphere and counterclockwise in the Southern Hemisphere. Commonly referred to as simply a HIGH.

Azimuth Angle — The arc of the horizon intercepted between a given point and an adopted zero point. In pilot-balloon observations made by the Weather Bureau, north is the zero point, east is 90°, etc.

Baroclinic — An atmospheric state in which the pressure depends upon other variables in addition to density: the isobaric surfaces do not, therefore, coincide with the surfaces of constant specific volume. In a baroclinic atmosphere the variation of the wind with elevation may be quite large.

Barogram — A trace made by a barograph.

Barograph — A barometer which makes a continuous record of the atmospheric pressure and pressure changes.

Barotropic — A state of the atmosphere in which isobaric surfaces coincide with surfaces of equal density. In a barotropic atmosphere the variation of the wind with elevation is slight.

Blocking — The retardation or deflection of eastward-moving pressure centers due to the stagnation of a HIGH (less frequently a LOW) in their paths.

Circulation — In a broad sense the general or primary wind-flow patterns of the atmosphere. It consists of the polar easterlies, the westerlies of the middle latitudes, and the easterlies south of the subtropical HIGH cells. The term is also applied to more localized wind patterns.

Convergence — The increase of mass within a layer of the atmosphere when the winds are such that there is net horizontal inflow into the layer.

Coriolis Force — The apparent force which, due to the rotation of the earth, causes winds in the Northern Hemisphere to be deflected to the right, and in the Southern Hemisphere to the left. It is a function of the sine of the latitude, being zero at the equator and a maximum at the poles.

Cyclogenesis — The processes which create a new cyclone or intensify an existing one.

Cyclone — An area of low pressure (with the lowest pressure at the center), around which the winds blow counterclockwise in the Northern Hemisphere and clockwise in the Southern Hemisphere. Commonly referred to as a LOW.

Deepening — The process by which the central pressure of a system (usually a LOW) decreases with time. Deepening is related to cyclogenesis and results in an increase in the wind speeds around a low-pressure area.

Divergence — In fluid motion, a net outflow of mass across the boundary surfaces of a volume. It is the opposite of convergence.

Doldrums — The equatorial belt of calms or light variable winds, lying between the trade-wind systems of the two hemispheres.

Dropsonde — A small radio transmitter, which is dropped from an aircraft by means of a parachute. As it falls, it transmits back to a receiving apparatus in the plane data on temperatures, pressure, and relative humidity.

Dry Adiabatic Lapse Rate — The rate at which dry air warms or cools during adiabatic descent and ascent. It is about 1° C. per 100 meters, or about 1° F. per 188 feet.

Easterly Wave — A trough of low pressure embedded in the easterly winds to the south of the subtropical high-pressure areas. The wave moves from east to west.

Entrainment — The mixing of environmental air with the rising currents that are present inside convective clouds, e.g., cumulus or cumulonimbus.

Eye of a Hurricane — The area in the center of a tropical cyclone. It is characterized by light winds (complete calm is very rare), little or no cloudiness or precipitation. Aloft, the temperature of the eye is much warmer than the surrounding atmosphere, and the air inside the eye is much drier.

Fetch — The length of the distance over water along which the wind blows in a relatively straight path. The height of wind waves are a function of the fetch.

Filling — The process (opposite to deepening) by which the central pressure of a cyclone increases.

Forerunner — The rise of the water level along a coast which occurs at some considerable distance ahead of the arrival of the center of the storm. It is partially produced by swells.

Gale — A wind of 40 mph or more.

Gradient — The rate of change in the value of any element with distance in any given direction.

Hurricane — A tropical cyclone with wind velocity of 74 mph or higher. Occasionally used to denote any type of wind of hurricane force.

Intertropical Convergence Zone — The zone near the equator along which the opposing trade winds of the two hemispheres meet. It is located in the same general region of the world as the doldrums, but the intertropical convergence zone does not imply light and variable winds. Frequently abbreviated as ITC.

Inversion — The condition that exists within the atmosphere when the temperature increases rather than decreases with height through a layer of air.

Isallobar — A line connecting points on a weather map having the same barometric change.

Isobar — A line connecting points of equal atmospheric pressure.

Isochrone — A line connecting points where a given event occurred at the same time.

Isohyet — Lines of equal rainfall.

Isotach — Lines of equal wind speed.

Jet Stream — A narrow band of strong winds usually found at elevations of 20,000 to 50,000 feet. It is usually located north of 30° N latitude, and wind speeds in the core of the jet stream frequently exceed 150 knots.

Knot — A unit of wind speed equal to one nautical mile (6,080 feet) per hour.

Lapse Rate — The rate of change of temperature with elevation.

Long Wave — Atmospheric waves (troughs and ridges) with wave lengths varying from 50° to 120° of longitude. They have large amplitude which increases upward in the troposphere. They move so slowly that they often appear as waves of large amplitude on five-day mean charts.

Meter — A unit of length equal to 39.37 inches. A meter per second (mps) is equal to about two knots.

Meridional Flow — A predominately north-south wind circulation.

Millibar (Abbreviated mb) — A unit of pressure equal to 1,000 dynes per square centimeter. An inch of mercury is equal to 33.86 mb.

Moist Adiabatic Lapse Rate — The rate at which saturated air cools as it rises. It is not constant but depends upon the temperature and to some extent upon the pressure. In the lower atmosphere it is about 0.6° C. per 100 meters.

Planetary Wave — Another name for a "long wave." *See also* Long Wave.

Polar Trough — A trough of low pressure embedded in the prevailing westerly winds of the middle latitudes. Normally it moves from west to east. Occasionally a well-developed polar trough extends into tropical regions, where it is forced aloft and overrides the lower easterly current to which it is opposed.

Radar — An ultrahigh-frequency pulsed radio signal. Upon striking a "target" (aircraft, prominent features of the terrain, or even drops of water) the radar signal is reflected back to the transmitter, where the receiving portion of the set detects the signal, amplifies it, and presents the target as a visible echo on the radarscope.

Radiosonde — A small radio transmitter sent aloft by means of a helium-filled balloon. In flight the radio transmits data on temperature, humidity, and pressure from the surface up to elevations of twelve to fifteen miles.

RAOB — An abbreviation for "radiosonde observation."

RAWIN — An abbreviation for "radio wind," or a wind aloft obtained by tracking a balloon by means of radio direction-finding equipment.

Recurvature — The turning of a tropical storm from an initial path toward the west or northwest to the north or northeast.

Resurgence — The rise in the water level in areas where it has been reduced by offshore winds. It is due to oscillation of the water surface following the relaxation of the winds that lowered the water level initially. A resurgence may cause the water to rise to dangerous levels.

Ridge of High Pressure — An elongated area of high pressure; it is distinguished from the anticyclone, or HIGH, by the lack of closed isobars.

SCR-658 — A radio direction-finding apparatus used for tracking radiosondes in order to obtain radio winds. It is now almost obsolete.

Seiche — An oscillation of the surface of a lake or other landlocked body of water; it is caused by winds, variations of atmospheric pressure, earthquakes, etc.

St. Elmo's Fire — A luminous brush discharge of static electricity from pointed objects to the air. It occurs on airplanes, ships, steeples, and even on the ears of horses, horns of cattle, etc.

Sferics — A contraction of "atmospherics"; it refers to natural electrical phenomena detected by means of radio.

Short Waves — Numerous wavelike disturbances present in the upper-level circulation of the atmosphere. They move rapidly, and their amplitude and wave length are small in comparison with the "long waves." They are associated with the migratory cyclones and frontal systems of the middle latitudes, of which they are the upper-level reflections.

Spiral Band — A long and narrow spiralling band found embedded within the wind circulation around a hurricane. It is along the spiral bands that convergence and rainfall reach a maximum. They are visible on radarscopes.

Squall Line — An advancing line along which thundershowers or rain squalls are concentrated. They frequently precede cold fronts, but sometimes they are present within the outer edges of hurricanes.

Stable — As applied to an air mass, stable means that vertical motion is suppressed, provided an element of air is in equilibrium with its environment.

When used in connection with a vortex or a disturbance, stable means that a "steady state" is approached, i.e., the disturbance displays little change in shape or intensity with time.

Stratosphere — That portion of the upper atmosphere within which the lapse rate is almost isothermal. It is separated from the lower atmosphere by the tropopause.

Subsidence — A slow sinking or settling of an air mass. It is accompanied by divergence.

Surge — A rapid rise in the water level along a coast coincident with the arrival of a storm center.

Swell — A wind wave that has moved away from the disturbance that caused it.

Tornado — A severe rotating windstorm of small diameter and great destructive power. It is the most violent natural meteorological phenomenon. Winds in tornadoes have been estimated as high as 500 mph.

Tropical Cyclone — Any cyclonic wind circulation that had its origin within the tropics. It includes hurricanes, typhoons, etc.

Tropopause — The region separating the stratosphere from the troposphere. It varies in height from seventeen to eighteen kilometers at the equator to six to seven kilometers at the poles.

Troposphere — The region of the atmosphere extending from the surface up to the tropopause. It makes up the body of the atmosphere, and most of the earth's weather occurs within this layer.

Trough of Low Pressure — An elongated area of low pressure; it has U-shaped or V-shaped isobars. It is distinguished from a cyclone by the absence of closed isobars.

Typhoon — A tropical cyclone with winds of seventy-four mph or more. It is the same as the hurricane but occurs in different parts of the world.

Virtual Temperature — The temperature at which dry air would have the same pressure and density as air with the current humidity and temperature.

Vortex — Any rotating wind system.

Vorticity — The tendency of a fluid to spin or rotate, or the rotational circulation of air about a center, the axis being in any direction whatsoever. It may be due to wind shear or motion in a curved path. Cyclonic vorticity is in a counterclockwise sense and anticyclonic vorticity is in a clockwise direction (in the Northern Hemisphere).

Waterspouts — Small, whirling storms over the oceans or inland waters. Their chief characteristic is a funnel-shaped cloud extending from the base of a cumuliform cloud to the water. They occasionally move inland and cause some damage, but they are much less severe than tornadoes, which they resemble in appearance.

Wind Shear — Wind speed change, with distance either horizontal or vertical

Zonal Flow — A predominantly west-east wind circulation.

APPENDIX B

HURRICANES AFFECTING THE UNITED STATES, BY SECTIONS

Intensity classification. It is extremely difficult to develop an intensity classification which is satisfactory for all purposes. If it is based on all possible criteria, these would include wind, pressure, tides, size, floods, damage, fatalities, and possibly other data. Since there is no unique correlation between many of these, classification on this basis would be complex. To simplify matters, a classification has been set up based principally upon the maximum winds and the minimum pressure in tropical cyclones but subjectively giving some weight to the other factors. The classification follows:

	Maximum Winds	Minimum Central Pressure
Minor............................	Less than 74	Above 996 mb (above 29.40 in.)
Minimal........................	74 to 100	983 to 996 mb (29.03 to 29.40 in.)
Major............................	101 to 135	949 to 982 mb (28.01 to 29.00 in.)
Extreme........................	136 and higher	948 mb or less (28.00 in. or less)

TABLE 26

Tropical Cyclones in New England

Year	Date	Area	Intensity	Miscellaneous Notes
1635	Aug. 15	Mass., R.I., Conn.	Extreme	20 ft. tide at Boston
1638	Aug. 3	Mass., R.I., Conn.	Extreme	High tides R.I.
1723	Oct. 30	Southeast portion	Major	High tides R.I. coast
1743	Sept. ?	Cape Cod	Minor	Ben Franklin's storm
1761	Oct. 24	Southeast coast	Major	Very severe R.I.
1770	Oct. 20	Cape Cod	Minimal	100 vessels wrecked
1788	Aug. 19	N.H., Mass., Conn.	Minimal	6 killed
1804	Oct. 9-10	Southeast coast	Minor	Gale at Newport
1815	Sept. 22-23	All sections	Extreme	Similar to 1938 storm
1821	Sept. 3	South portion	Major	High winds and tides
1829	July 24	Boston	Minor	Questionable
1841	Oct. 3	Southeast coast	Minor	Strong R.I., Mass. coasts

TABLE 26 (Continued)
Tropical Cyclones in New England

Year	Date	Area	Intensity	Miscellaneous Notes
1854	Sept. 10-11	All sections	Minor	Dissipating hurricane
1866	Oct. 30	Southeast coast	Major	High tides
1869	Sept. 8	South portion	Major	Heavy property damage
1877	Oct. 4-5	Southeast coast	Minimal	High tides R.I.
1878	Oct. 23-24	All sections	Minimal	Path inland
1879	Aug. 20	Cape Cod	Minor	Severe at sea
1893	Aug. 24	Western sections	Minimal	Heavy damage Conn., R.I.
1893	Aug. 29	Western sections	Minor	Overland storm
1896	Sept. 10	East portion	Minimal	Hurricane R.I. to Me.
1896	Oct. 12-13	Coast R.I., Mass.	Minimal	More severe off coast
1903	Sept. 16	Western sections	Minor	Several persons killed
1904	Sept. 14-15	All sections	Minimal	Damage $1,000,000
1916	July 21	R.I., Cape Cod	Minor	
1924	Aug. 26	R.I., Cape Cod	Minimal	Severe at Block Island
1933	Sept. 17	Cape Cod	Minor	Center remained offshore
1934	Sept. 8-9	South portion	Minor	
1936	Sept. 19	Cape Cod	Minor	Center remained offshore
1938	Sept. 21	All sections	Extreme	See descr. pp. 272-75
1944	Sept. 14-15	Coastal areas	Extreme	390 killed $100,000,000 damage
1950	Sept. 11	Cape Cod	Minor	Center remained offshore
1954	Aug. 31	All sections	Extreme	60 killed, $450,000,000 damage
1954	Sept. 11	Coastal areas	Extreme	21 killed, $40,600,000 damage
1955	Aug. 18-19	South portion	Extreme flood	82 killed, $800,000,000 damage, no wind or sea damage
1958	Aug. 29	Cape Cod	Minor	Center 75 mi. off coast

TABLE 27
Tropical Cyclones in the Middle Atlantic States

Year	Date	Area	Intensity	Miscellaneous Notes
1743	Sept. ?	Coast	Minor	Ben Franklin's Storm
1766	Sept. 11	Virginia	No data	
1785	Sept. 22-24	Virginia	Minor	Damage slight
1788	Aug. 19	Eastern N.Y.	Minimal	Much damage eastern N.Y.
1815	Sept. 22	Coast	Major	Heavy damage coast N.Y. & N.J.

TABLE 27 (Continued)
Tropical Cyclones in the Middle Atlantic States

Year	Date	Area	Intensity	Miscellaneous Notes
1821	Sept. 2-3	Coast	Major	Tide rose 13 ft. in 1 hr. in N.Y. City
1830	Aug. 16-17	Va. Capes	Minor	Moved overland from S.C. & Ga.
1854	Sept. 9	Philadelphia	Minimal	Moved overland from Ga.
1876	Sept. 17-18	Eastern half	Minor	Damage slight to moderate
1878	Oct. 23	All sections	Major	Resembled Hazel of 1954
1879	Aug. 18-19	Coast	Minimal	High tides
1889	Sept. 9-12	Coast	Minimal	40 killed, $2,356,000 damage
1893	Aug. 23-24	Coast N.J.; N.Y.	Minor	
1893	Aug. 28-29	All sections	Minor	Moved overland from Ga.
1893	Oct. 13	All sections	Minimal	Another Hazel
1894	Oct. 9-10	All sections	Minor	Moved overland from NW Fla.
1896	Sept. 29-30	All sections	Major	16 killed, damage $3,828,000
1896	Oct. 10-11	Va. Capes	Minor	Storm center off coast
1899	Aug. 18-19	Va., Del., N.J. coast	Minor	Storm center off coast
1899	Oct. 31	Coast	Minor	High winds & tides
1903	Sept. 15-16	Coast	Minor	
1904	Sept. 14-15	Inside coast	Minimal	Damage $1,000,000
1923	Oct. 23-24	Chesapeake Bay	Minimal	82 mph at Atlantic City
1925	Dec. 2-3	Va. Capes to N.J.	Minor	2 killed
1928	Sept. 19-20	Va. Capes inland	Minor	3 killed, damage sev'l. million
1929	Oct. 2	All sections	Minor	Overland from NW Fla.
1933	Aug. 23-24	Coast	Major	Damage $21,000,000
1934	Sept. 8	N.J., N.Y. coast	Minor	65 mph at Sandy Hook
1936	Sept. 18	Va. Capes	Minimal	2 killed, $500,000 damage Va.
1938	Sept. 21	Coast	Minimal	Damage $6,000,000 N.Y.
1944	Sept. 14-15	Coast	Major	63 killed, damage $22,500,000
1954	Aug. 30-31	Coast	Minor	Damage $6,250,000 mostly N.Y.
1954	Sept. 10-11	Coast	Minor	Damage $2,100,000 mostly N.Y.
1954	Oct. 15 (Hazel)	All sections	Major	74 killed, damage $88,595,000
1955	Aug. 12-13	All sections	Minimal	22 killed, damage $6,200,000
1955	Aug. 17-18	Va. to L.I.	Major flood	98 killed, damage $112,840,000
1955	Sept. 19	Va. Capes	Minor	

TABLE 28
Tropical Cyclones in the South Atlantic States — Carolinas and Georgia

Year	Date	Area	Intensity	Miscellaneous Notes
1700	Sept. 16	Charleston	Major	Several ships lost
1713	Sept. 16-17	S.C.	Major	Very high tides
1728	Aug. ?	Charleston	No data	
1728	Sept. 14	S.C.	Major	High tide & ships damaged
1752	Sept. 15	Both Carolinas	Major	10 ft. tide at Charleston
1752	Sept. ?	S. C.	Minimal	
1753	Sept. 15	Charleston	Minimal	
1758	Aug. 23	S.C.	Minimal	
1761	June 1	S.C.	Minimal	
1770	June 6	Charleston	Minimal	
1777	Aug. 10	Carolinas	Minimal	
1783	? ?	Near Charleston	Minimal	
1787	Sept. 19	S.C.	Major	23 drowned, great damage
1791	? ?	N.C.	Major	High tides
1797	Sept. 5	S.C.	Major	High tides overflowed wharves
1800	Oct. ?	Charleston	Major	
1804	Sept. 7	Ga., S.C.	Extreme	More than 500 drowned
1811	Sept. 10	Near Charleston	Minimal	Many killed
1812	? ?	Ga.	Major	
1813	Aug. 27-28	S.C.	Extreme	Tides very high, many drowned
1814	July 1	S.C.	Minimal	Tornado near Charleston
1815	Sept. 28	S.C.	Minor	Centered off coast
1821	Sept. 2-3	Morehead City	Major	
1822	Aug. ?	Carolinas	Minimal	Centered off coast
1822	Sept. 27-28	Carolinas	Major	200 drowned S.C.
1827	July 30	N.C.	Minimal	
1827	Aug. 24-25	N.C.	Major	Severe around Cape Fear
1830	Aug. 15-16	Carolinas	Minimal	Worst in S.C.
1837	Aug. ?	Ga., S.C.	Minimal	Center near Darien, Ga.
1837	Sept. 1	Ga.	Minor	Overland from NW Fla.
1837	Oct. 9	Carolinas	Minimal	90 marine casualties
1840	? ?	N.C.	Minimal	
1841	Sept. 16	Charleston	Minor	
1842	July 15	N.C.	Major	About 40 ships wrecked
1842	Aug. 24	N.C.	Minimal	Heavy shipping losses
1844	Sept. 14	S.C.	Minor	
1846	Aug. 16	S.C.	No details	
1850	Aug. 24	S.C.	No details	May have come in 1851
1851	Aug. 24	Carolinas	Minor	Overland from NW Fla.

TABLE 28 (Continued)
Tropical Cyclones in the South Atlantic States — Carolinas and Georgia

Year	Date	Area	Intensity	Miscellaneous Notes
1852	Aug. 27	S.C.	Minor	Overland from Mobile
1853	Sept. 7	N.C.	Minimal	Center off coast
1854	Sept. 7-9	Entire coast	Minimal	Center near Savannah
1856	Sept. ?	Wilmington area	Minimal	Destructive tides
1861	Oct. ?	Cape Hatteras	Minimal	Federal fleet scattered
1871	Aug. 19	Tidewater areas	Minor	Overland from Fla.
1873	Oct. 16	S.C., Ga.	Minimal	Some loss of life
1874	Sept. 28	Carolinas	Minimal	2 killed S.C.
1876	Sept. 16-17	N.C.	Minimal	Center inland S of Cape Hatteras
1877	Oct. 3-4	Tidewater areas	Minor	Overland from NW Fla.
1878	Sept. 11-12	Carolinas	Minor	Few fatalities
1878	Oct. 22-23	N.C.	Major	Many marine casualties
1879	Aug. 18	N.C.	Extreme	Estimated max. wind 165 mph
1881	Aug. 27	Ga., S.C.	Major	Over 700 killed
1881	Sept. 9	Wilmington area	Minimal	
1882	Oct. 11	S.C.	Minor	Center remained at sea
1883	Sept. 11	Carolinas	Major	53 killed in N.C.
1885	Aug. 25	Coastal sections	Extreme	21 killed in S.C.
1885	Oct. 12	N.C.	Minor	High tides—center offshore
1887	Aug. 21	Cape Hatteras	Minimal	
1888	Oct. 11	Carolinas	Minimal	Inland N of Charleston
1889	Sept. 23-24	All sections	Minor	Overland from Mobile
1893	Aug. 23	Cape Hatteras	Minimal	Center remained at sea
1893	Aug. 27-28	All sections	Extreme	1,000 to 2,000 killed S.C.
1893	Oct. 13	Carolinas	Major	22 killed in N.C.
1893	Oct. 22	N.C.	Minor	Inland SW of Cape Hatteras
1894	Sept. 27	Coastal sections	Minor	Overland from Fla.
1894	Oct. 9	All sections	Minor	Overland from NW Fla.
1896	Sept. 29	Ga., S.C.	Minimal	30 killed
1898	Aug. 31	Georgia	Minimal	Center over Tybee Is.
1898	Oct. 2	Coastal sections	Extreme	179 killed in Ga.
1899	Aug. 17-18	Cape Hatteras	Extreme	7 ships wrecked
1899	Oct. 31	Carolinas	Major	High tides
1900	Oct. 13	Cape Hatteras	Minor	
1901	July 10	N.C.	Minimal	Damage minor
1903	Sept. 15-16	Cape Hatteras	Minimal	Center remained offshore
1904	Sept. 14-15	Carolinas	Minimal	Damage minor
1906	Sept. 17	Myrtle Beach	Major	Bar. 27.90 in. at Cape Fear

TABLE 28 (Continued)
Tropical Cyclones in the South Atlantic States —
Carolinas and Georgia

Year	Date	Area	Intensity	Miscellaneous Notes
1906	Oct. 20	S.C.	Minor	Center remained offshore
1908	July 30-31	N.C.	Minimal	Tide high at Wrightsville B.
1908	Aug. 31–			
	Sept. 1	Cape Lookout	Minimal	Center offshore
1910	Oct. 19-20	Coast	Minor	Overland from Fla.
1911	Aug. 27-28	Ga., S.C.	Major	17 killed near Charleston
1912	July 14-15	Ga., S.C.	Minimal	Center near Tybee Beach
1913	Sept. 3	N.C.	Minimal	5 killed
1913	Oct. 8	S.C.	Minimal	Inland near Georgetown
1916	July 13-14	S.C.	Minimal	Severe floods
1920	Sept. 22-23	Carolinas	Minimal	Damage slight
1924	Aug. 25	Cape Hatteras	Minimal	Center offshore
1924	Sept. 16-17	Ga., S.C.	Minor	Heavy rains
1925	Dec. 2	N.C. capes	Minimal	Damage slight
1927	Oct. 3	All sections	Minor	
1928	Sept. 17-19	Tidewater sections	Minor	12- to 16-in. rains
1929	Oct. 1-2	All sections	Minor	Heavy rains
1933	Aug. 22-23	Cape Hatteras	Minimal	Damage moderate
1933	Sept. 16	Cape Hatteras	Major	21 killed
1935	Sept. 5	All sections	Minor	4 tornadoes
1936	Sept. 18	Cape Hatteras	Major	Extreme off coast
1940	Aug. 11-12	Ga., S.C.	Major	34 killed, damage $7,000,000
1944	Aug. 1	N.C.	Minimal	Damage $2,000,000
1944	Sept. 14	Cape Hatteras	Major	Bar. 27.97 in. at Cape Hatteras
1944	Oct. 19-20	S.C., Ga.	Minor	Damage $350,000
1945	June 25	N.C. Capes	Minor	
1945	Sept. 17	Paris Island	Minimal	Damage $7,000,000
1947	Oct. 15	Savannah	Minimal	Damage $3,000,000
1949	Aug. 24	N.C. coast	Minimal	Center off coast
1949	Aug. 28	Interior sections	Minor	Overland from Fla.
1952	Aug. 30-31	All sections	Minimal	Damage $3,000,000 S.C.
1953	Aug. 13-14	N.C. Capes	Minimal	Damage $1,000,000
1954	Aug. 30	Cape Hatteras	Minimal	Major off coast
1954	Sept. 10	Cape Hatteras	Minimal	Major off coast
1954	Oct. 15	Carolinas	Extreme	20 killed, damage $163,000,000
1955	Aug. 12	Morehead City	Minimal	Damage $40,000,000
1955	Aug. 17	N.C.	Minimal	Damage $65,000,000
1955	Sept. 19	Morehead City	Minimal	7 killed, damage $88,035,000
1958	Sept. 27	Cape Fear	Extreme	Damage $11,000,000

TABLE 29
Tropical Cyclones in Florida

Year	Date	Area	Intensity	Miscellaneous Notes
1559	Sept. 19	Pensacola	Major	Earliest known hurricane in Fla.
1565	Sept. 20	St. Augustine, Matanzas	Minimal	
1566	Sept. 16	East coast	?	
1736	?	Pensacola	Major	Pensacola destroyed
1740	Sept. 12-13	Pensacola	?	
1757	?	East coast	?	
1758	?	NW Fla.	?	40 drowned at St. Marks
1759	Sept. ?	S Fla.	Major	High tides Dry Tortugas to Miami
1766	Oct. 22	NW Fla.	Major	12 ft. tide at St. Marks.
1769	Aug. 30	East coast	?	
1769	Oct. 29	?	?	
1787	Aug. 15	?	?	
1804	Sept. 6	East coast	Minimal	Intense off coast
1824	?	St. Augustine	Minimal	Center probably off coast
1831	June 10	?	?	Probably west coast
1837	July 31	East coast	?	
1837	Aug. 6	East coast	?	
1837	Aug. 30	NW Fla.	?	
1842	Aug. 4	Key West	?	
1842	Oct. 5	NW Fla.	?	Bad around Cedar Keys
1843	Sept. 13	NW Fla.	Major	Port St. Joe and St. Marks destroyed
1844	Oct. 4-5	Key West—Miami	Minimal	Matanzas, Cuba, bar. 28.00 in.
1844	Oct. 12	Key West	?	
1846	Oct. 11-12	Key West	Extreme	Key West almost destroyed, bar. 27.06 in. at Havana
1848	Sept. 25	Tampa Bay	Major	Tampa tide 15 ft., bar. 28.18 in.
1848	Oct. 12	Tampa Bay	Minimal	Tide 10 ft. above normal
1850	Aug. 23	Apalachicola	?	
1851	Aug. 23	Apalachicola	Minimal	
1852	Oct. 9	?	?	
1854	Sept. 7-8	Northeast coast	Minimal	Very severe offshore
1871	Aug. 17-18	East coast	?	
1873	Oct. 5-7	Punta Rassa	Major	Punta Rassa destroyed, tide 14 ft.
1874	Sept. 28	East coast	Minimal	Center remained offshore
1876	Sept. 16	Southeast coast	Minimal	Center remained offshore

TABLE 29 (Continued)
Tropical Cyclones in Florida

Year	Date	Area	Intensity	Miscellaneous Notes
1876	Oct. 19-20	Southeast coast	Minimal	Tide 8 to 10 ft. above MLW at Miami
1877	Aug. 2	?	?	
1877	Oct. 2	NW Fla.	Minimal	12 ft. tide at St. Marks
1878	July 11-12	Jacksonville	?	
1878	Sept. 11	Jacksonville	Minimal	13 wrecks northeast coast
1878	Oct. 21-22	Southeast coast	Minimal	
1879	Oct. 27	Tampa to Cedar Keys	Minimal	
1880	Aug. 28-29	Most of state	Major	Severe Palm Beach— Okeechobee
1880	Oct. 8	Cedar Keys	?	
1881	Aug. 27	Southwest coast	Minor	
1881	Oct. 6	Jacksonville	?	Questionable
1882	Sept. 9-10	NW Fla.	Minimal	In Gulf ship bar. 28.01 in.
1882	Oct. 9-11	Near Cross City	Minimal	
1885	Aug. 23	East coast	Minimal	Center off shore
1885	Sept. 28-30	Near St. Joe	Minimal	
1885	Oct. 10-11	Pinellas County	Minimal	High tides
1886	June 21	Apalachicola	Major	High tides
1886	June 30– July 1	Apalachicola	Minimal	Several killed
1886	July 18	N of Cedar Keys	Minor	
1886	Aug. 17-18	Fla. Straits	Minimal	
1887	July 27	NW Fla.	Minimal	
1887	Oct. 29	Southwest coast	Minor	
1888	Aug. 16	Extreme south	Minimal	Hurricane winds at Miami
1888	Sept. 7-8	Central Fla.	Minor	Considerable damage at Micco
1888	Oct. 10-11	N of Cedar Keys	Minimal	Sea rose 9 ft. in 30 min.
1889	June 17	S of Cedar Keys	Minimal	
1889	Oct. 5	Southeast coast	Minor	
1891	Aug. 24	Southeast coast	Minor	
1891	Oct. 7	Ft. Myers to Palm Beach	Minimal	
1892	June 10	Ft. Myers to Pompano	Minor	
1892	Oct. 24	N Fla.	Minor	
1893	June 15	NW Fla.	Minimal	High tides N of Tampa Bay
1893	Aug. 27	NE coast	Minimal	Severe offshore
1893	Oct. 2-3	Pensacola	Minor	Center W of this area
1893	Oct. 11-13	East coast	Major	Center remained offshore
1893	Oct. 21	Extreme south portion	Minor	

TABLE 29 (Continued)
Tropical Cyclones in Florida

Year	Date	Area	Intensity	Miscellaneous Notes
1894	Sept. 25	Southwest coast	Major	Extreme wind Key West 104 mph
1894	Oct. 8	Apalachicola	Minimal	Many killed
1895	Aug. 16	Pensacola	Minor	
1895	Oct. 1-2	Southeast coast	Minor	
1895	Oct. 16	Southeast coast	Minor	
1895	Oct. 21-22	Southeast coast	Minimal	
1896	July 7	Pensacola	Major	Extreme wind Pensacola 100 mph
1896	Sept. 28-29	Cedar Keys	Major	Over 100 killed
1896	Oct. 8	Ft. Myers	Minimal	
1897	Sept. 21	Northern peninsula	Minor	
1898	Aug. 2-3	Most of state	Minimal	12 or more killed
1898	Oct. 2	Northeast coast	Minimal	A few killed
1899	Aug. 1	Carabelle	Minimal	6 killed
1899	Aug. 12-14	East coast	Minor	6 killed, very severe offshore
1899	Oct. 29-30	Southeast coast	Minor	Center offshore
1900	Sept. 5-6	Straits	Minor	
1901	Aug. 10-14	Straits & NW Fla.	Minor	Wind Pensacola 70 mph
1901	Sept. 17	Pensacola	Minor	
1902	June 14	Apalachee Bay	Minor	
1903	Sept. 11-13	S and NW Fla.	Minimal	14 killed & heavy shipping losses
1904	Oct. 16-19	Southeast coast	Minimal	5 or more killed
1906	June 12	Apalachicola	Minor	
1906	June 17	Extreme south	Minimal	
1906	Sept. 27	Pensacola	Major	34 killed, most severe at Pensacola in 170 years
1906	Oct. 18	Southeast coast	Major	164 killed, Miami bar. 28.55 in.
1907	Sept. 28	NW Fla.	Minor	
1909	Oct. 11	Keys	Major	15 killed, damage $1,000,000
1910	Oct. 17-18	Entire peninsula	Major	30 killed, damage $365,000
1911	Aug. 11	NW Fla.	Minimal	
1912	Sept. 13	Pensacola	Minimal	Center moved W of Mobile
1915	Sept. 4	Apalachicola	Minimal	Some loss of life
1916	July 5	Pensacola	Major	Pensacola wind 104 mph
1916	Oct. 18	Pensacola	Major	Pensacola wind 114 mph
1916	Nov. 15	Straits	Minimal	
1917	Sept. 28-29	Pensacola	Major	Pensacola wind 103 mph
1919	Sept. 9-10	Key West	Major	Marine casualties 300 plus

TABLE 29 (Continued)
Tropical Cyclones in Florida

Year	Date	Area	Intensity	Miscellaneous Notes
1920	Sept. 29-30	Cedar Keys	Minor	
1921	Oct. 25	West-central coast	Major	6 killed, damage $1,000,000
1923	Oct. 16	Pensacola	Minor	Center Louisiana coast
1924	Sept. 15	St. Joe	Minimal	Damage $275,000
1924	Sept. 29	Cedar Keys	Minor	
1924	Oct. 20-21	Extreme south	Minimal	Jutias Bay, Cuba, bar. 27.20 in.
1925	Nov. 30–Dec. 1	S Fla.	Minimal	50 killed, damage $1,600,000
1926	July 27-28	East coast	Minimal	Damage $3,000,000
1926	Sept. 18-20	Miami, NW Fla.	Extreme	Miami bar. 27.61 in., wind 138 mph
1926	Oct. 21	Southeast coast	Minimal	Center remained offshore
1928	Aug. 7-9	N of Palm Beach	Minimal	2 killed, damage $235,000
1928	Aug. 14	Apalachicola	Minimal	
1928	Sept. 16-17	Entire peninsula	Extreme	1,836 killed, damage $25,000,000
1929	Sept. 27–Oct. 1	Key Largo, NW Fla.	Extreme	Key Largo bar. 28.00 in.
1930	Sept. 9-10	Northern peninsula	Minor	
1932	Aug. 29–Sept. 1	Extreme S & NW Fla.	Minimal	
1932	Sept. 14	Cedar Keys	Minor	
1933	July 30-31	Central Fla.	Minimal	
1933	Aug. 20	Apalachicola	Minor	
1933	Sept. 1	Straits	Minor	Havana bar. 28.92 in., wind 94 mph
1933	Sept. 3-4	Peninsula	Major	Jupiter bar. 27.98 in., wind 125 mph
1935	Sept. 2-4	Keys, Taylor Co.	Extreme	Keys bar. 26.35 in., wind 200 mph +
1935	Sept. 28	Southeast coast	Minimal	Bimini bar. 27.90 in., wind 120 mph
1935	Nov. 4	Extreme south	Minimal	Miami bar. 28.73 in., wind 75 mph
1936	June 14-15	Extreme south	Minor	8 to 15 in. of rain
1936	July 28-31	Extreme S, NW Fla.	Minimal	6 ft. tides in Gulf
1936	Aug. 21	Northeast coast	Minor	
1937	July 29	N of Tampa	Minor	
1937	Aug. 30-31	Northeast coast	Minor	15 sailors drowned Panama City

TABLE 29 (Continued)
Tropical Cyclones in Florida

Year	Date	Area	Intensity	Miscellaneous Notes
1937	Sept. 20-21	Apalachicola	Minor	
1938	Oct. 23-24	N of Tampa	Minor	
1939	June 16	NW Fla.	Minor	Center near Mobile
1939	Aug. 11-13	Central & NW Fla.	Minimal	
1941	Oct. 6-7	Extreme south, Carabelle	Major	S Miami wind 123 mph
1941	Oct. 20	Cedar Keys	Minor	10 to 15 in. rain
1944	Oct. 18-19	Peninsula	Major	18 killed, damage $60,000,000
1945	June 24	N of Clearwater	Minimal	
1945	Sept. 4	Extreme south	Minor	
1945	Sept. 15-16	Extreme south	Extreme	Homestead bar. 28.09 in., wind 170 mph
1946	Oct. 7-8	West coast	Minimal	Tides high, damage $5,200,000
1946	Nov. 1-2	Palm Beach	Minor	Damage several millions
1947	Sept. 17-18	S Fla.	Extreme	Pompano bar. 27.97 in., wind 155 mph
1947	Sept. 23	N of Clearwater	Minor	St. Leo bar. 29.22 in.
1947	Oct. 12	S Fla.	Minimal	5 to 13 in. rain
1948	Sept. 22	Southern portion	Major	Key West bar. 28.45 in., wind 122 mph
1948	Oct. 5	S Fla.	Minimal	Miami bar. 28.92 in., wind 86 mph
1949	Aug. 26-27	S Fla.	Extreme	2 killed, damage $45,000,000
1950	Aug. 30	Pensacola	Minor	Damage $550,000
1950	Sept. 3-7	Peninsula	Major	Cedar Keys bar. 28.30 in., wind 125 mph
1950	Oct. 17-18	Peninsula	Major	Miami bar. 28.20 in., wind 122 mph
1951	Oct. 2	Southwest coast	Minor	Damage $2,000,000
1952	Feb. 2-3	S Fla.	Minor	Miami wind 68 mph, gusts 84 mph
1953	June 6	NW Fla.	Minor	
1953	Sept. 26	NW Fla.	Minimal	Damage $150,000
1953	Oct. 9	SW Fla.	Minor	Okeechobee City bar. 29.15 in.
1956	Sept. 24	NW Fla.	Minimal	7 killed, damage $2,000,000
1957	June 8	Apalachee Bay	Minor	5 killed, damage $52,000
1957	Sept. 8	Fort Walton	Minor	
1957	Sept. 18	Pensacola	Minor	Center SE La. coast
1958	Sept. 2-3	Keys	Minor	Winds 50 to 60 mph

TABLE 30
Tropical Cyclones in Louisiana, Mississippi, and Alabama

Year	Date	Area	Intensity	Miscellaneous Notes
1559	Sept. 19	Mobile	Major	
1711	Sept. 11-13	New Orleans	Major	High tide at Mobile
1722	Sept. 12-13	New Orleans	Minimal	Ships sunk in harbor
1723	?	Mobile	?	
1732	?	New Orleans	Major	Many buildings destroyed
1740	Sept. 12	La. to Pensacola	Major	Lasted 12 hrs. in Mobile
1746	?	Gulf coast	?	
1772	Sept. 2-4	La. to Mobile	?	Severe in Mobile
1776	?	New Orleans	Minimal	Some damage in New Orleans
1779	Aug. 8	New Orleans	?	Gálvez' ships destroyed
1779	Oct. 10	New Orleans	?	
1780	Aug. 24	Louisiana	Major	Every ship in Miss. Delta sunk
1781	Mid-Aug.	New Orleans	?	
1800	Mid-Aug.	New Orleans	?	
1811	?	New Orleans	?	
1812	Mid-Aug.	New Orleans	?	
1813	Aug. 19	Gulf coast	Major	Very destructive
1819	Aug. 27-28	All sections	Major	Great destruction
1821	?	New Orleans	Minor	
1822	July 11	Mobile	Minimal	
1831	Aug. 16-17	New Orleans	Major	
1837	Oct. 6-7	Entire area	Minimal	
1846	?	New Orleans	Minor	
1852	Aug. 23-25	Mobile	Minimal	Tide 8.8 ft. above MLW
1856	Aug. 10-11	Ile Dernière	Major	400 killed
1856	Aug. 30	Mobile	Minimal	
1860	Aug. 11	Mobile	Minor	Tide 18 in. lower than 1852
1860	Sept. 15	Mobile	Minimal	High tides
1865	Sept. ?	Louisiana	Minimal	
1870	July 3 or 30	Mobile	Minor	
1877	Sept. 19-20	Entire coast	Minor	Center remained off coast
1879	Aug. 23	Louisiana coast	Minor	
1880	Aug. 30	Mobile	Minimal	
1882	Sept. 9	All coasts	Major	Severe on Alabama coast
1882	Sept. 14-15	Entire coast	Minimal	Port Eads wind 92 mph
1885	Sept. 25-28	Gulf coast	Minor	
1886	Oct. 11	Louisiana	Minimal	50 killed Cameron Parish
1887	Oct. 18-19	SE La.	Minimal	Heavy damage in New Orleans
1888	Aug. 19-20	Coastal areas	Minimal	New Orleans wind 90 mph

TABLE 30 (Continued)
Tropical Cyclones in Louisiana, Mississippi, and Alabama

Year	Date	Area	Intensity	Miscellaneous Notes
1889	Sept. 22-23	Coastal areas	Minor	
1892	Sept. 11-12	SE La.	Minor	
1893	Sept. 7-8	Louisiana	Minimal	Much damage small area
1893	Oct. 1-2	Coastal areas	Extreme	1,000 to 2,000 killed
1894	Aug. 6-7	Coastal areas	Minor	
1895	Aug. 16	Mobile	Minor	
1897	Sept. 12	Louisiana	Minimal	
1898	Sept. 20	Louisiana	Minimal	
1900	Sept. 7	Louisiana	Minimal	Famous Galveston storm
1900	Sept. 12-13	Coastal areas	Minor	
1901	June 13	Mobile	Minor	
1901	Aug. 14-15	Miss. Delta to Mobile	Minimal	Considerable loss of life
1902	Oct. 10-11	Mobile	Minor	
1904	Nov. 2	Miss. Delta	Minor	
1905	Sept. 29	Louisiana	Minor	
1906	Sept. 27	Delta eastward	Major	Bar. 28.30 in., estimated
1907	Sept. 21	Louisiana	Minor	
1909	Sept. 20-21	Louisiana	Extreme	Tide 15 ft., 350 killed
1911	Aug. 11	Mobile	Minor	
1912	June 13	Louisiana	Minor	
1912	Sept. 13-14	Mobile	Minor	Tide 5.2 ft. above MLW
1915	Aug. 17	Louisiana	Minor	Center remained offshore
1915	Sept. 29-30	Louisiana	Extreme	275 killed, damage $13,000,000
1916	July 5	Miss., Ala.	Major	4 killed, damage $3,000,000
1916	Oct. 18	Burrwood eastward	Minimal	Center passed over Pensacola
1917	Sept. 28	Miss. eastward	Minimal	Center between Mobile & Pensacola
1918	Aug. 6	W La.	Extreme	34 killed, damage $5,000,000
1920	Sept. 21-22	E La.	Minimal	1 killed, damage $1,450,000
1923	Oct. 16	Louisiana	Minimal	
1926	Aug. 25-26	Louisiana	Major	25 killed, damage $4,000,000
1926	Sept. 20-21	Miss., Ala.	Major	Perdido Beach, Ala., bar. 28.20 in.
1931	July 14-15	Louisiana	Minor	
1932	Sept. 1	Miss., Ala.	Minimal	
1932	Sept. 19	Morgan City, La.	Minor	
1932	Oct. 15	La., Miss.	Minor	
1934	June 16	Morgan City	Minimal	6 killed, damage $2,605,000
1936	July 27	Louisiana	Minor	
1937	Sept. 19	E La.	Minor	

TABLE 30 (Continued)
Tropical Cyclones in Louisiana, Mississippi, and Alabama

Year	Date	Area	Intensity	Miscellaneous Notes
1937	Oct. 3	Atchafalaya Bay	Minor	
1938	Aug. 14	W La.	Minor	Damage $243,000
1939	June 16	Mobile	Minor	
1939	Sept. 26	New Orleans eastward	Minor	Damage $1,743,550
1940	Aug. 7	W La.	Minor	Center S of coast
1943	Sept. 19	W La.	Minor	Damage $190,000
1944	Sept. 10	Mobile	Minor	7 to 11 in. rain
1947	Aug. 22	Grande Isle	Minor	
1947	Sept. 8	Biloxi–Mobile	Minor	
1947	Sept. 19	E La. eastward	Major	34 killed, damage $53,000,000
1948	Sept. 4	E La. eastward	Minimal	Damage $888,000
1949	Sept. 4	Louisiana	Minor	
1950	Aug. 30-31	Miss., Ala.	Minimal	1 killed, damage $2,550,000
1954	July 29	Vermillion Bay	Minor	
1955	Aug. 1	La., Miss.	Minor	2 killed
1955	Aug. 27	E La.	Minor	4 killed
1956	June 13	Louisiana	Minor	5 killed
1956	Sept. 24	E La. eastward	Minimal	8 killed, damage $22,000,000
1957	June 27	W La.	Extreme	550 killed, damage $150,000,000
1957	Aug. 9	Louisiana	Minor	2 killed
1957	Sept. 18	E La. coast	Minor	3 killed

TABLE 31
Tropical Cyclones in Texas

Year	Date	Area	Intensity	Miscellaneous Notes
1766	Sept. 4	Galveston Bay	?	Mission destroyed
1818	Sept. or Oct.	Northern coast	Major	4 Lafitte's ships sunk
1828	?	Lower coast	Minimal	High tides reported
1829	Sept. 10	Lower coast	Minimal	High tides
1831	Aug. 18	Lower coast	Minimal	
1834	Sept. ?	Lower coast	Minimal	
1835	Aug. 18	Upper coast	Minimal	
1835	Sept. 18	Brownsville	Minimal	Center S of Brownsville
1837	Oct. 3-6	Entire coast	Minimal	Severe offshore
1838	?	Lower coast	Minimal	High tides
1839	Nov. 5	Galveston	Minimal	

TABLE 31 (Continued)
Tropical Cyclones in Texas

Year	Date	Area	Intensity	Miscellaneous Notes
1840	?	Brownsville	Minimal	
1842	Sept. 7-8	Brownsville	Minor	Severe in Mexico
1842	Oct. 5	Galveston	Minor	
1844	Aug. 6	Brownsville	Major	70 killed
1847	?	Galveston	Minimal	
1848	Oct. 17	Lower coast	Minimal	High tides
1854	Sept. 16-18	Galveston southward	Major	Matagorda leveled
1857	?	Port Isabel	?	
1866	?	Galveston	Minimal	This or another at Port Isabel
1867	Oct. 3	Galveston southward	Major	Damage at Galveston $1,000,000
1871	June 4	Galveston	Minor	Rainfall 15.57 in.
1871	June 9	Upper coast	Minor	
1871	Oct. 3	Galveston	Minimal	SS *Hall* sunk, all hands lost
1872	?	Port Isabel	Minimal	
1874	July 2-4	Indianaola	Minimal	Damage at Corpus Christi
1874	Sept. 6	Lower coast	Minor	Center struck Mexico
1875	Sept. 16	Indianaola	Extreme	176 killed
1877	Sept. 16-17	Entire coast	Minimal	High tides
1879	Aug. 23	Upper coast	Minor	
1880	Aug. 13	Lower coast	Major	Center struck Matamoras, Mexico
1880	Oct. 12-13	Brownsville	Major	Brownsville nearly destroyed
1881	Aug. 12-13	Lower coast	Minimal	"Violent" Padre Island
1885	Sept. 17-20	Entire coast	Minimal	Center remained offshore
1886	June 14	Upper coast	Minor	Center remained offshore
1886	Aug. 19-20	Entire coast	Extreme	Destroyed Indianaola
1886	Sept. 23-24	Lower coast	Minimal	25.98 in. rain near Brownsville
1886	Oct. 12	Upper coast	Minimal	Tidal wave drowned 100 Sabine
1887	Sept. 21	Brownsville	Minimal	14 sailors lost
1888	June 17	Upper coast	Minimal	Center moved SW of Galveston
1888	July 5	Upper coast	Minor	
1891	July 4-5	Entire coast	Minimal	Part of Galveston inundated
1895	Aug. 29	Lower coast	Minor	Center hit Mexico 80 mi. S of Brownsville
1895	Oct. 6	Lower coast	Minor	

TABLE 31 (Continued)
Tropical Cyclones in Texas

Year	Date	Area	Intensity	Miscellaneous Notes
1897	Sept. 12	Upper coast	Minimal	13 killed, damage $150,000
1898	Sept. 27-28	Upper coast	Minor	
1900	Sept. 8-9	Upper coast	Extreme	6,000 killed, damage $30,000,000
1901	July 10	Upper coast	Minor	
1902	June 26	N of Corpus Christi	Minimal	
1909	June 30	Lower coast	Minor	
1909	July 21	Velasco	Major	41 killed, damage $2,000,000
1909	Aug. 27-28	Lower coast	Minimal	Major in Mexico, over 1,500 killed
1910	Aug. 31	Lower coast	Minor	
1910	Sept. 14	Lower coast	Minimal	Padre Island wholly inundated
1912	Oct. 15-16	Lower coast	Minimal	Damage $28,000
1913	June 27	Lower coast	Minor	Torrential rains
1915	Aug. 16-17	Upper coast	Extreme	275 killed, damage $50,000,000
1916	Aug. 18	Lower coast	Extreme	20 killed, damage $1,800,000
1919	Sept. 14	Corpus Christi	Extreme	300–600 killed, damage $20,270,000
1921	June 22	Entire coast	Minimal	
1921	Sept. 7-10	Lower coast	Minor	51 killed from floods
1922	June 15-16	Rio Grande	Minor	Floods on Rio Grande
1925	Sept. 6-7	Lower coast	Minor	Center entered Mexico
1929	June 28	Port O'Connor	Minimal	3 killed, damage $675,000
1931	June 28	Lower coast	Minor	Heavy rains
1932	Aug. 13	Freeport	Major	40 killed, damage $7,500,000
1933	July 6	Lower coast	Minor	Center entered Mexico
1933	July 22-23	Matagorda Bay	Minor	Heavy rains
1933	Aug. 5	Brownsville	Minimal	
1933	Sept. 4-5	Brownsville	Major	40 killed, damage $12,000,000
1934	July 25	Rockport	Minimal	11 killed, damage $1,500,000
1934	Aug. 26-31	Entire coast	Minor	Center remained offshore
1936	June 27	Port Aransas	Minimal	Damage $550,000
1936	Sept. 13	Lower coast	Minor	
1938	Oct. 17	Upper coast	Minor	
1940	Aug. 7	Upper coast	Minimal	Damage moderate
1940	Sept. 23	Upper coast	Minor	Center remained offshore
1941	Sept. 14	Upper coast	Minor	

TABLE 31 (Continued)
Tropical Cyclones in Texas

Year	Date	Area	Intensity	Miscellaneous Notes
1941	Sept. 23	Matagorda	Minimal	4 killed, damage $6,000,000
1942	Aug. 21	Upper coast	Minimal	Damage $790,000
1942	Aug. 30	Matagorda Bay	Major	8 killed, damage $11,500,000
1943	July 27	Galveston	Minimal	19 killed, damage $16,550,000
1943	Sept. 19	Upper coast	Minor	Remained offshore
1945	Aug. 26-27	Middle coast	Extreme	3 killed, damage $20,133,000
1946	June 16	Port Arthur	Minor	
1947	Aug. 1	Lower coast	Minor	Rain damage $2,000,000
1947	Aug. 24	Galveston	Minimal	1 killed, damage $757,000
1949	Oct. 3-4	Freeport	Major	2 killed, damage $6,700,000
1954	June 25	85 miles S of Brownsville	Minor	17 killed by floods
1955	Sept. 6-7	Corpus Christi	Minimal	17.02 in. rain Flour Bluff
1957	Aug. 9	Beaumont	Minor	
1957	June 27	Near La. border	Minimal	(Audrey) 7 killed, damage $8,000,000
1958	June 15	Extreme southern coast	Minimal	
1958	Sept. 6	Corpus Christi	Minimal	

APPENDIX C

CHRONOLOGICAL ACCOUNT OF HURRICANES OF THE TWENTIETH CENTURY

Tannehill in Chapter 14 of his *Hurricanes* [102] gave a chronological account of hurricanes beginning with 1901 and in his last edition ending with the year 1955. Since many persons interested in tropical cyclones have found the descriptions helpful, the account has been continued.

1956

The 1956 hurricane season was mild from both the standpoints of number and intensity. Two storms (Figure 89) reached the United States coast line along the Gulf of Mexico. Total damage in the United States was $30,007,605 and $37,829,201 in other areas. There were nineteen fatalities in the United States and fifty-seven elsewhere of which twenty-seven were in Mexico and eighteen in the French West Indies.

The first tropical storm of the season (unnamed) developed in the Bay of Campeche and reached the Louisiana coast on June 13. The highest wind, 55 mph, was reported at Grande Isle, Louisiana. The tide was 4.7 feet above normal at Biloxi, Mississippi. Four persons were drowned and damage was about $50,000.

Hurricane Anna, the first of the season, developed in the Bay of Campeche on July 25 and moved inland south of Tampico early on the evening of the twenty-sixth. Hurricane winds apparently existed for only about three hours prior to landfall. The lowest pressure reported was 29.26 and maximum winds were 81 mph. There were no deaths and damage was estimated at $50,000.

The strongest hurricane of the season was Betsy, which developed east of the Lesser Antilles on August 9, crossed over Puerto Rico on the twelfth and then recurved east of the United States mainland. As

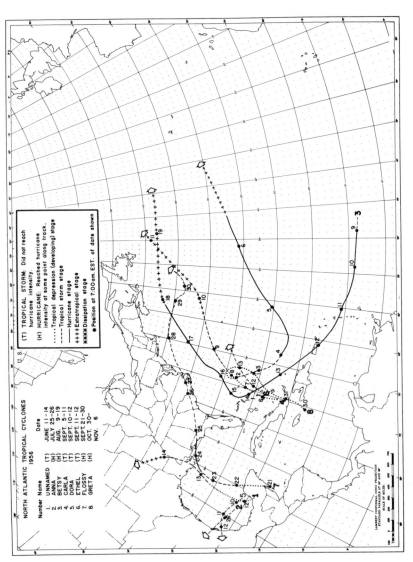

Fig. 89. Tracks of tropical cyclones of 1956.

the hurricane passed through the French Antilles damage was heavy and winds of 100 to 120 mph swept over Guadeloupe and Marie Galante. Damage amounted to $10,000,000. The hurricane passed over Puerto Rico on the twelfth with gusts of 115 mph, resulting in nine fatalities and $25,500,000 damage. At San Salvador in the Bahamas winds reached 132 mph in gusts and 5 inches of rain fell in five hours. The tracking and forecasting of hurricane Betsy was aided by radar which picked it up as it approached Puerto Rico and kept it under surveillance until it was well northeast of Miami, Florida.

Tropical storm Carla formed north of eastern Cuba, remained out at sea, and was unimportant.

Tropical storm Dora formed and moved in the same area as Anna. It passed inland on September 12 near Tuxpan, Mexico. The accompanying heavy rains caused a landside in which thirteen persons were killed and there were fourteen other fatalities from floods and other phenomena associated with the storm.

Tropical storm Ethel was very short-lived developing on September 11 and 12 in the eastern Bahamas. On the afternoon of the twelfth research aircraft found a well-developed eye and maximum winds of 75 mph in a squall in the northeast quadrant. No hurricane winds were found in any other sector. By late on the thirteenth, the storm had assumed extratropical characteristics and lost intensity.

Hurricane Flossy probably formed in a disturbance which moved across Guatemala from the Pacific. The storm reached hurricane intensity in the Gulf of Mexico on the twenty-third and crossed the Mississippi Delta near Pilottown, Louisiana, early on the twenty-fourth. It seems to have reached maximum intensity at Burrwood with the highest wind 84 mph and lowest pressure 29.03 inches. Tides reached 7.4 feet above mean sea-level at Laguna Beach, Florida. Rainfall totaled 16.70 inches at Golden Meadow, Louisiana, and almost as much at Gulf Shores, Alabama. Three tornadoes were reported in northwestern Florida and another near Savannah, Georgia. Total damage in Louisiana, Florida, Alabama, and Mississippi was $24,774,000, and in Georgia, the Carolinas, and Virginia $100,000. Deaths, mainly from plane and automobile accidents attributed to the storm, totaled fifteen.

A late season tropical cyclone, which began on October 30 and reached hurricane intensity on November 4 concluded the season. The circulation formed by hurricane Greta and the large anticyclone to the north covered a tremendous expanse of the Atlantic Ocean and the long fetch of the strong winds set up much larger waves and swells than indicated by the normal wind-sea-swell relationships. Shore erosion damage was heavy along the Florida coast and throughout the Antilles. Eighty per cent of the port installations were destroyed at Basse Terre, Guadeloupe. Total damage, $3,579,806, was almost entirely from sea action. The hurricane acquired its greatest intensity on November 5 when aircraft found a central pressure of 28.64 inches and maximum winds in excess of 100 mph.

1957

The hurricane season of 1957 was a little under the normal number for the past several decades with eight tropical cyclones but only three of full hurricane intensity. However, five of the storms reached the United States coast line — all on the Gulf Coast between eastern Texas and northwestern Florida (Figure 90). One of these was Audrey, one of the most destructive June hurricanes on record. Property damage in the United States amounted to $152,500,000. Audrey left 390 known dead and the total may have exceeded 500 since there were 192 persons reported missing.

An unnamed tropical storm developed on June 7 and 8 in the south-central Gulf of Mexico. It moved northeastward to Apalachee Bay, and exposed places along the Florida Gulf coast from Sarasota to north of Cedar Keys experienced winds of 40 mph or more and tides 2 to 3 feet above normal. Exceptionally heavy rain attended the passage of the storm with amounts of 15 inches at official stations and some unofficial amounts of 19 inches. At least nine tornadoes or damaging windstorms were reported in northeastern Florida on the afternoon and evening of the eighth. One small craft capsized in the Gulf of Mexico and five of the seven persons aboard were apparently drowned. Damage was about $52,000.

Audrey, the major hurricane of the season, was described on pages 258 to 265.

Tropical storm Bertha developed about 100 miles south of the mouth of the Mississippi River on August 8 and crossed the Louisiana coast near Cameron late on August 9. Highest winds were estimated by ships and land stations at 50 to 70 mph and 10.73 inches of rain fell at Livingston, Texas. There were two fatalities but damage was slight.

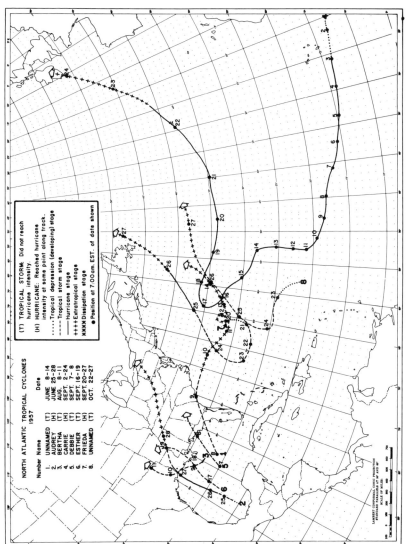

Fig. 90. Tracks of tropical cyclones of 1957.

Hurricane Carrie was in existence in one form or another from September 2 to 24, but during its tropical stages was entirely over the open ocean. The hurricane was quite severe over a long portion of its history and on the twenty-first the German sailing ship *Pamir* was sunk southwest of the Azores with a loss of 80 of her 86 crew members. While assuming extratropical characteristics Carrie lashed the British Isles with high winds and waves on the twenty-fourth and twenty-fifth. The hurricane was charted over one of the longest hurricane tracks of record — approximately 6,000 miles.

Tropical storm Debbie was in existence only on September 7 and 8. The storm went inland near Fort Walton, Florida. Highest winds were 40 mph at St. Marks and 52 mph in a squall at Tampa. In Apalachee Bay tides were 2.5 to 4 feet above normal and Crawfordville, Florida, reported 9.10 inches of rain. Four fatalities were attributed indirectly to the storm.

Another tropical storm, which was named Esther, developed in the Gulf of Mexico on September 16 and crossed the southeastern Louisiana coast about daybreak on the eighteenth. The Pensacola airport reported winds of 52 mph and gusts to 75 mph. There were three fatalities and damage totaled $1,500,000.

Hurricane Frieda spent its life at sea and was of hurricane intensity only a few hours on the morning of September 25.

The last tropical storm of the season (unnamed) developed and moved over the Atlantic north of the Windward Islands. During its history the lowest pressure reported was 29.32 and the highest winds 50 to 60 mph.

1958

Ten tropical cyclones, seven of full hurricane intensity developed in Atlantic waters during 1958 (Figure 91). Disturbances in the tropics became quite active after the first week in August and continued so until mid-October. While no hurricane center reached the United States mainland, Helene caused hurricane winds of major intensity on the North Carolina coast. Only two deaths in the United States were attributable directly to tropical cyclones and total damage was estimated at between eleven and twelve million dollars, mostly in the Carolinas in connection with Helene. In the Antilles tropical cyclones killed six

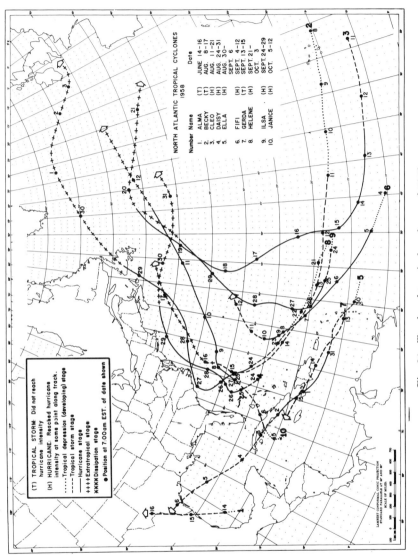

Fig. 91. Tracks of tropical cyclones of 1958.

or seven persons in Cuba, thirty-five or more in Haiti, three in Puerto Rico and two in the Bahamas.

Abnormally heavy shower activity was noted on June 9 and 10 over the western and central Caribbean Sea. Soon a weak circulation appeared and, attended by heavy rains, moved across Yucatan into the Bay of Campeche, where it developed into tropical storm Alma on the fourteenth, some 150 miles east of Tampico. The lowest pressure reported was 29.44 inches and the highest wind of 58 mph was encountered by a Coast Guard aircraft 50 miles south of Port Isabel, Texas. Heavy rains fell over the hill country west of San Antonio, with as much as 20 inches falling a little to the west of Medina, Texas. Accompanying floods caused considerable damage to crops and property, and one death by drowning occurred near Galveston.

Tropical storm Becky could be followed either as a storm or a disturbance over a long trajectory from the Cape Verdes to north of Puerto Rico and then on a recurvature well off the east coast of the United States. Although hurricane force squalls were reported briefly in the northeastern semicircle on August 14, it never reached full hurricane intensity.

Hurricane Cleo, which moved through the mid-Atlantic from August 11 to 21, was quite severe but remained far from any land area. On the fourteenth a minimum pressure of 28.41 inches and maximum winds of 146 mph were reported. On the fifteenth the aircraft found an even lower central pressure of 27.96 inches, but it is doubtful that it encountered the highest winds that were occurring at the time.

Daisy formed just east of the Bahamas on August 24 and became a hurricane the next day. The center passed about 75 miles east of Cape Hatteras on the twenty-eighth and 75 miles southeast of Nantucket on the twenty-ninth. Fringe gales were felt on the North Carolina capes and along the southern New England coast. A Texas tower, 120 miles east of Cape Cod, experienced a sustained wind of 69 mph and gusts to 87 mph. Maximum intensity was attained on August 28 with minimum pressure of 27.61 inches and estimated winds in excess of 150 mph.

A developing tropical depression moved through the Windward and Leeward Islands on August 30 with heavy rains and squalls of 35 to 40 mph. This storm named Ella intensified rapidly as it moved westward and by the late forenoon of the thirty-first winds had increased to 85 mph and by midnight to 110 mph. The center skirted along the south coast of Hispaniola causing torrential rains and resulting in considerable damage along the southern mountain slopes. The center passed inland over the Sierra Maestra in eastern Cuba a short distance west of Santiago and weakened. It continued on a west-northwest course across the Gulf of Mexico but never regained hurricane intensity. Grand Isle, Louisiana, reported gusts of 75 mph during a squall on the morning of the fifth. Flooding caused heavy damage in southern Haiti. Thirty persons were drowned in a flash flood near Aux Cayes; six to eight persons were also drowned in Cuba. Galveston Airport reported 13.60 inches of rain during a three-day period with 8.44 inches on September 7. One man was washed overboard from a snapper boat near Galveston.

Hurricane Fifi moved on a parabolic course east and north of the Antilles during the period September 4-12. It appears to have reached maximum intensity on the sixth with highest winds of 92 mph.

A minor disturbance moved through the Windward Islands on September 13. It broke up over the mountains of the Dominican Republic on the fourteenth. The lowest known pressure in tropical storm Gerda was 29.65 inches with maximum winds of 69 mph.

Hurricane Helene was one of the most intense storms of 1958 and the most destructive. A disturbed condition which had been followed for some time began to intensify on September 23 and became a hurricane late on the twenty-fourth. It approached the South Carolina coast on the twenty-sixth attaining the greatest intensity around midnight some 80 miles east of Charleston with a minimum pressure of 27.55 inches. The next day as the hurricane recurved the western edge of the hurricane eye came within approximately 10 miles of the coast at Cape Fear, North Carolina, and a portion of the terrific winds under the wall cloud passed over land in this area. The Weather Bureau at Wilmington recorded a maximum wind of 88 mph and a peak gust of 135 mph. This exceeded all previous records there. At Cape Fear sustained winds were estimated at 125 mph with gusts from 150 to 160 mph. Although property damage was estimated at $11,000,000 in North Carolina, no lives were lost directly as a result of the hurricane and only one indirectly.

Hurricane Ilsa immediately followed Helene but recurved northward east of Puerto Rico and Bermuda. The minimum pressure in Ilsa was 27.52 inches on the twenty-sixth and the storm had deepened 48 mb in twenty-four hours. Winds were in excess of 125 mph.

The last hurricane of the season began developing on the fourth and fifth of October south of central Cuba. Janice reached hurricane intensity during the evening of the sixth as it passed through the Bahamas. Minimum pressure was 28.58 inches on the tenth with maximum winds of 90 mph. Rains in excess of 20 inches caused floods in Jamaica and one man was drowned in Nassau harbor. Damage was from $200,000 to $300,000 in the Bahamas.

1959

Eleven tropical cyclones were noted in Atlantic waters during 1959 (Figure 92) compared with an annual average of ten. There is considerable doubt whether one storm — Edith — fully met all the criteria of a tropical cyclone. Except for hurricanes Gracie and Hannah in late September and early October, average intensity was unusually weak. Three hurricanes — two barely of hurricane intensity — and four tropical cyclones not of full hurricane intensity, reached the coast line of the United States. Damage from these storms in the United States totaled about $23,500,000 with twenty-four fatalities, twenty-two resulting from Gracie. Except for thirty-three deaths in Nova Scotia from the hurricane of June 17-21, there were no other known deaths or even significant damage in North and Central America outside the United States.

The first storm Arlene developed in the southeastern Gulf of Mexico on May 28 and moved northward across the Louisiana coast on the thirtieth between Weeks Island and Point Au Fer. This was the earliest tropical storm of record to reach the Louisiana coast. Highest sustained winds were 55 mph with gusts to 74 mph and lowest central pressure was 29.52 inches. Eleven to thirteen inches of rain fell in southeastern Louisiana and heavy rains were associated with Arlene east-northeastward to northern Georgia. One man was drowned in the surf at Galveston and total damage was around $500,000.

Tropical storm Beulah developed in the far southwestern Gulf of Mexico on June 16 and moved inland south of Tampico on the eighteenth. Maximum wind reported was 70 mph and lowest pressure 29.15 inches.

At about the same time a weak closed circulation appeared in the east-central Gulf on the seventeenth. While it was moving across central Florida on the night of June 17-18, tornadoes were reported at Miami and near Jupiter around 10:00 p.m. The former caused damage

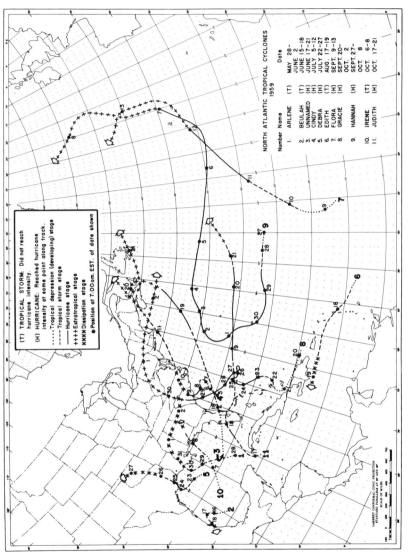

Fig. '92. Tracks of tropical cyclones of 1959.

of $1,500,000 in the Miami area and many injuries but no deaths. Tides 2.5 to 3 feet above normal eroded beaches from Naples to St. Petersburg to the extent of $156,000. After passing into the Atlantic the storm deepened to 28.76 inches with winds approaching 100 mph.

The fourth tropical cyclone of the season — Cindy — attained hurricane force just before it reached the coast north of Charleston, South Carolina, on July 8. Block Island, Rhode Island, reported a gust of 65 mph as the storm recurved a short distance south of the New England coast.

Debra reached storm intensity some distance off the Texas coast on July 23 and passed inland between Freeport and Galveston on the twenty-fourth. The lowest reported pressure was 29.07 inches and maximum winds 90 mph with gusts to 105 mph. Rainfall was heavy throughout eastern Texas with 14.42 inches at Orange. There were no casualties but damage amounted to $6,685,000.

Tropical storm Edith passed through the Windward Islands on August 18 with 55 mph and minimum pressure 29.74 inches. No good circulation apparently existed and the storm dissipated in the eastern Caribbean.

Flora moved northward through the eastern Atlantic September 9-13. Maximum winds reported were 74 mph and minimum pressure 29.35 inches.

Gracie, a major hurricane, was the most troublesome tropical cyclone of the season to forecast. Its development and intensification northeast of the Bahamas was sudden and her erratic movement between the twenty-second and twenty-seventh of September, when at one time or another it moved in every direction of the compass, proved impossible to forecast in detail. On the twenty-seventh, however, Gracie began to move steadily toward the west-northwest and passed inland on the South Carolina coast near Beaufort around noon on the twenty-ninth. The Marine Corps Auxiliary Air Station at Beaufort reported a minimum barometer reading of 28.05 inches and gusts to 138 mph. Gusts were estimated at 173 mph closer to the eye. A series of tornadoes attended the passage of the dying storm through Virginia and twelve persons were killed near Charlottesville. Ten others lost their lives in South Carolina and Georgia, mainly due to storm induced automobile accidents, falling trees, and live wires. Damage was described as the most severe in history at Beaufort and estimated at $14,000,000, about half occurring in Charleston County, South Carolina.

Hurricane Hannah, which lasted from September 27 to October 8 spent her entire life over the open ocean and was never a serious threat to any land area. By the thirtieth central pressure had dropped to 28.32 inches with maximum winds of 124 mph. The hurricane maintained about the same intensity for the next three days and then it began to lose strength.

Tropical storm Irene developed in the central Gulf of Mexico on October 6 and moved north-northeastward to the extreme northwest Florida coast. The lowest pressure reported by the hurricane hunter planes was 29.56 inches and the highest winds were 55 mph in squalls at Pensacola. There were no deaths and damage was insignificant.

A squally area was detected in the eastern Caribbean on October 10 and 11 but no intensification occurred until the seventeenth when a circulation began to develop near the western tip of Cuba. Late in the day a ship reported hurricane winds near Dry Tortugas in an apparently brief squall. The center reached the Florida Gulf coast near Boca Grande Island between 8:00 and 9:00 a.m. Fort Myers reported a sustained wind of only 40 mph, gusts to 53 mph, total rainfall 7.57 inches and tides 2.5 feet above normal. Gusts of 55 mph occurred at Miami. Shortly after passing out over the Atlantic, Judith attained hurricane intensity.

1960

The hurricane season of 1960 was subnormal from the standpoints of both frequency and intensity. Seven tropical cyclones developed in the Atlantic and four reached hurricane intensity (Figure 93). The only major hurricane was Donna, which was the most destructive tropical cyclone ever to strike Florida and one of the most damaging ever to affect the United States. It is also believed to have caused hurricane winds over a greater proportion of the United States coast line than any other storm. This was the first major hurricane to affect Florida since 1950.

Donna was found by a Navy hurricane hunter plane on September 2 near latitude 14° N and longitude 49° W. It was already a fully developed hurricane with maximum winds of 138 mph and central pressure of 28.73 inches. It is believed that the disturbance can be traced back to the African coast. An active easterly wave passed over Dakar on August 29 attended by heavy rain which contributed to an

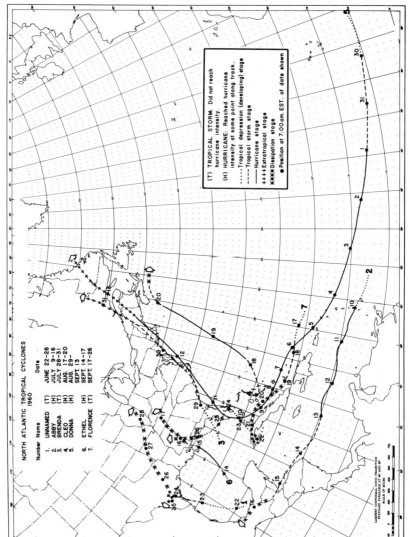

Fig. 93. Tracks of tropical cyclones of 1960.

airliner crash there with heavy loss of life. Heavy rain occurred in the Cape Verde Islands on the thirty-first. It is believed the disturbance reached hurricane intensity on September 1 near longitude 40° W.

Donna moved west-northwestward on approximately the climatological track, but at a slightly faster-than-average rate of about 19 mph. This course took the hurricane through the Leeward Islands during the evening of September 4, with the eye passing over Barbuda and Saint Maarten. Damage on these and nearby islands was severe. Maximum gusts were 60 mph in the Virgin Islands and 38 mph in Puerto Rico as the main body of the hurricane passed to the north. However, a combination of heavy rains, 4- to 6-foot storm tides and heavy surf drowned 107 persons — 84 at Humacao.

By September 6 the central pressure had dropped to 27.76 inches and Donna was a severe hurricane approaching the southern Bahamas. Turks Islands, south of the center, escaped with little damage and winds of 50 to 60 mph. Other islands were not so fortunate. The eye passed over or very near Mayaguana, Acklins Island, Fortune Island, and Ragged Island. No deaths were reported, but only a few of the more substantial buildings were left standing. Mayaguana was battered by hurricane winds for thirteen hours, and the anemometer at Ragged failed at 150 mph.

The eye of Donna passed over the middle Florida Keys a few hours after midnight on the tenth with the hurricane at its peak intensity. Central pressure was now 27.46 inches and under the wall cloud around the eye prevailed sustained winds of 140 mph and gusts to 180 and possibly 200 mph. During this period Donna was moving quite slowly at about 8 mph. The storm surge reached as much as 13 feet above normal levels at points on Islamorada and was generally 8 to 12 feet some 40 miles to the northeast of the center and 20 miles to the southwest. Destruction from the combination of wind and water ranged from major to almost complete. Although there are now nine times as many people living in the area, in contrast to the Labor Day hurricane of 1935, when between 400 and 500 persons were killed on the Florida Keys, there were only three fatalities in Donna. The effect of the hurricane on the flora and fauna of the Everglades National Park has been studied by Robertson and Paulson.* After the hurricane, observers in

---

*Robertson, W. B., Jr., and Paulson, D. R., 1961: Florida Region. Audubon Field Notes, 15, No. 1.

the main storm area found a world without one green leaf, the vegetation browned as if by fire. The largest stand of big mangrove trees in the world is located near the southern tip of Florida and was 50 per cent or more killed with a complete kill in some areas. The great white heron, only found in the United States in extreme southern Florida and once in danger of extinction, suffered about a 35 to 40 per cent loss but some 600 of these beautiful birds survived.

After leaving the Keys, Donna moved on a broad recurve with the eye passing over Naples and Fort Myers. Sustained winds of 100 mph with gusts from 115 to 150 mph occurred in these areas as the hurricane began slowly to weaken; damage was severe. Donna had diminished to barely hurricane intensity by the time it passed out to sea over in the vicinity of Daytona Beach. Rapid reintensification, however, occurred over the Atlantic. As it moved north-northeastward off the South Carolina coast several small tornadic storms were reported in South Carolina and southeastern North Carolina.

Late on the eleventh the hurricane began to accelerate and it re-entered the coast just northeast of Wilmington and passed out to sea again near the Virginia line about 0500 EST the next morning. An interesting feature was the large eye which had expanded from 50 to 80 miles in diameter and later to 100 miles as it moved along off the New Jersey coast. Minimum pressures in North Carolina were in the 28.29 to 28.55 inch range and highest winds ranged from 80 to 100 mph with higher gusts. Damage was heavy. Now moving at 35 to 40 mph Donna crossed Long Island into New England on the twelfth. Gusts of 115 mph or higher were reported at Montauk, Long Island, and Block Island, Rhode Island. Blue Hill Observatory clocked 90 mph winds with gusts to 140 mph.

Altogether there were 164 fatalities from Donna, 13 in Florida, 8 in North Carolina, 29 in other states, and 114 in the Antilles and the Bahamas. Damage was $300,000,000 in Florida, $56,500,000 in North Carolina, $30,000,000 in other states, and $13,000,000 in the Antilles and the Bahamas.

Donna was unique in that it caused hurricane winds in Florida, North Carolina, the Middle Atlantic states and New England. Although it was one of the most destructive hurricanes of all times, loss of life in the United States was remarkable low. The accuracy of the warnings was in large part a reflection of continuous tracking by aircraft and land-based radar, which was the most complete of any up to this time.

The first tropical cyclone of the season was poorly organized and was never named. It drifted northward from the Bay of Campeche. Early on June 24 it moved inland about 30 miles west of Corpus Christi, Texas, with lowest reported pressure 29.60 inches and maximum gusts of 60 mph. Port Lavaca reported 29.76 inches of rain for the period of June 23-26. Fifteen persons were drowned either in the high seas or subsequent floods. Damage mostly from floods was estimated at $3,600,000.

Early on July 10 a small vortex passed just to the north of Barbados. By 1100 EST reconnaissance aircraft found a small hurricane, which was named Abby, with winds of 90 to 100 mph. The hurricane moved on a general westerly course, skirting the coast of Honduras, and moved inland over southern British Honduras on the fifteenth. Damage was minor in British Honduras, but six lives were lost on St. Lucia with damage of $435,000.

On July 28 a weak cyclonic circulation began to deepen some 150 miles west of Tampa Bay. Brenda moved northeastward across northern Florida and eventually reached New England on the thirty-first with the center always remaining over or near land. It did not reach hurricane intensity but a gust of 65 mph was measured at the Cape Cod canal. Thirteen inches of rain fell around Tampa and 3- to 5-foot storm tides were reported on the Gulf coast near Tampa. No lives were lost but damage along the Florida Gulf coast was reported at $5,000,000.

Hurricane Cleo formed northeast of the Bahamas on August 18 and moved north-northeastward over the Atlantic dissipating south of Nova Scotia on the twentieth. High wind was about 90 mph when the hurrican was south of the New England coast.

Hurricane Ethel was discovered by MAMOS (Marine Automatic Meteorological Observing Station — later called NOMAD) anchored in the central Gulf of Mexico. Late in the afternoon aircraft reconnaissance reported a central pressure of 28.70 inches and winds 160 mph. Shortly after this cooler and drier air began to enter the system and it was barely of hurricane intensity when it reached the coast near Biloxi, Mississippi. The total storm damage was estimated at around $1,000,000.

Florence, the last tropical cyclone of the season, was never well defined. Vero Beach, Florida, reported 52 mph winds in a squall. It produced rains of 3 to 6 inches over much of extreme southern Florida, which together with Donna and frequently heavy showers brought

September rainfall totals to over 30 inches in some sections along the lower east Florida coast.

1961

Tropical cyclones in 1961 numbered ten (Figure 94). The season was remarkable for the lack of activity June through August and the very high cyclone frequency September through November. Eight of the storms were of full hurricane intensity. Indeed all could have been classified as hurricanes since Gerda was attended by hurricane-force winds at the Texas towers off the New England coast when only partly tropical, and ships in Inga reported 74 mph winds on one or two occasions. Carla, Esther, and Hattie were major hurricanes — all had central pressures under 27.52 inches. On September 11 there were four fully developed hurricanes: Carla in the Gulf of Mexico; Betsy, Debbie, and Esther in the mid-Atlantic at approximately latitudes 22°, 29°, and 48°.

Anna, the first hurricane of the year, began developing a short distance east of the Windward Islands on July 19. It passed through the Grenadines on the night of the nineteenth with winds up to 50 mph and attained hurricane force by the next afternoon. Anna maintained a course slightly north of due west through the Caribbean crossing the coast line of southern British Honduras on the twenty-fourth. Minor damage was reported from Trinidad and Grenada and on the southern coast of British Honduras. Damage was extensive on the islands off the coast of Honduras, total damage being estimated at $300,000 with one fatality.

Four hurricanes developed in quick succession: Betsy on September 2, Carla on the third, Debbie on the sixth, and Esther on the eleventh. Betsy and Debbie kept on a course through the mid-Atlantic, with Debbie eventually reaching the British Isles with hurricane force and causing considerable damage and eleven fatalities in Ireland. While the center of Esther remained off shore, peripheral effects caused five to ten million dollars damage in southern New York and New England.

Carla, one of the major Atlantic hurricanes of the twentieth century, was faintly evident as a weak perturbation in the intertropical convergence zone in the eastern Caribbean as early as September 1. The disturbed area was more pronounced by the third, and at 1100 EST on the

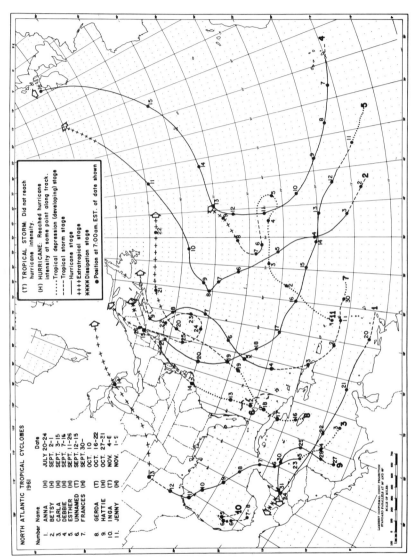

Fig. 94. Tracks of tropical cyclones of 1961.

fourth the first bulletin was issued announcing that it had reached the depression stage and that further intensification was expected. Regular advisories began late that day and continued until the storm was no longer a threat to life and property. From its inception until the hurricane center approached the Texas coast intensification was remarkably regular and steady reaching hurricane force on the sixth, east of the Yucatan peninsula; its lowest central pressure 27.49 inches occurred on the afternoon of the eleventh. The center of Carla was under surveillance of land-based radars at Lake Charles, Louisiana, and Galveston and Brownsville, Texas, for some forty-eight hours. All radars showed a strong cycloidal track and even a complete loop during the period immediately preceding landfall.

Carla was one of the largest, most intense and destructive hurricanes ever to strike the Gulf coast. At one time gale or stronger winds were prevailing over more than two-thirds of the Gulf of Mexico. Sustained hurricane force winds were reported from Corpus Christi to Galveston with hurricane gusts along almost the entire length of the Texas coast. High tides began affecting the upper Texas coast on September 8, and waves and tides continued to batter the area with ever increasing fury until the center moved inland three days later. Highest tides were 16.6 feet MSL at Port Lavaca, 14.5 feet at Port O'Connor, 15.2 feet at Matagorda and 14.8 feet on the upper Houston ship channel. A high waterline varying from 15.7 to 22.0 feet was established from the debris near the head of Lavaca Bay. The unusually slow movement of the storm of 6 to 9 mph resulted in exceptionally prolonged hurricane conditions.

Peak gusts of 175 mph were estimated at Port Lavaca. The lowest reported pressure there was 27.62 inches and it remained at that value from 1545 to 1735 CST. Although the hurricane eye was never closer to Galveston than 120 miles, the maximum wind there was 80 mph with peak gusts to 112 mph. Tides at Galveston were 9.3 feet and 11.0 feet at Texas City. Between 2:00 a.m. and 9:00 a.m. on September 12, a series of five tornadoes occurred in the Galveston area. Two of the tornadoes were very destructive — eight persons were killed and forty-nine injured. About 40 per cent of the total hurricane damage on Galveston Island was caused by the tornadoes. The loss of life from the tornadoes might have been much heavier if there had not been such a complete evacuation. Altogether eight tornadoes were associated with Carla in Texas and ten in Louisiana.

Total damage in Texas was estimated as at least $300,000,000, with approximately two-thirds of the total for property damage and one-third for crop damage; the U.S. Engineers, however, estimated the damage as more than $400,000,000. Fatalities numbered thirty-four in Texas, six in Louisiana, five in Kansas, and one in Missouri; persons injured in Texas totaled 465. Building destruction was itemized: 1,915 homes, 568 farm buildings, and 415 other buildings, with 7,398 homes, 1,382 farm buildings and 1,219 other buildings receiving major damage.

Timely and accurate hurricane advisories resulted in the largest evacuation of persons from danger areas in the nation's history. An estimated 350,000 persons fled inland from the coastal areas of Texas and Louisiana. This evacuation was responsible for the comparatively low death toll, in contrast to September, 1900, when 6,000 persons died, mostly from drowning, in this area. An improved warning system, better dissemination of warning information through television, radio, and the newspapers, and efficient community preparedness were responsible for the saving of thousands of lives.

A tropical depression formed north of Andros Island in the Bahamas on September 12 and reached the North Carolina coast near Wilmington still a depression on the fourteenth. As it moved northeastward along the New Jersey coast, radars observed an eye and spiral bands. By this time it had reached storm intensity. Point Judith, Rhode Island, reported winds of 70 mph, and winds of hurricane force occurred in Maine. At Cutler, at the top of an 800-foot radio tower, 100 mph winds were recorded. It was at least partially extratropical, however, at this time with the storm embedded in an extratropical low pressure system.

Frances reached storm intensity a short distance east of the French Antilles on September 30 and caused 50 to 60 mph winds as it passed through that area. The mountains of Dominica and Guadeloupe temporarily disrupted the storm but it reached hurricane intensity on October 4 east of the Bahamas. The hurricane passed west of Bermuda on the sixth and threatened Maine on the eighth. Then it turned abruptly eastward and dissipated over Nova Scotia. Maximum intensity was reached west and northwest of Bermuda with lowest pressure 27.99 inches and maximum winds 127 mph. Damage was minor and confined to flooding along the south coast of Puerto Rico.

The first indication of the next tropical cyclone — Gerda — was heavy rain which set in over Jamaica on October 15. By the morning of the sixteenth the barometer at Kingston had fallen to 29.68 inches. The poorly organized disturbance moved across Cuba on the seventeenth and later winds north of the Bahamas increased to 60 mph. Gerda moved northward to a position just off Nantucket on the twentieth and a Texas tower off the Massachusetts coast reported winds of hurricane force for short periods. Subsequently Gerda turned to the east-northeast and gradually lost intensity. Extensive flooding resulted in seven deaths in eastern Cuba and five in Jamaica.

Hurricane Hattie was the killer storm of the 1961 hurricane season, although property damage was much greater in Carla; approximately 275 people perished in Hattie. Not since hurricane Janet in 1955, had such an intense hurricane visited the Yucatan peninsula. The first indication of the developing tropical cyclone was a ship report from the Caribbean about 120 miles south-southeast of San Andres Island. The center of Hattie passed over or just to the west of San Andres during the late afternoon of October 27. The barometer fell to 29.26 inches with sustained winds of near 80 mph and gusts to 105 mph. On San Andres one person was killed, fifteen injured, and property damage was $300,000. This was only the fourth hurricane of record to affect the island.

From this point Hattie continued on a generally northerly course for the next thirty-six hours, steadily intensifying with the minimum pressure reaching 28.11 inches as it crossed latitude 15° N. By 1900 EST, October 29, a change to a more westerly and later west-southwesterly course became evident. (The west-southwest to southwest movement of the hurricane in this area was most unusual.) Around 1700 EST on October 30 as the hurricane approached the coast of British Honduras it reached its greatest intensity with a minimum barometer reading of 27.17 inches. Around sunrise on the thirty-first the eye of hurricane Hattie crossed the coast about 20 miles southeast of Belize, the capital of British Honduras. The lowest pressure on the barograph at Stanley Field, Belize, was 28.70 inches, indicating a gradient of 1.3 to 1.5 inches in the approximately 25 miles between that point and the center of the eye. Sustained winds reached 150 to 160 mph with gusts to 200 mph. Storm tides of 10 to 11 feet along the Belize waterfront were general and other locations near Belize reported tides of 14 feet. Seventy-five per cent of Belize was either destroyed or severely damaged. Destruction was estimated at $60,000,000 — a staggering figure

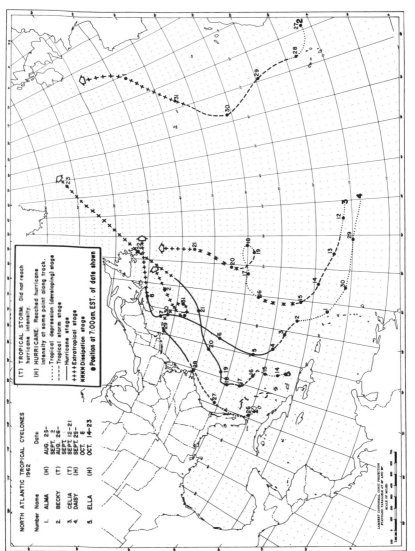

Fig. 95. Tracks of tropical cyclones of 1962.

for the small, thinly populated country. Some 262 person
British Honduras, 11 in Guatemala, and 1 in Honduras. The
of British Honduras stated that Hattie was much more sever
hurricane of 1931 when two thousand persons perished, I
lower death toll because of the excellent warnings which r
extensive evacuation.

Tropical storm Inga moved very erratically in the Gulf c
east of Tampico and Vera Cruz during the period Novemb
was quite possibly a hurricane on the fourth when the SS i
estimated winds at 75 to 85 mph. On the sixth it seems l
center dissipated and another formed to the south.

Hurricane Jenny was first observed as a depression in the
Islands. Beginning on November 1 it meandered in a general
east direction over the mid-Atlantic until it dissipated on the
reached maximum intensity on the sixth with lowest pressu
inches and winds of just about hurricane intensity.

1962

From the overall standpoints of number, intensity, and
1962 hurricane season was the quietest in over thirty years. T
no major hurricane; no tropical cyclones were noted in the C
Sea and Gulf of Mexico (Figure 95) and none caused winds
cane force on the mainland of the United States. Consequently
and casualties were the lowest in many years. At no time was t
relatively small eye and concentrated organization of the class
ricane.

The first development of a tropical cyclone of storm intei
curred on August 26, the latest date for the first occurren
1941. A weak disturbance was photographed by Tiros V on
14 in the vicinity of 12.5° N., 51° W. During the next
days it moved at a constant speed of some 10 knots for som
miles without any significant change in intensity. It began to i
slowly on the twenty-sixth and reached hurricane intensity ne
Hatteras on the twenty-eighth. On the North Carolina cape
Head reported gusts of 53 mph and Hatteras 48 mph. Tides wei
2 feet above normal in the Hatteras-Norfolk area and 3 feet i
Head. Coastal areas of Massachusetts and Rhode Island were bufi
northerly gales gusting to 60 mph. More than one hundre

pleasure craft were sunk along the Massachusetts coast. Hurricane Alma reached maximum intensity on the afternoon of the twenty-eighth when aircraft reconnaissance reported a sustained wind of 92 mph.

Reports from the Cape Verde Islands strongly indicated a tropical disturbance on August 27. On the twenty-ninth photographs from Tiros V showed a cloud system which had all the characteristics of a fully developed tropical storm. On August 30 a ship near 30.7° N., 29.2° W. reported a northerly wind of 52 mph. Tropical storm Becky began a gradual decrease in intensity thereafter as it moved east of the Azores and it apparently dissipated on September 1. Climatologically speaking Becky followed a very rare track. Indeed this is the farthest east an observed storm has ever moved north in the period extending back to 1886. It is not unlikely, however, that some tropical cyclones in this area have gone unnoted.

The third tropical storm in 1962 was first observed as a depression near 18.4° N., 50.7° W. on September 12. It moved first west-north-westward and then northward near longitude 60° W. eventually dissipating in the mid-Atlantic on the twenty-first. Intensity fluctuated from one day to the next but the highest wind was apparently 65 mph late on the twelfth, while the lowest pressure 29.38 inches was reported the next day.

The first indication of Daisy, the fourth tropical cyclone of the season, was reported on September 28 by the weather satellite and by ships. It was not until October 3 that it finally reached hurricane intensity. On October 6 the hurricane passed northward well west of Bermuda with 100 mph winds and a barometer reading of 28.5 inches; on reaching Nova Scotia October 7 it turned sharply eastward. As the hurricane moved northeastward offshore from New England it immediately followed a "northeaster." The combined impact of the two storms produced widespread and heavy damage. Flood damage occurred in eastern Vermont, New Hampshire, and southwestern Maine. A near record rainfall of 10 to 12 inches was reported in Middlesex and Essex Counties, Massachusetts. Highest winds were experienced along the Maine coast with velocities of 60 to 70 mph. Lobster fishermen suffered heavy losses and hundreds of small boats were sunk or damaged. Acre-size Mt. Desert Rock, twenty-two miles offshore from Southwest Harbor, Maine, was pounded and washed by mountainous waves, some of which reportedly reached elevations 50 feet above sea level. Damage was said to be the heaviest in the Coast Guard's 115-year history there.

The depression which was to grow into hurricane Ella developed in the southeastern Bahamas on October 14. As it drifted northward it reached storm intensity on the fifteenth and hurricane intensity on the seventeenth. The hurricane reached maximum intensity on the twentieth about midway between Bermuda and Cape Hatteras with about 100 mph winds and central pressure of 28.35 inches. Property damage along the Atlantic coast was minor, but two fishermen, who set out in a 14-foot outboard motor boat from near Charleston, South Carolina, lost their lives in the fringes of the hurricane during its closest approach to the coast.

Altogether the hurricane damage in 1962 in the United States was only slightly more than $2,000,000 — the lowest in many years. There were four fatalities: two in South Carolina, one in New England, and one in Nova Scotia.

1963

Nine tropical cyclones were observed in the Atlantic during the 1963 season and all but two were of hurricane intensity, although several were barely so. This is close to the normal number of ten which has been the average during the past three decades. The majority of the tropical cyclones developed initially between the Antilles and Africa but none attained hurricane intensity east of latitude 48° (Figure 96). The number of hurricane days greatly exceeded the average. For the second consecutive year the continental United States was not affected by any major hurricane. However, from the standpoint of loss of life, this was the second most disastrous hurricane season of record in the Atlantic area as a whole and will be long remembered in Cuba and Haiti. Statistics on casualties and damage for the 1963 hurricane season are included in Table 32. As of March 1, 1964, final evaluation of these figures had not been completed in the Dominican Republic, Haiti, and Cuba.

Hurricane Arlene was first detected by the Tiros VI satellite at 1505Z on July 31 in its embryonic depression stage. On August 2, Navy hurricane-hunter planes found that it had reached full hurricane intensity. Arlene moved on a parabolic trajectory, passing a short distance north of Antigua and later over Bermuda; it lost tropical characteristics on August 11. The most unusual development was a marked loss of intensity during the night of August 3-4 in an area where this

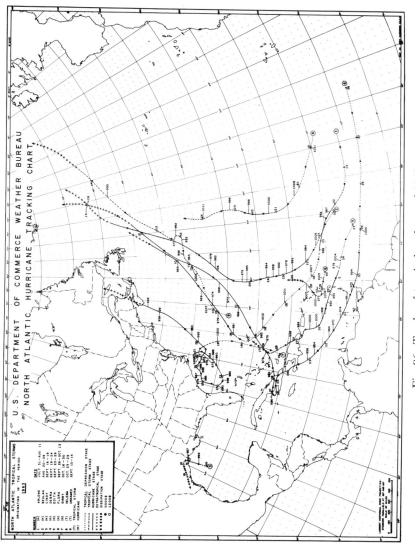

Fig. 96. Tracks of tropical cyclones of 1963.

TABLE 32

Casualties and Damage for the 1963 Hurricane Season

Cyclone	In-tensity	Date	Damage	Deaths	Injuries	Principal Area Affected
Arlene	H	July 31-Aug. 11	$ 300,000	0	0	Bermuda
Beulah	H	Aug. 20-28	——	0	0	
Unnamed	T	Sept. 10-15	——	0	0	
Cindy	H	Sept. 16-19	12,560,000	3	0	Texas, La.
Debra	H	Sept. 19-24	——	0	0	
Edith	H	Sept. 23-29	46,622,600	10	50	Lesser Antilles
Flora	H	Sept. 26-Oct. 13	528,550,000	7193	*	Haiti, Cuba
Ginny	H	Oct. 16-30	400,000	7	0	Fla., N.C., New Eng.
Helena	T	Oct. 25-29	500,000	5	14	Guadeloupe
Total			$588,932,600	7218	*	

* many

rarely occurs. There were no lives lost in Bermuda although there was $300,000 property damage. The lowest pressure was 28.78 inches. Highest winds at Bermuda were from the east-southeast with gusts to 98 mph and tides were estimated at 4 feet above normal.

Hurricane Beulah developed some 350 miles east of the Lesser Antilles and remained well out in the mid-Atlantic. Maximum intensity was reached early on August 24 with a central pressure of 28.29 inches and maximum winds of 120 mph.

The hurricane season began in earnest on September 10 when the next tropical cyclone developed. This was never named since it remained well out in the Atlantic and there was some question at the time whether it was tropical. On September 12 the *Freiburg* reported 78 mph winds, 27-foot seas, and a barometer reading of 29.39 inches.

Hurricane Cindy, the first in the Gulf of Mexico in two years, formed in a trough of low pressure located about 200 miles east-north-east of Brownsville, Texas, on the morning of September 16. By 2:00 p.m., the central eye developed sufficiently to be located about 200 miles east of Corpus Christi by the WSR-57 radar at Galveston. At the same hour, a report from the *SS Sabine* near the storm center indicated hurricane force winds. Cindy moved northward at an average speed of 8 mph during the afternoon and night of the sixteenth, remaining relatively small in area and with no further increase in intensity, although most of the circulation was still over the warm Gulf waters. Winds and tides along the coast from the Galveston area eastward increased during the evening, with winds reaching maximum values during the early morning hours of the seventeenth. Over the Gulf, highest sustained winds were estimated at 80 mph and highest gusts on the coast were 80 mph, measured near the eastern tip of Galveston Island. The Weather Bureau office at Galveston recorded a fastest mile at the rate of 50 mph and a peak gust of 74 mph on the seventeenth. In the Port Arthur area, the highest gusts were from 40 to 50 mph; while in Louisiana gusts were estimated as high as 60 mph at Grand Chenier and 45 mph at Cameron, but were generally in the 25 to 35 mph range.

The central eye of Cindy, some 20 miles in diameter, moved on shore around High Island, about midway between Galveston and Port Arthur. The Corps of Engineers there reported "light winds and near calm" between 7:30 and 11:00 a.m. CST on the seventeenth and a low barometer reading of 29.44 inches at 10:00 a.m. A slightly lower pressure, 29.41 inches, was recorded at Anáhuac between 2:27 and 2:45 p.m. The storm center became almost stationary for about eighteen hours shortly after moving inland, then drifted very slowly westward and south-westward with slowly decreasing intensity through the Texas coastal plain on September 18 and 19. This unusual slow movement during the decay of the storm resulted in an extended period of heavy rainfall in the northeastern sector over extreme southeastern Texas and southwestern Louisiana. Storm rainfall totals were 15 to 20 inches in portions of Jefferson, Newton, and Orange counties, Texas, and Calcasieu and Vermilion parishes, Louisiana. The heaviest rain occurred at Deweyville, in southern Newton County: a three-day total of 23.50 inches, including 20.60 inches in twenty-four hours between 7 a.m. CST observations on September 17 and 18.

Considerable damage was produced by the flooding of streams and drainage canals and ponding of water in the areas of extremely heavy rainfall over the lower Sabine Basin in both Texas and Louisiana. The flood waters were most severe in the Port Arthur-Port Acres area of Jefferson County. Waters entered about 4,000 homes in Jefferson, Orange, and Newton counties, remaining in some areas for extended periods. Overall property damage — primarily from the flooding — was estimated at $11,700,000. Principal crop damage (estimated near

$500,000 in Texas and $360,000 in Louisiana) was to unharvested rice. Fortunately most of the crop had already been combined and rainfall in most areas was considered more beneficial than damaging to crops and ranges. One man was drowned when he fell from a crew boat evacuating personnel from the offshore oil rigs south of Cameron, Louisiana, and two young twin girls drowned at Port Acres on September 22 in the persistent flood waters still covering that section.

Hurricane Debra formed in the mid-tropical Atlantic and moved on a course well removed from any land areas. On September 21, a reconnaissance aircraft found 75 mph winds and a central pressure of about 29.53 inches. Debra at best was barely a minimal hurricane for no more than twenty-four hours.

Hurricane Edith formed in the Atlantic east of the Lesser Antilles on September 24. Early morning reconnaissance found winds of 70 mph and a short time later Edith was reported to be of hurricane intensity with 80 mph winds. This location was some 120 miles east of Barbados. Edith passed over the north portion of St. Lucia between midnight and daybreak on the twenty-fifth and was at her maximum intensity at about this time. The lowest pressure computed in Edith was 28.88 inches on September 24. The hurricane then moved on a general west-northwesterly course to a point some 120 miles south of Puerto Rico, where it turned to a more northwesterly course passing over the eastern portion of the Dominican Republic before dissipating as it moved out north of Hispaniola. Edith was weakened considerably by passing over the mountains of the Lesser Antilles and, thereafter, was barely of hurricane intensity as she moved across the northeastern Caribbean and the Dominican Republic.

Martinique was heavily damaged to the extent of $40,000,000 with ten persons killed and fifty injured. Storm tides of 8 feet above normal were noted, and Fort-de-France reported a minimum pressure of 29.38 inches with maximum winds at 127 mph. Winds reached 80 mph in gusts on Dominica, where damage amounted to $2,611,600; there was no loss of life. On St. Lucia, 40 to 50 per cent of the bananas were destroyed and the cocoa crop was a total loss; tides were 8 to 10 feet above normal and Port Castries reported a dead calm, beginning at 2:00 a.m., which lasted seventy-five minutes. Maximum winds here were 90 mph with no loss of life but damage totaled $3,465,000. On Barbados winds reached 60 to 65 mph in squalls on the northern tip of the island and damage was estimated at $145,000. In the Dominican Republic damage was minor, but 50 to 60 mph winds along the south and south-western coasts of Puerto Rico, together with heavy rains, caused damage of $400,000.

At 8:50 a.m. EST on September 26, the National Hurricane Center in Miami received an advisory from the Weather Bureau's satellite section stating that Tiros VII at 4:40 a.m. EST had sighted a poorly organized vortex at approximately latitude 11.5° N, longitude 38.0° W, with a central overcast area about 4° in diameter with some banding to the north and east.

On the next day, September 27, Tiros VII photographed the same complex cloud system which retained a rather remarkable resemblance to that of the day before. The cloud mass had grown somewhat in size but there were still no indications of spiral bands and apparently it was still associated with an ordinary depression in the ITC. The satellite was not in a position to photograph the cloud system on Saturday and Sunday and there were not sufficient ship reports to indicate the existence of a circulation. However, on Sunday, the San Juan Hurricane Center requested surface observations from all ships in the area, and a Navy hurricane reconnaissance flight was arranged for daybreak Monday morning.

A series of ship reports began to arrive early Monday morning. A much delayed weather observation from the *Sinon* arrived around 3:30 a.m. The report stated that the barometer at 5:30 p.m. the afternoon before had dipped to 29.54 inches with a wind shift from northwest to southwest but nothing was said about the strength of the winds. The *SS Del Alba* forwarded an observation made at 1:00 a.m. EST, which arrived around 4:30 a.m., indicating winds from the northeast of 35 knots and a barometer reading of 1006.8 mb with a fall of 5 mb in the past three hours. At 10:00 a.m. EST much too late for adequate warning to Tobago, the *Del Alba* sent in a complete report as follows:

PASSED THROUGH STORM AREA COMMENCING 4 PM ON THE 29TH — PASSED NORTH OF CENTER 2 AM ON THE 30TH — ESTIMATED POSITION AT 6 AM 11.0 57.5 — WINDS FROM THE NORTHWEST AT 4 PM TO NORTHEAST 28 MPH AT 10 PM TO EAST 40 MPH AT 2 AM — PRESENT POSITION AT 10 AM 10.9N 56.3W WIND EASTSOUTHEAST TO SOUTHEAST 16 MPH BAROMETER 29.94 INCHES RISING SOUTHEAST SEAS ROUGH WITH MODERATE HEAVY SWELL — HAVE PASSED STORM.

At 9:07 a.m. EST the hurricane hunter plane reached the center of the storm, found a well-defined circular eye, central pressure 29.35 inches, surface winds in excess of hurricane force and the wall cloud around the eye 8 miles wide. This observation indicated that Hurricane Flora was the most concentrated and best organized tropical cyclone of the past two years.

The eye of Hurricane Flora passed over Tobago at 1:40 p.m. EST with lowest pressure 28.77 inches (uncorrected) and maximum sustained winds 90 to 100 mph. Twenty-four persons were killed and crop and property damage was around $30,000,000. On Trinidad, maximum winds were estimated at about 55 mph in extreme gusts from the southwest. There was only minor damage over most of Trinidad due to the protection afforded by the mountain range along the north coast. However, when the wind shifted to the southwest, many small boats in the harbor, which is an open roadstead to the west, were sunk. The large vessels had put out to sea. On Grenada damage was minor but six persons lost their lives by drowning.

After leaving the southern Windward Islands, Hurricane Flora moved on a fairly smooth and regular track toward the southwestern Haitian peninsula gradually acquiring a more northly component. Flora intensified slowly until it began to deepen rapidly on October 3. At 11:20 a.m. EST the Navy reconnaissance plane reported a central pressure of 27.65 inches. Flight level winds of 167 mph were measured on the second and about the same on the third. Probably some further intensification continued on the third until the center reached the coastline around 8:00 p.m. EST. At this time it was estimated that sustained winds on the surface were around 140 mph with gusts from 180 to 200 mph. Thus at this time, Flora was comparable to Hurricane Donna when it crossed the Florida Keys in 1960 and Carla in 1961 when it reached the Texas coast.

The vortex entered the south coast at Côtes-de-Fer and calms were noted at Fond-des-Nègres and Anse-à-Veau. Winds of 102 mph were noted at Côtes-de-Fer at 1900E on October 3 and 120 mph at the army base near Durez. The total rainfall at Miragoâne during the period when western Haiti was under the influence of Flora probably exceeded 75 inches. On October 6-8 when Miragoâne was under the principal rain band feeding into Flora, the rain gauge at the Reynolds Haitian Mines, Inc., which holds nineteen inches was observed overflowing three times and was emptied. Thus at least 57 inches fell during this three-day period; this figure does not include rainfall during the passage of the center nearby on October 3 and 4, as well as some rain which fell on the fifth. Destruction over the mountainous terrain of the Haitain peninsula ranged from severe to complete. Flash floods washed away sections of many towns and landslides buried others. The height of the storm surge on the south shore is unknown but could easily have been 12 feet or more. Crops were totally destroyed. About 3,500 bodies were counted and several thousand persons are missing to date. Of the missing, normally about half are eventually found to be casualties and half turn up sooner or later in their own or some other locality. Therefore, an estimate of 5,000 deaths appears reasonable. Property and crop damage is estimated at $125,000,000 with some reliable figures as high as $180,000,000.

In the Dominican Republic, preliminary information indicates that damage (mostly from floods but to some extent from wind) to agriculture, livestock, communication lines, etc., is estimated at $60,000,000. There was also considerable damage to bridges and roads. Floods were most extensive of record, with 10,000 square kilometers inundated in the western section of the republic. The known loss of life is twenty-nine but is estimated in excess of four hundred. Several months after the storm, roads were still impassable and communication channels in many western sections unrestored.

Flora entered Cuba about 30 miles east of Guantánamo Bay late on the forenoon of Friday, October 4. For portions of the next five days — completely boxed in by the high pressure areas to the west, the north, and the east — the hurricane meandered back and forth over eastern Cuba with winds of hurricane or near hurricane force and torrential rain. Although Flora did not completely regain its former intensity by the time it entered Cuba, winds of 70 to 100 mph lashed eastern Cuba for one hundred hours or more. Cuba's productive valleys and low lands remained flooded for many days and crop damage was tremendous. Rainfall amounts were enormous. Radio broadcasts from Cuba mentioned a total of 90 inches near Velasco. At Guantánamo Bay the rainfall from Hurricane Flora greatly exceeded the recorded amount for the entire year of 1962. (Dr. Luis Larragoiti Alonso, Director of the National Observatory, has forwarded rainfall accumulations in Cuba during the storm period, see Table 33.)

The last official total of fatalities announced was 1,159 with more than a thousand persons missing. Applying the same procedure as in

TABLE 33
Rainfall Accumulations in Cuba During Hurricane Flora

Climatological Station	Rainfall	Geographical Position
Francisco	41.89 inches	20°48′N 77°35′W
Elia	52.60	20°58′N 77°27′W
Manati	42.03	21°19′N 76°57′W
Palma	45.71	20°15′N 75°59′W
Alto Cedro	45.35	20°34′N 75°57′W
Baguanos	66.22	20°46′N 76°02′W
Boston	47.68	20°54′N 75°44′W
Tacajo	79.72	20°51′N 75°59′W
Preston	41.26	20°46′N 75°40′W
Union	42.09	20°13′N 75°51′W
Santiago de Cuba	41.38	20°01′N 75°50′W
Santiago de Cuba (Refineria)	64.84	—— ——
Santa Ana	64.21	20°16′N 75°54′W

Haiti, the death toll is probably at least 1,750. No official estimate of crop and property damage has been released by the Cuban government so far. Based on reports emanating from Cuba, damage estimates to the sugar crop range from 15 to 60 per cent; tobacco 15 to 50 per cent; coffee and cocoa 25 to 100 per cent; and rice 50 to 75 per cent. There were heavy losses to cattle, poultry, vegetables, bananas, pineapples, and cotton as well as extensive damage to factories, roads, and bridges. Estimates of total damage have ranged upward to $500,000,000 but at the present time it is believed $300,000,000 is reasonably realistic. (As of February 20, 1964, press reports from Havana continue to quote the Cuban government's estimate of the total damage in Cuba as $500,000,000.)

Only peripheral effects were felt in Jamaica, but there was considerable damage as follows: waterworks $420,000; bananas $5,-600,000; other crops $1,400,000; roads and bridges $4,200,000; houses, etc. $280,000; or a total of $11,900,000. There were eleven fatalities due mostly to flash floods. Some rainfall amounts (in inches) were: Palisadoes Airport 16.70; Hermitage Dam 44.32; Hope Filter Plant 21.99; Seaview 31.94; Cavaliers 19.72; Jack's Hill 22.36; Gordon Town 35.00; Castleton Gardens 47.00; Cedar Valley 51.7; and Spring Hill 60.00.

Hurricane Flora passed through the southeastern Bahamas on the night of October 8. On Inagua, Flora was described as the "worst hurricane ever experienced there within living memory." Winds were estimated at 75 to 80 mph. Two wharves were destroyed, the sea wall was damaged, and there was extensive damage to crops, roofs, and roads. The eye passed over Mayaguana shortly after midnight with maximum winds at 1:30 a.m. of 83 mph. The sea wall was washed away and crop destruction was total. There was extensive damage to roofs and communication lines. One person was drowned. Exuma, Long, Acklins Island, Crooked Islands, and Long Cay reported some damage to roads and property with crop damage ranging from moderate to total.

Flora is a historical hurricane — the second most deadly tropical cyclone ever to occur in the Atlantic area. The currently estimated total of 7,193 deaths considerably exceeds that of the Galveston hurricane of 1900. Also, there are a considerable number of small boats missing in the Caribbean with two to seven or more crewmen and passengers aboard each. These missing persons have not been included but may total one hundred or more. In the great hurricane which devastated the Windward and Leeward Islands from October 10-12, 1780, nearly 20,000 persons apparently perished: 4,326 on Barbados; 9,000 on Martinique; 4,500 on St. Eustatius; 2,000 sailors in the Spanish Fleet under Don Bernardo de Galvez, and a smaller number of fatalities on other islands.

The damage to crops and property of some $528,550,000 is conservative (Table 34). There are, of course, indirect additional losses which will be incurred from loss of work and long period effects on crops which, in some cases, will materially lessen crop production for the next five to eight years. Since the time of Columbus' discovery of the New World, no hurricane has dealt such a devastating blow to the countries of Haiti and Cuba.

The depression which grew into Hurricane Ginny developed in the southeastern Bahamas during October 16. The depression was not tropical and neither was the storm which developed later on the nineteenth. There was no warm core. Even though hurricane force winds were observed on the twentieth, it was not until the morning of the twenty-second that air reconnaissance found a thermal structure that was more like a hurricane, rather than the hybrid, late season type of the previous days. An eye of 20 miles diameter had formed on the

TABLE 34
Estimated Casualties and Damage for Hurricane Flora

Location	Killed	Damage
Tobago	24	$ 30,000,000
Trinidad	——	100,000
Grenada	6	25,000
Haiti	5000	125,000,000
Dominican Republic	400+	60,000,000
Cuba	1750	300,000,000
Jamaica	11	11,900,000
Bahamas	1	1,525,000
Florida	1	——
Total	7193	$528,550,000

morning of the twenty-second, however, definition was reportedly poor.

The track of Ginny was most unusual although not unique. Many hurricanes have looped and a few others have had rather long trajectories toward the southwest. The reader is referred to the "Yankee Storm" of October 30-November 8, 1935 (102), and Hurricane Able of May 15-24, 1951.* It would seem that these two storms and Ginny certainly had an affinity for the warm Gulf Stream. Operationally, aside from the erratic track, Ginny was a most difficult hurricane in that a large part of her life history was uncomfortably close to land. For eight consecutive days while Ginny was meandering off the southeast coast, the center was within 250 nautical miles of the United States mainland and, during one day, the wall cloud was less than 50 miles from the Cape Kennedy–Daytona Beach area. Indeed, considerable restraint was exercised in posting warnings. Hurricane warnings were only in effect from Charleston to Cape Fear and at Cape Hatteras at one time or another, and this represented about one-sixth of the coast that was threatened. Highest winds at any land station were 70 mph, with gusts to 100 mph reported at Cape Fear at the Oak Island observation point when the center took a temporary odd turn toward the North Carolina coast. Later the hurricane threatened New

---

*Moore, P. R., and Davis, W. R., 1951: A Pre-Season Hurricane of Subtropical Origin. Mon. Wea. Rev., 79, 189-195.

England but gale warnings which were in effect were ample. The fastest mile on the New England coast was 65 mph reported at Nantucket. The Coast Guard vessel *Cowslip,* off Portland, Maine, reported seas 30 to 40 feet high; the anemometer broke at about 105 mph; and its lowest barometer reading was 28.98 inches.

Ginny was probably more beneficial than damaging in that muchneeded rain fell along the Carolina coasts and in southeastern New England and Maine. Six to eighteen inches of snow occurred in north and central Maine in the cold air which pushed southward on the west side of the hurricane center. Apparently two persons perished in the snow storm and there was one other fatality. Possibly four others were lost on the tug *Otho.* Other damage resulted from minor beach erosion and relatively small structural loss to boats, houses, automobiles, etc., mainly in Maine and on Cape Cod. Total damage in the United States probably did not exceed $400,000. According to reports, damage in the Canadian Maritime Provinces was confined to small boats, with minor flooding but no known deaths.

Tropical storm Helena developed in an easterly wave a short distance east of the Lesser Antilles on October 25. Two ships in the disturbed area during the early afternoon of October 25 reported southerly winds of 32 and 40 knots with continuous rain. A reconnaissance aircraft later in the day found similiar conditions and a central pressure of 29.68 inches. The system was described as ill-defined with no wall cloud but with squall bands in the eastern semicircle. The storm intensified slightly as it moved west-northwestward but later weakened to below storm force after passing between Dominica and Guadeloupe — the 5,000-foot mountains of the islands evidently disrupted the poorly organized circulation. During the night of the twenty-sixth, Helena became almost stationary then turned northward and intensified slightly the next day. Central pressure dropped to 29.59 inches and reconnaissance aircraft reported winds of 58 mph in squalls between Guadeloupe and Dominica. Most of the squalls were confined to a small area in the eastern quadrant of the storm as the center moved northeastward from the vicinity of Antigua on the night of the twenty-seventh. During the next twenty-four hours the storm assumed a more northerly course and gradually weakened. Reconnaissance aircraft on the twenty-ninth found only an area of squally weather with highest winds about 23 mph.

Although Helena was never a well-defined storm, it caused considerable damage to small craft and roads in the Windward Islands. On Guadeloupe, 5 persons were reported dead, 500 homeless, and 14 seriously injured. A number of barges and fishing craft were sunk or seriously damaged. Total damage is estimated at no more than $500,000.

REFERENCES

1. Arakawa, H., and Suda, K., 1953: Analysis of Winds, Wind Waves, and Swells Over the Sea to the East of Japan During the Typhoon of September 26, 1935. Mon. Wea. Rev., *81*, 31-37.
2. Ballenzweig, E.M., 1957: Seasonal Variation in the Frequency of North Atlantic Tropical Cyclones Related to the General Circulation. National Hurricane Research Project, Report No. 9, 32 pp.
3. Bangs, N.H., 1929: Effects of the 1926 Florida Hurricane Upon Engineer Designed Buildings. Bull. Amer. Met. Soc., *10*, 46-47.
4. Beerbower, G.M., 1926: Hurricane Effects on Buildings at Hollywood, Florida. Engineering News Record, *97*, 752.
5. Boughner, C.C., 1955: Hurricane Hazel. Weather, *10*, 200-205.
6. Braham, R.R., 1958: An Exploratory Experiment in Hurricane Seeding. Proceedings, Technical Conference on Hurricanes, Miami Beach, Fla., November 20-22, 1958.
7. Brooks, C.F., 1939: Hurricane Hazard in New England. Geographical Review, January, 1939.
8. Cline, I.M., 1926: Tropical Cyclones. MacMillan Company, New York, N.Y., 301 pp.
9. Colón, J.A., 1953: A Study of Hurricane Tracks for Forecasting Purposes. Mon. Wea. Rev., *81*, 53-66.
10. Colón, J.A., 1956: On the Formation of Hurricane Alice, 1955, with notes on other cold-season tropical storms. Mon. Wea. Rev., *84*, 1-14.
11. Conner, W.C., Kraft, R.H., and Harris, D.L., 1957: Empirical Methods for Forecasting the Maximum Storm Tide Due to Hurricanes and Other Tropical Storms. Mon. Wea. Rev., *85*, 113-116.
12. Douglas, Marjory Stoneman, 1958: Hurricane, Rinehart & Co., New York, N.Y., 393 pp.
13. Deppermann, C.E., 1939: Some Characteristics of Philippine Typhoons. Bureau of Printing, Manila, P.I.
14. Drumm, W.M., 1905: The Pioneer Forecasters of Hurricanes. Havana, Cuba.
15. Duane, J.E., Jr., 1935: The Hurricane of September 2, 1935, at Long Key, Florida. Bull. Amer. Met. Soc., *16*, 238-239.
16. Dunn, G.E., 1940: Cyclogenesis in the Tropical Atlantic. Bull. Amer. Met. Soc., *21*, 215-229.
17. Dunn, G.E., 1956: Areas of Hurricane Development. Mon. Wea. Rev., *84*, 47-51.

18. Dunn, G.E., 1951: Tropical Cyclones. In Compendium of Meteorology, Amer. Met. Soc., Boston, Mass., 887-901.

19. Dunn, G.E., Davis, W.R., and Moore, P.L., 1955: Hurricanes of 1955. Mon. Wea. Rev., *83*, 315-326.

20. Fassig, O.L., 1913: Hurricanes of the West Indies. Bull. No. 13, U.S. Weather Bureau, Washington, D.C., 28 pp.

21. Fawbush, E.J., Miller, R.C., and Starrett, L.G., 1951: An Empirical Method of Forecasting Tornado Development. Bull. Amer. Met. Soc., *32*, 1-9.

22. Fletcher, R.D., 1955: Computation of Maximum Winds in Hurricanes. Bull. Amer. Met. Soc., *36*, 246-250.

23. Flora, S.D., 1953: Tornadoes in the United States. University of Oklahoma Press, Norman, Okla., 194 pp.

24. Frankenfield, H.C., 1896: The Tornado of May 27, 1896, at St. Louis, Mo., Mon. Wea. Rev., *24*, 77-81.

25. Garriott, E.B., 1900: Forecasts and Warnings. Mon. Wea. Rev., *28*, 371-377.

26. Garriott, E.B., 1906: The West Indian Hurricane of September 1906. Mon. Wea. Rev., *34*, 416-417.

27. Garriott, E.B., 1909: Weather, Forecasts and Warnings for the Month. Mon. Wea. Rev., *37*, 829-831.

28. Gentry, R.C., 1955: Wind Velocities During Hurricanes. Paper No. 2731, Trans. Amer. Soc. of Civil Engineers, *120*, 169.

29. Gentry, R.C., Moore, P.L., and Marshall, A.M., 1950: Hoist Hurricane Warnings. Weather Vane Publications, Miami Springs, Fla.

30. Hales, J.V., 1955: An Evaluation of the Effects of Cloud Seeding in Southern Utah. Bull. No. 46, Utah University, 39 pp.

31. Harris, D.L., 1957: Meteorological Aspects of Storm Surge Generation. Unpublished manuscript, U.S. Weather Bureau, Washington, D.C., 16 pp.

32. Haurwitz, B., 1935: The Height of Tropical Cyclones and of the Eye of the Storm. Mon. Wea. Rev., *63*, 45-49.

33. Higgs, R.L., 1954: Severe Floods of October 12-15, 1954, in Puerto Rico. Mon. Wea. Rev., *82*, 301-304.

34. Hoover, R.A., 1957: Empirical relationships of the Central Pressures in Hurricanes to the Maximum Surge and Storm Tide. Mon. Wea. Rev., *85*, 167-174.

35. Horiguti, Y., 1927: Memoirs of the Imperial Marine Observatory, Kobe, Japan, Nos. 2 and 3, 1926-1927.

36. Hubert, L.F., 1955: Frictional Filling of Hurricanes. Bull. Amer. Met. Soc., *36*, 440-445.

37. Hubert, L.F., 1955: A Case Study of Hurricane Formation. J. Met., *12*, 486-492.

38. Hubert, L.F., and Clark, G.B., 1955: The Hurricane Surge. U.S. Weather Bureau, Washington, D.C., 34 pp.

39. Hubert, L.F., and Berg, O., 1955: A Rocket Portrait of a Tropical Storm. Mon. Wea. Rev., *83*, 119-124.

40. Hughes, L.A., 1952: On the Low-level Wind Structure of Tropical Storms. J. Met., *9*, 422-428.

41. Humphreys, W.J., Biographical Sketch of Mr. William C. Redfield. New York Academy of Sciences. Date unknown.

42. Jordan, E., 1952: An Observational Study of the Upper Wind Circulation Around Tropical Storms, J. Met., *9*, 340-346.

43. Jordan. C.L., 1957: A Mean Atmosphere for the West Indies. National Hurricane Research Project, Report No. 6, 17 pp.

44. Jordan, C.L., 1957: Estimating the Central Pressures of Tropical Cyclones from Aircraft Data. National Hurricane Research Project, Report No. 10, 12 pp.

45. Jordan, C.L., 1957: Mean Soundings for the Hurricane Eye. National Hurricane Research Project, Report No. 13, 10 pp.

46. Kessler, Edwin III, 1958: Eye Region of Hurricane Edna, 1954. J. Met., *15*, 264-270.

47. Klein, W.H., and Winston, J.S., 1947: The Path of the Atlantic Hurricane of September 1947 in Relation to the Hemispheric Circulation. Bull. Amer. Met. Soc., *28*, 447-452.

48. Knox. J.L., 1955: The Storm Hazel. Bull. Amer. Met. Soc., *36*, 239-246.

49. Krueger, A.F., 1954: The Weather and Circulation of October 1954. Mon. Wea. Rev., *82*, 296-300.

50. Krueger, D.W., 1957: A Relation Between the Mass Circulation Through Hurricanes and Their Intensity. University of Chicago, Dept. of Met., 12 pp.

51. Laban, J., 1955: Sequence of Weather Events, Hurricane Janet, September 26-27, 1955. Swan Island, West Indies. Weatherwise, *9*, 121-124.

52. Ligda, M.G.H., 1955: Analysis of Small Precipitation Areas and Bands in the Hurricane of August 23-28, 1949. Mass. Inst. of Tech., Tech. Note No. 3, Cambridge, Mass.

53. Ludlum, F.H., *et al.*, Artificial Control of Clouds and Hydrometeors. World Met. Organization, Tech. Note No. 13.

54. Malkin, W., and Galway, J.G., 1953: Tornadoes Associated with Hurricanes. Mon. Wea. Rev., *81*, 299-303.

55. Malkus, J., 1958: On the Thermal Structure of the Hurricane Core. Proceedings, Technical Conference on Hurricanes, Miami Beach, Fla., November 20-22, 1958.

56. Malkus, J., 1958: On the Structure and Maintenance of the Mature Hurricane Eye. J. Met., *15*, 337-349.

57. Malkus, J., and Riehl, H., 1958: On the Dynamics and Energetics of the Hurricane Area. Proceedings, Technical Conference on Hurricanes, Miami Beach, Fla., November 20-22, 1958.

58. McDonald, W.F., 1942: On a Hypothesis Concerning Normal Development and Disintegration of Tropical Hurricanes. Bull. Amer. Met. Soc., *23*, 73-78.

59. Miller, B.I., 1958: On the Maximum Intensity of Hurricanes. J. Met., *15*, 185-195.

60. Miller, B.I., 1958: The Three Dimensional Wind Structure Around a Tropical Cyclone. National Hurricane Research Project, Report No. 15, 41 pp.

61. Miller, B.I., 1958: The Use of Mean Layer Winds As a Hurricane Steering Mechansim. National Hurricane Research Project, Report No. 18, 24 pp.

62. Miller, B.I., 1958: Rainfall Rates in Florida Hurricanes. Mon. Wea. Rev., *86*, 258-264.

63. Miller, B.I., and Moore, P.L., 1958: A Comparison of Hurricane Steering Levels. Proceedings, Technical Conference on Hurricanes, Miami Beach, Fla., November 20-22, 1958.

64. Mitchell, C.L., 1924: West Indian Hurricanes and Other Tropical Cyclones of the North Atlantic Ocean. Mon. Wea. Rev., Supplement No. 24, 47 pp.

65. Mook, C.P., and Kutschenreuter, P.H., 1956: Hurricane Rains and Floods of August 1955 Carolinas to New England. U.S. Weather Bureau Tech. Paper No. 26, Washington, D.C., 146 pp.

66. Mook, C.P., Hoover, E.W., and Hoover, R.A., 1957: Analysis of the Movement of the Hurricane Off the East Coast of the U.S., October 12-14, 1947. Mon. Wea. Rev., *85*, 243-248.

67. Moore, R.L., 1946: Forecasting the Motion of Tropical Cyclones. Bull. Amer. Met. Soc., *27*, 410-415.

68. Namias, J., 1955: Long Range Factors Affecting the Genesis and Paths of Tropical Cyclones. Proceedings, UNESCO Symposium on Typhoons, Tokyo, November 9-12, 1954, pp. 213-219.

69. Namias, J., 1955: Tropical Cyclones Related to the General Circulation. Trans. New York Academy of Science.

70. Namias, J., 1958: Forms of the General Circulation Related to Hurricane Genesis and Path. Preceedings, Technical Conference on Hurricanes, Miami Beach, Fla., November 20-22, 1958.

71. Namias, J., and Dunn, C.R., 1955: The Weather and General Circulation of August 1955. Mon. Wea. Rev., *83*, 163-170.

72. Norton, G., c1947: Hurricane Forecasting. Unpublished manuscript, Weather Bureau Office, Miami, Fla., 53 pp.

73. Norton, G., 1949: Florida Hurricanes (by R.W. Gray, revised by G. Norton), U.S. Weather Bureau Publications, Washington, D.C., 6 pp.

74. Olascoaga, M.J., 1950: Some Aspects of Argentine Rainfall. Tellus, *2*, 312-318.

75. Palmén, E., 1948: On the Formation and Structure of Tropical Hurricanes. Geophysica No. 3, 26-38.

76. Palmén, E., 1956: Dynamics of Hurricanes. Lecture at Caribbean Hurricane Seminar, Ciudad Trujillo, D.R., 18 February, 1956.

77. Piddington, H., 1851: The Sailor's Hornbook, London.

78. Redfield, A.C., and Miller, A.R., 1955: Memorandum On Water Levels Accompanying Atlantic Coast Hurricanes, U.S. Weather Bureau, Washington, D.C.

79. Reid, W.F., 1917: Forecasts and Warnings. Mon. Wea. Rev., *45*, 457-461.

80. Riehl, H., 1945: Waves in the Easterlies and the Polar Front in the Tropics. Dept. Meteor., University of Chicago, Misc. Reports No. 17.

81. Riehl, H., 1951: Aerology of Tropical Storms. In Compendium of Meteorology, Amer. Met. Soc., Boston, Mass., 902-913.

82. Riehl, H., 1954: Tropical Meteorology. McGraw-Hill Book Company, New York, N.Y., 392 pp.

83. Riehl, H., Haggard, W.H., and Sanborn, R.W., 1956: On the Prediction of 24-hour Hurricane Movement. J. Met., *13*, 415-420.

84. Riehl, H., and Palmén, E., 1957: Budget of Angular Momentum and Energy in Tropical Cyclones. J. Met., *14*, 150-159.

85. Riehl, H., 1958: On the Production of Kinetic Energy from Condensation Heating. National Hurricane Research Project, Report No. 22, 25 pp.

86. Riehl, H., 1958: Comments On the Formation of Hurricanes. Proceedings, Technical Conference on Hurricanes, Miami Beach, Fla., November 20-22, 1958.

87. Rockney, V.D., 1956: Hurricane Detection By Radar and Other Means. Tropical Cyclone Symposium, Brisbane, Australia, 19 pp.

88. Rossby, C.G., 1949: On the Mechanism for the Release of Potential Energy in the Atmosphere. J. Met., *6*, 163-180.

89. Schoner, R.W., 1957: Frequency and Distribution of Areal Rainfall Averages Associated With Tropical Storms Entering the Texas Coast. Unpublished manuscript, U.S. Weather Bureau, Washington, D.C., 9 pp.

90. Schoner, R.W., and Molansky, S., 1956: Rainfall Associated With Hurricanes. National Hurricane Research Project, Report No. 3, 305 pp.

91. Senn, H.V., Hiser, H.W., and Bourett, R.C., 1957: Studies of Spiral Bands As Observed On Radar. University of Miami, Coral Gables, Fla., 21 pp.

92. Senn, H.V., and Hiser, H.W., 1958: The Origin and Behavior of Hurricane Spiral Bands As Observed On Radar. Proceedings, Seventh Weather Radar Conference, Miami Beach, Fla., November 17-20, 1958, 46-55.

93. Sherman, L., 1950: On the propagation of Hurricanes, Trans. Amer. Geophys. Union, *31*, 531-535.

94. Simpson, R.H., 1946: On the Movement of Tropical Cyclones. Trans. Amer. Geophys. Union., *27*, 641-645.

95. Simpson, R.H., 1952: Exploring the Eye of Typhoon Marge, 1951. Bull. Amer. Met. Soc., *33*, 286-298.

96. Simpson, R.H., 1954: Hurricanes. Scientific American, June, 1954.

97. Simpson, R.H., 1955: On the Structure of Tropical Cyclones As Studied By Aircraft Reconnaissance. UNESCO Symposium on Typhoons, Tokyo, November 9-12, 1954, pp. 129-150.

98. Simpson, R.H., and Riehl, H., 1958: Mid-tropospheric Ventilation As a Constraint On Hurricane Development and Maintenance. Proceedings, Technical Conference on Hurricanes, Miami Beach, Fla., November 20-22, 1958.

99. Staff, National Hurricane Research Project, 1958: Details of Circulation in the High Energy Core of Hurricane Carrie. National Hurricane Research Project, Report No. 25, 15 pp.

100. Sverdrup, H.U., 1942: Oceanography for Meteorologists. Prentice-Hall, Inc., New York, N.Y., 243 pp.

101. Tannehill, I.R., 1936: Sea Swells in Relation to the Movement and Intensity of Tropical Storms. Mon. Wea. Rev., *64*, 231-238.

102. Tannehill, I.R., 1938: Hurricanes, Their Nature and History. Princeton University Press, Princeton, N.J., 304 pp.

103. Tannehill, I.R., 1954: Hurricane Hunters. Dodd, Mead, and Company, New York, N.Y., 271 pp.

104. Tepper, M., 1958: A Theoretical Model for Hurricane Radar Bands. Proceedings, Seventh Weather Radar Conference, Miami Beach, Fla., November 17-20, 1958.

105. U.S. Army, Corps of Engineers, 1956: Hurricanes Affecting the Texas Coast from Galveston to the Rio Grande. Tech. Memo. No. 78, March, 1956.

106. U.S. Navy, Bureau of Aeronautics, 1955: Marine Climatic Atlas of the World. Vol. I, North Atlantic Ocean.

107. U.S. Navy, Bureau of Aeronautics, 1956: Intensification of Tropical Cyclones, Atlantic and Pacific Areas. Fourth Research Report, Project AROWA, Norfolk, Va., 28 pp.

108. U.S. Weather Bureau, 1938: Atlas of Climatic Charts of the Oceans. Washington, D.C.

109. Veigas, K.W., and Miller, R.G., 1958: Probabilistic Prediction of Hurricane Movement by Synoptic Climatology. Technical Conference on Hurricanes, Miami Beach, Fla., November 20-22, 1958.

110. Viñes, B., 1898: Investigation of the Cyclonic Circulation and the Translatory Movement of West Indian Hurricanes. U.S. Weather Bureau, Washington, D.C.

111. Visher, S., 1925: Tropical Cyclones of the Pacific. Bernice P. Bishop Museum, Bull. No. 20, Honolulu, T.H.

112. Weems, John E., 1957: A Weekend in September. Henry Holt and Co., New York, N.Y., 180 pp.

113. Wexler, H., 1947: Structure of Hurricanes As Determined By Radar. Annals of New York Academy of Science, *48*, 821-844.

114. Willett, H.C., 1955: A Study of Tropical Hurricanes Along the Atlantic and Gulf Coasts of the United States. Inter-regional Insurance, New York, N.Y., 63 pp.

115. Winston, J.S., 1954: The Weather and Circulation of August 1954, Including a Discussion of Hurricane Carol in Relation To the Planetary Waves. Mon. Wea. Rev., *82*, 228-236.

116. Yeh, T.C., 1950: The Motion of Tropical Storms Under the Influence of a Superimposed Southerly Current. J. Met., *7*, 108-113.

INDEXES

NAME INDEX